The Complete Book of Game Conservation

The Complete Book of
Game Conservation

Edited by Charles Coles OBE, VRD

Stanley Paul
London Melbourne Auckland Johannesburg

Stanley Paul & Co. Ltd

An imprint of Century Hutchinson Ltd

Brookmount House, 62–65 Chandos Place,
Covent Garden, London WC2N 4NW

Century Hutchinson Publishing Group (Australia) Pty Ltd
16–22 Church Street, Hawthorn, Melbourne, Victoria 3122

Century Hutchinson Group (NZ) Ltd
32–34 View Road, PO Box 40–086, Glenfield, Auckland 10

Century Hutchinson Group (SA) Pty Ltd
PO Box 337, Bergvlei 2012, South Africa

First published 1971
Second edition 1975
Reprinted 1978
Third edition 1984
Reprinted 1986

© 1971, 1975, 1984 by Imperial Metal Industries (Kynoch) Ltd

Set in Baskerville by Wyvern Typesetting Ltd, Bristol

Printed and bound in Great Britain by
Anchor Brendon Ltd, Tiptree, Essex

ISBN 0 09 156940 0

Contents

Introduction

by Lord Netherthorpe

Having enjoyed a lifelong connection with the land, I have seen many changes in its use. The first significant fact is that there has been a material depletion in the area of unencroached country-side, though what remains has become progressively farmed more intensively. This is imperative because indigenous agricultural production is indispensable to our survival. But in the wake of an increasingly efficient and productive agriculture, inevitable consequential pressures bear on nearly all forms of wildlife, including, and by no means least, their impact on gamebirds.

Happily for the sportsman in these islands the Game Conservancy, of which I have the honour to be the President,* maintains a staff of scientists and advisers to study the inherent problems and thereby help to sustain the game population and minimise its erosion.

This book is concerned with the art and science of game conservation and is a distillation of a great many years of experimental and practical work in the field. I believe it will be of the greatest value both to owners of the 'rough shoot' and the 'keepered estate' alike.

The maxim of the true sportsman is not to exploit his privilege, but rather to put back more into his sport than he takes out. The contents of this book point the way to the realisation of this desirable objective.

---

* HRH The Prince of Wales is now President of the Game Conservancy.

Editor's Preface

Gamebirds no longer survive as they did ten or twenty years ago. Modern farming has created conditions against which they cannot compete without man's help. This must include the new technology as well as the old crafts and skills.

If good shooting is to continue in our shrinking countryside we believe this book – the result of over fifty years' research work undertaken by the Game Conservancy (and its predecessor the Eley Game Advisory Station) – will fulfil an urgent need.

It is planned to appeal mainly to the sportsman who wants to know how to produce more game and better shooting on his land. His problems are likely to include the choice of an incubator, pheasant rearing, wild partridge keepering, warming-up draughty coverts, planting food patches, trapping stoats and a host of similar practical issues. In addition to discussing such operations in detail, essential game management and breeding techniques are described which, it is hoped, will be of interest to the serious student of wildlife biology. Though not legally 'game', a section on wildfowl is included, also notes on snipe and woodcock.

Third edition
Since the first edition was published in 1971 we have made many advances in the field of game conservation. In this edition an enlarged chapter has been included on game diseases, and another on the red-legged partridge. Radical alterations have been made to the sections on game forestry and shooting crops. We know more about the ideal habitat for pheasants and how their territories are made up. There is new thinking on wildfowl and grouse; the problems of grey partridge chick survival are more clearly defined.

The Game Conservancy – its Aims

The main objective of the Game Conservancy is, as the name suggests, to promote the conservation of game in the British countryside. We provide advice to landowners and shoot-managers to enable them to improve the habitat for game species. To be able to do this we must know, in considerable detail, the exact requirements of each species and then be able to assess how these requirements can be integrated with farming and forestry practices in today's world. This involves extensive research into pesticides, crop management, hedgerows, moorland, wetlands and woodland.

If we are to retain a countryside where we can still enjoy a day's shooting with an abundance of game in attractive surroundings that also shelter other wildlife species, then action to enable us to carry out further research is required now.

Current research
Our research programme is currently based at three regional centres which cater for uplands, wetlands and lowlands.

Uplands and red grouse
Our uplands research is based on our specially funded North of England Grouse Research Project. Here we are investigating the cause of the large fluctuations found in grouse populations so that management methods can be developed to reduce the extreme 'lows' of this highly cyclical species. This project, with a smaller study in Scotland, is also concerned with the problems of over-grazing with sheep, and the effect of sheep tick, which, in conjunction with the disease Louping-ill, can decimate a grouse population. We are keenly aware that if grouse management fails, many upland moors will either be over-grazed or planted with spruce. Either way they will then be lost as open heather and

9

moorland, with the consequent disappearance of many birds other than grouse.

Wetlands and wildfowl

As much of our traditional marshland is inevitably drained, the emphasis of our wetland research, which operates from the Amey Roadstone-financed research laboratory in Buckinghamshire, is on developing areas of new water. Flooded gravel pits, reservoirs, even farm ponds can become breeding refuges for our wildfowl species if they are managed in the correct manner. The early stages of this research revolved around ways of improving the nesting habitat for breeding duck. These problems have now been largely solved and most of our attention is being directed towards increasing the survival of ducklings, many of which die through lack of food on these often rather sterile waters.

Lowlands: farm and woodland game

Our longest research studies have centred on lowland game – partridges, pheasants, woodcock and hares. The extreme pressure of modern farming and forestry practices make this the area with the widest scope and greatest need. As agriculture becomes ever more intensive, so game and wildlife are increasingly in danger of being squeezed out.

This book is based on our research findings; though, for reasons of length, some of the lesser projects have been omitted and others summarised.

Historical Note

It was in 1932 when the Eley Game Advisory Station initiated their studies of gamebirds. The first headquarters was situated at Knebworth in Hertfordshire, where I.C.I. Ltd leased an experimental shoot as their field laboratory. The research programme was financed by the Company's Eley cartridge interests at Witton.

The creation of the department was due to the imagination of Major H. G. Eley. A. D. Middleton, then at the Oxford Bureau of Animal Population, and Dr Phyllis Clapham, of the Commonwealth Bureau of Parasitology, were engaged as biologist and pathologist respectively. C. L. Coles joined the service in 1937, in due course undertaking operational research and writing many of the game management booklets.

In 1946 the unit moved to Fordingbridge, Hampshire, where

10

for 14 years they rented a shooting estate at Damerham. It was here that many of the secrets of the wild partridge were uncovered, census techniques worked out, habitat requirements evaluated and pioneer work undertaken on new methods of game rearing, the prevention of disease and many other problems. Scientists and gamekeepers worked together.

T. H. Blank continued the partridge ecology studies started by A. D. Middleton, and Nigel Gray became the first of the field consultants and a specialist in game and forestry studies.

In 1969 the Eley Game Advisory Station became independent and was re-named the Game Conservancy. A generous grant was continued by the original founders, together with some additional financial assistance from the shooting industry as a whole; the Amey Roadstone Corporation (for wildfowl research on wet gravel pits) has already been mentioned.

The main income now comes from the members of the Game Conservancy, who pay an annual subscription. Part of the royalties of this book are put towards the cost of research. The organisation became a registered charity in 1980.

The present Director is Richard Van Oss and the Director of Research is Dr G. R. Potts.

Acknowledgements

It is impossible to mention by name all those whose work has contributed to this book, but grateful acknowledgement is made of the work of all the anonymous technicians, field workers, laboratory assistants, keepers, shoot owners and others, whose interest in wild game has helped towards the production of this volume.

Two of our headkeepers deserve especial mention: Mr Bob Aitchison and the late Mr Bert Ambrose – men with a lifetime's experience and love of partridges.

The chapter on 'Grouse Management' was written by Dr Adam Watson, Director of the Unit of Grouse and Moorland Ecology, and 'Heather Management' by Dr Gordon Miller, then of the Nature Conservancy.* New information on grouse has been added by Dr Peter Hudson of the Game Conservancy's North of England Grouse Research Project.

Two plates, facing pages 59 and 203, are reproduced from paintings by Alex Jardine. Other plates, facing pages 35 and 227, are from paintings by C. F. Tunnicliffe and David Binns. 'Grey Partridges', facing page 202, is from a painting by Philip Rickman, with kind permission of The Tryon Gallery Ltd, Dover Street, London. The drawing of partridges (Figure 12) is reproduced by permission of Winifred Austen. The colour plates facing pages 34 and 226 are reproduced by permission of the Trustees of the British Museum (Natural History). The black and white drawings and photographs have been contributed by the Game Conservancy staff, except for photographs kindly lent by *Farmer's Weekly*, Fisons Pest Control Ltd, John Tarlton, A. W. P. Robertson, G. L. Carlisle, Douglas England, J. Marchington and P. Moxon.

---

* Now re-named the Institute of Terrestrial Ecology.

Chapter 1
Game as a Farm Crop

The term 'game conservation' is self-explanatory, but the precise *function* of game management may be worth defining briefly.

The objective is to treat game as a manageable crop and its pursuit as a pleasurable and profitable form of land use. Inevitably there are – and probably always will be – good and bad partridge seasons just as there are good and bad years for acorns and mushrooms. One of the principal functions of game management, therefore, is to level out the ups and downs rather than leave things to nature. This is effected mainly by trying to alter the environmental conditions that hold down the natural increases of game.

Limiting the bag alone is rarely successful and often has the opposite effect, because in time it results in many sportsmen losing interest. As Professor Aldo Leopold, the American game biologist, said: 'Management seeks the same end (as restricting the amount of game shot) but by more versatile means. We seem to have two choices: try it, or hunt rabbits.'

This was written over 50 years ago when rabbits were with us in pest proportions!

The art of game conservation has been practised for many centuries. The Emperor Kublai Khan (AD 1259–94) planted special food patches for his partridges and quail, and regulated – albeit rather selfishly – the number of birds that could be taken annually. And even before the great Khan, other hunters were taking simple practical steps to ensure that their quarry – whether enjoyed as food, sport or both – was given some form of protection.

The basic concept of game management has changed little – only the methods used.

Today more and more farmers think of game in accordance with the above definition – as a valuable by-product of the land: a secondary crop that can be produced and harvested much like any other crop. The farmer's ordinary implements will be the first tools he needs for wildlife management. Then for a modest outlay on traps and perhaps a few rearing pens and some food, he can further encourage pheasants, partridges, wildfowl or whatever species may be suitable.

In many areas where natural conditions for the increase of *wild* game are potentially good, the rearing of birds may be unnecessary. Instead it will be important to maintain the right habitat, improving it wherever possible. The birds' food supply – particularly in winter – is often a key factor, and some control of their natural enemies may be necessary at certain seasons. The farmer must also do what he can to prevent casualties caused by agricultural or forestry operations. This man-made wastage can be very high.

In some places the game may simply need *initial* encouragement. Reared birds of a wild or hardy strain can be 'planted out' as seed stock, and if properly looked after will, in due course, establish themselves.

Most of the conservation work will fit in with the daily routine on a farm. On a modest shoot the extra labour involved will take up no more time than maintaining a normal garden.

Some farmers and landowners are so keen on their shooting that they will give their game every consideration: they will make concessions to wildlife. On the other hand there are farmers who will pull up every hedge and bush, cultivating every square inch of soil until they have a highly efficient food factory, neatly boxed in with barbed wire. Under this type of management the game simply has to take its chance with farm machines and chemicals – although the farmer nevertheless often expects some sport.

The man who shoots over dogs will also have a different outlook from the man who prefers driven birds on a more organised day.

It is not easy to make proposals that will appeal to every type of farmer or shooter. In this book, therefore, we intend to discuss a range of game management ideas, in the hope that each person will adopt those suggestions which suit his particular farm and the amount of time and money he has available.

Incidentally, some readers may be puzzled why we still feature the partridge as the main species to be considered in terms of game quarry, when the pheasant is clearly the more important bird today.

Part of the reason may be summed up in the old keepers' saying: 'If you look after the partridges, the wild pheasants will look after themselves.' This is still true today. The other reason is that the partridge is what scientists call an 'indicator species'. It is a fairly accurate barometer of what is happening to other species that use the same type of habitat. In other words, if we continue to plan and manage our farmland for wild partridges – even though modern agriculture has loaded the dice against them – we shall be doing all the right things for many other species – both game and non-game.

Keepers – professional and amateur
Unfortunately, with the increase of intensive farming and the sprawl of urban development, in most areas wild game no longer thrives entirely unaided. It needs a helping hand – the best helping hand, of course, being a skilled

14

gamekeeper. On a shoot where it is not possible to employ a professional keeper, a profitable amount of amateur keepering in the form of predator control, winter feeding, nest salvage, game rearing where necessary, improving the woodlands and so on, can be undertaken without vast experience. Experts have often been surprised at the stock of game on groups of small farms 'keepered' by the staff.

The owner-farmer

The farmer has the best chance to have a reasonably good shoot. He very largely controls where the gamebirds live, what is available for them to eat and what degree of protection they have from their natural enemies. *By planning his crops so as to form the right pattern for growing and sheltering gamebirds, he holds the key to the carrying capacity of the land.* Natural food, nesting places, escape cover and winter crops should be evenly dispersed over the whole game range. This he is usually in a position to undertake at no cost, though possibly at a little inconvenience, when first he decides to integrate his game crop with his farm crops.

Living on the spot, he will be able to salvage nests disturbed by farming operations and put the young reared birds back on the farm. He must naturally exercise the greatest care when using chemical sprays or seed dressings. Their *indirect* effect on wildlife can be as important as the direct consequences.

Farm habitat

'No single event had a greater impact on farm wildlife than did the coming of the barbed-wire fence.' These words, written by an American game biologist, are as true in Britain as in the United States. The wire fence, replacing warm, friendly hedgerows, is the most obvious modern alteration to gamebird habitat in the countryside. At their present rate of removal – roughly 7,000 miles (11,265 km.) each year – hedgerows could have disappeared before the end of the century! Luckily, scientists have now proven new values of hedgerows to both farmer and wildlife conservationist, and ideas are changing.

It should be realised by everyone interested in shooting that the foundation stone upon which all management is based is *habitat*. A varied pattern of fields and woods, hedges and open ground, is the natural range of the important British game species – particularly the pheasant, which is a bird of the 'fringe', continually moving from cover into the open and back again. Even grey and red-legged partridges, although they are normally seen out on fields or grassland, need a proportion of taller cover if they are to survive and breed successfully.

Hedgerows in general

In Britain hedgerows answered the nesting needs of gamebirds for centuries, but the recent trend towards intensive farming has deprived them of even a minimum of nesting sites in some parts of the country.

15

Of course, hedges are not the only source of cover. Between the wars, in the famous partridge areas of Hungary there were very few hedgerows, but other suitable cover was available – particularly the strip crops of 'peasant husbandry'. In Beauce, the granary of France where partridges still prosper, the winter wheat is forward enough to provide nesting cover. Assuming there is enough natural food, partridges will still thrive wherever there are areas of rough, ungrazed grass to give secure nesting sites and shelter – even under disturbed conditions such as those on airfields, artillery ranges or large areas of cereals criss-crossed with wide grassy tracks.

Major nest losses among partridges occur when a proportion of hedgerow cover has been removed and the hens are forced to resort to insecure sites in the open. Under these conditions many eggs will be lost to crows, rooks and other predators. The other main source of losses (particularly destructive since so many hens are killed) is the cutting out of sitting birds in grass crops.

When consultants are called in to advise on methods of making a farm more profitable, one of the first moves is invariably to bulldoze out the hedges in order to increase field sizes. (The Agricultural Development and Advisory Service consider fields of 50–60 acres [20–25 h.] quite large enough to be efficiently worked by modern machinery. The partridge herself would chose 30 acres [12 h.].) But when all things are taken into consideration hedge removal is not always the best policy.

It can be short-sighted and less economically sound than might at first appear. There is no case for the retention of tiny hedged fields, but there is a great deal to be said in favour of retaining hedges in place of fences for the remaining divisions when fields are enlarged. The physical benefits of hedges are:

1. They give shelter for sheep and cattle in extremes of temperature, preventing excessive weight loss or reduction in milk yield.
2. They act as windbreaks, preventing soil erosion.
3. They raise the soil temperature and reduce the rate of evaporation (water loss) due to wind.
4. They provide nesting cover for many beneficial birds.
5. They provide reservoirs of predatory insects, which help to control pests such as aphids in cereal crops, thereby reducing the need for the volume of chemicals used. This *integrated* control is preferable.

Hedgerow management for game has reached the greatest perfection in north-west Norfolk, where thorn hedges provide essential shelter for crops and stock – and also help to maintain partridges at a higher breeding density than anywhere else in Britain. These hedge banks are about 7 ft. (2 m.) across, from furrow to furrow, and usually 2–2½ ft. (0·6–0·75 m.) high. They provide food and shelter in a landscape which can otherwise be extremely bleak during winter, and give good nesting cover in the spring. The hedge bank aids predator control and may be used as a driving hedge. The diagram (Figure 1) shows a typical hedge in May, with a nest sited on the screened, well-drained bank.

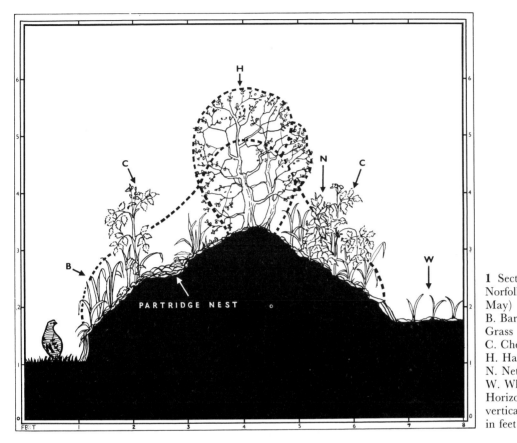

1 Section across a Norfolk hedge (early May)
B. Barren Broom Grass
C. Chervil
H. Hawthorn
N. Nettle
W. Wheat
Horizontal and vertical scale in feet

The type of hedge most useful to both farmer and game preserver is a neat, well-kept thorn hedge, with narrow grassy banks which offer safe nesting cover. Nobody wants the straggling, unkempt hedge which can harbour only pigeons, rabbits and crows. Although even a tidy thorn hedge can shelter rabbits, except in isolated areas their numbers are now generally at such a low level that any new burrows can be spotted at once and attended to without difficulty. Hedgerows that are truly dual-purpose, in that they take up the minimum cropping space and yet provide shelter for crops and stock as well as nesting cover for game, are still to be found in many parts of East Anglia.

In Wiltshire, a few miles from the Game Conservancy at Fordingbridge, some excellent thorn hedges were noted that had been laid eight years after planting, hand trimmed for two years and then cut by machine for the past six years. At 16 years, they varied in height from 4 ft. to 9 ft. (1–2½ m.), according to the site, but all were about 6 ft. (2 m.) wide (except the lowest, which had been

17

trimmed to only 3 ft. [1 m.] wide). The thorns were planted 18 in. (46 cm.) apart in double rows, with 9 in. (23 cm.) between the rows.

In Kent there are many tall, razor-thin hedges – the actual thorn growth being only 9 in. (23 cm.) across – grown to protect the fruit orchards from frost damage. They are usually about 10 ft. (3 m.) high and would be perfect for partridge nesting and driving in the shooting season if the chemical sprays had left sufficient gamebirds to use them! The same sort of hedge can be found round some of the hop gardens.

In parts of Denmark, spruce belts are planted to prevent erosion on the light sandy soils. They are topped at about 9 ft. ($2\frac{3}{4}$ m.) and require no maintenance. Although they lack the variety of bird life and plant specimens to be found in a thorn hedge, the grass verge at the bottom is sufficient for gamebirds to nest in. Occasionally these Danish hedges are improved in appearance by being planted up with whitebeam on one side.

The value of hedges for providing shelter for cattle is well known, and there is evidence to show that cattle in exposed areas require more food to maintain themselves. Wind is the principal force that has an effect on animals; cattle will react to wind speeds of around 15 m.p.h. (24 k.p.h.) under dry conditions, while sheep react to even lower speeds. If rain is falling, the reactions of cattle and sheep occur at quite low wind speeds.

Soil erosion is not the only damage caused by wind in exposed areas. When the soil starts moving, many plants are buried, some are cut off at ground level and others are torn and blasted beyond hope of recovery. One of the favourite coloured slides used during lectures at Fordingbridge shows a dust storm in Cambridgeshire in which 30 acres (12 h.) of sugar-beet seed are blowing merrily across the main Newmarket road.

Hedges have a considerable ecological value. In an article in *Agriculture* two ecologists* made the following statement:

> 'As a national asset the loss of hedges at the present rate is disastrous and it is likely that the long-term effect will be to the disadvantage of agriculture in general.'

A well-kept hedge also provides nesting cover for many birds useful to the farmer. Among these are blackbirds, thrushes, hedge sparrows, linnets, yellowhammers, whitethroats, chaffinches, greenfinches and occasionally warblers. Between them they eat an enormous number of insect pests and weed seeds. Bullfinches can be a pest to the fruit farmers, but they are only locally common.

The value of the hedgerow to game is obviously immense. It provides nesting cover, food, shelter from the weather and a refuge from winged predators. It is also a natural travel lane for stoats, weasels, rats and other predators, and

---

* *Agriculture*, December 1963, J. M. May and B. N. K. Davis.

18

makes control by tunnel-trapping comparatively easy. The lee of a hedge provides an excellent place for winter feeding by hand or by hopper.

A hedge takes many years to grow to maturity, but may be removed in a matter of days. Its beneficial effects may not become apparent until after the damage is done.

Removing hedges: the farmer's point of view

When discussing the advantages of hedge removal with farmers, the four main reasons put forward are invariably increased cropping, couch control, saving of labour and maintenance, and ease of cultivation in larger, regular-shaped fields.

Increased cropping

Taking this factor first, it is interesting to calculate how much extra ground may be gained by enlarging the fields on a 1,000-acre (400 h.) unit. If the existing fields average 30 acres (12 h.) each and sufficient hedges are bulldozed out to double the field size into 60-acre (24 h.) units, the amount of ground gained will be only 3·7 acres (1·5 h.). This is allowing for hedges 9 ft. (3 m.) across. Norfolk hedges, including the grassy bank, are about 7 ft. (2·3 m.) across, which is quite sufficient for a partridge nest.

If the field size remains at 30 acres (12 h.) but barbed-wire fences are substituted for thorn hedges, what happens? If the 17 miles (27 km.) of hedges (7ft. [2 m.] wide) are replaced by barbed-wire fences (3ft. [0·9 m.] wide), the overall gain on the whole 1,000 acres (400 h.) would be about 8 acres (3 h.). By the time the farm income is taxed the financial gain cannot be very great.

What has been lost from the wildlife point of view by removing this length of hedgerows (over 6,000 yds. [5,500 m.])? On a partridge shoot with a density of a pair to 10 acres (4 h.), a possible 20 nests have been written off. If the ground is good partridge country, with a breeding potential of a pair to 5 acres (2 h.), a possible 40 nests or 600 eggs, have been sacrificed.

In America, the Wisconsin Conservation Department has shown that the reduction of bobwhite quail was directly related to the loss of hedgerow cover on a study area of 4,500 acres (1,820 h.). The population fell from a 'high' of 433 quail in 1933 to nil in 1959. When there was 1 mile (2 km.) of hedgerow to 450 acres (180 h.), the quail population averaged 23 birds per mile. When this ratio dropped to 1 mile (2 km.) of hedge per 650 acres (265 h.), the quail population disappeared completely.

Admittedly a partridge is not so dependent on hedgerows for nesting as a bobwhite quail, but in a hedge a gamebird is relatively safer than out in a farm crop, provided the area is effectively protected by tunnel traps.

19

2 Well maintained
hedges take up little
cropping space

3 Birds can dust
without disturbance
where a cultivated
strip is used for
couch control,
pedigree seed
growing and so on

20

Weed control

This is the biggest problem at present. Undoubtedly it will be solved economically within the next few years – one hopes before most of the hedges have been pulled out. Three methods of controlling couch are recommended:

1. Harrowing and burning. Probably the most common method, especially on flinty soils. It is cheap but not always very effective.

2. Controlled rotavating, which is very effective on medium and lighter soils: it should be carried out carefully when good growing conditions prevail. The technique is to chop the couch rhizomes continually, causing exhaustion and death by excessive growth (each individual rhizome running out of food reserves). Three rotary cultivations are usually required for a complete kill, and comparative trials have shown there is no need to wait for dry weather. The rhizomes must not be allowed to root and should be rotavated as soon as shoots 2 or 3 in. (5 or 7½ cm.) long appear, the timing being vital to the success of this method.

3. Chemical control using 'Gramoxone' or 'Round-Up'. One suggestion is that a 'no-man's land' of one or two sprayers' width should extend alongside the hedge, the chemical being sprayed and cultivated into the soil to stop the couch spreading from the hedge into the field. The hedges themselves should be tackled in rotation, as after spraying insufficient herbage will be left for nesting cover. In this way some hedge banks will always be available for cover.

Maintenance

Practical farmers seem to suggest that there is little economy to be gained by grubbing up a hedge, only to find that it must be replaced by wire fencing. An experienced agricultural consultant recently reported that wire fence maintenance costs, including crop loss, would not differ greatly from the maintenance cost of a normal well-kept hedge. Such a hedge will be far more durable than a fence, for many of Britain's hedges are over 200 years old and still stockproof, whereas a barbed-wire fence begins to deteriorate after 10 years. Many fences will be badly damaged if accidentally struck by a plough or a spray-boom, while a hedge accepts such knocks lightly.

There is also a mistaken impression that a hedge cannot be properly maintained by machine, but there is plenty of evidence to show that new thorn hedges can be kept in good shape by mechanical cutting, provided they have been laid once in their lifetime. As one of the winners of a national hedging championship said, 'You must have a frame to work on.'

The trimming of the bank is important, because grass and weed growth at the foot of the hedge grow faster than the hedge itself. This growth blocks out the sunlight from the hedge bottom, forcing the lower laterals to shoot upwards, eventually leaving a hedge which is inclined to grow out at the top and become bald at the bottom.

From then on it is only a short step to filling up the gaps with rusty bedsteads and finally bulldozing it right out. Old established thorn hedges, full of elder, hazel and privet, will naturally have to be weeded by hand, or the thorn will be killed out at the base. Unfortunately this is a skilled, expensive task, unless it can be a 'winter job' on the farm – to be fitted in whenever the weather calls a halt to other operations.

From the game point of view hedges should, if possible, be left undisturbed from two weeks before the commencement of nesting, i.e. about 14th March until 14th July, to allow any nesting birds, including the very early and the very late, to lay and hatch their broods and for the chicks to be old enough to fly away from working machinery. If this is not possible, the main danger period for pheasants and partridges is from 16th April to 30th June.

New hedges

New hedges should preferably be planted in a north–south line wherever possible so that one side of the hedge will not be in permanent shade, as is the case with an east–west hedge line. The Ministry of Agriculture will make a grant of nearly one quarter of the approved cost of the new hedge, provided protective fencing is erected to keep out stock and rabbits where required. But grants are always changing and it would be wise to consult the local ADAS officer.

Artificial nesting cover

If the surrounding nesting cover is poor, leys (temporary grass for mowing or grazing) can be a mixed blessing, for although they provide food during the winter they can become death traps at nesting time. Much, therefore, depends on the siting of the leys, but if there is no alternative, one can provide nesting sites along barbed-wire fences in the form of clumps of thorn-hedge trimmings – 3–4 yds. (3–4 m.) in length, pegged down if necessary. They will draw up the wild grasses, which can be further encouraged with a handful of fertiliser. These tiny nesting sanctuaries take up very little farming land – 250 cover just over a quarter of an acre ($\frac{1}{10}$ of a hectare). Field corners can also be wired off and planted up with suitable wild shrubs or thorns. The bases of electric power pylons can be treated in the same manner (these also make good sites for winter-feeding hoppers).

Dense overgrown hedges, which are often avoided by partridges – although usually suitable for pheasants – can be made more attractive to nesting birds if a wide bay is trimmed out of the thick cover. Nests will often be found among the new herbage and the stumps of elder, hazel or other shrubs which have been cut down. Some of the trimmings should be left on the ground to encourage the

22

4 Thorns planted in a wired-off corner provide a nesting sanctuary

5 Previously unproductive ground at the junction of two farm tracks has been planted with *Lonicera nitida*, *Crataegus prunifolia* and *Cotoneaster frigida* to give game cover on our Rockbourne study area

23

grass. It need hardly be said that it is inadvisable to plough right up to the edge of the fields, with the tractor wheel running down the bank.

New research results on hedgerows

Since the first edition of this book two major research projects have been undertaken on the importance of hedgerows to game and wildlife conservation. One of these is currently examining the use of hedges by beneficial predatory insects that may help to control cereal aphid outbreaks. The second concentrated on how hedge removal and management affected partridge breeding stocks. The practical implications of these projects are as follows:

1. When hedges are removed it will reduce the partridge population, but the severity of this will depend on two factors. Firstly, the amount of hedgerow remaining (i.e. the grubbing out of 1 km. of hedge is less damaging when there are 6 km. of hedgerow per km.² than when there are only 3 km. per km.²).

Secondly, the value of any particular hedge to partridges depends on its *quality*. Many hedges could be removed with little consequence; or better, improved by changes in their structure and so increase their attractiveness for partridges.

2. Simple changes to hedges can radically improve their quality. For instance, hedge width should be confined to between 2 m. and 3 m. since beyond these limits predation rates are higher. Similarly hedges should be kept between 1 and 2·5 m. in height. Lower hedges have poor ground cover, while higher ones suffer greater losses to predators. Where possible earth banks should be retained, or built up at the base of the hedge. This facilitates nest site drainage and also slightly reduces nest losses. For grey partridges at least 25 per cent of the base area of a hedge in January and February should be covered with residual dead grass (but no more than 50 per cent). In the case of the red-legged partridge, nettle is more important, and the preferred range is from 15 to 30 per cent.

3. These vegetation conditions are most often found, and easily maintained, in hedges that are cut once every other year. As we have already pointed out, stock should not be given access to the hedge bottoms, since they graze out residual cover; and mowing of grasses alongside the hedge should not be carried out between early March and end of June.

4. Beneficial insect predators which overwinter in hedges may also be found in grass strips between fields or beneath shelter belts of mature deciduous trees. As long as the boundary to a field is reasonably distinct from the field itself in terms of structure (raised banks) or vegetation (dead grasses, hedgerow trees and shrubs), predatory insects will take refuge there during the winter. This aspect of the biology of hedgerows is an added bonus to those who already maintain cover for nesting partridge.

Chapter 2
Some Effects of Farming Operations on Game

The shooting man who is not himself a farmer may fail to appreciate just how necessary it is for an efficient agriculturist to carry out the many operations which can have a detrimental effect on game and wildlife. The farmer who is keen on shooting will usually be able to combine both aspects of land use – producing food and enjoying good shooting.

As has been said, the pressures from agriculture are on two main fronts: first, the loss of good habitat, and secondly, direct or indirect harm to game from certain chemicals and machines. Even the farm tracks, which on intensively farmed areas are often the only 'drying-out' areas available to gamebirds, can become death-traps for young birds in June and July. Whole broods of young pheasants or partridges which, given a little time, could have run to safety, are often crushed beneath the wheels of speeding tractors and faster vehicles.

These losses tend to be accentuated by the labyrinth of wires which now surround and cross over so many fields. Parts of the countryside have been referred to as 'birdcage Britain'! These barbed-wire fences, telegraph and electric cables, which under normal conditions the birds may avoid, can exert a heavy toll on gamebirds in panic flight, particularly at dusk. Farm workers can be helpful in reducing this type of disturbance when they drive home in the evenings.

Losses in grass crops
It has proved impossible to assess with any degree of accuracy the actual losses of sitting gamebirds, their eggs and young, during hay and silage making, as many of the smashed eggs and dead birds remain hidden under swaths of grass. The casualties vary from season to season and farm to farm, but from sample records collected on several estates over a great number of years, it is believed that the total damage sustained is very great.

When attempting to limit the losses, there are two lines to pursue – offensive and defensive. First one should endeavour to *discourage* the birds from nesting in the grass, but if these efforts fail an attempt must then be made to save lives at cutting time.

A March partridge pair count will indicate where the breeding stock is heaviest and – related to the alternative shelter available – will give an idea of where trouble may be expected. Obviously fewer birds will nest in the grass crops if there is a good distribution of hedgerow cover. Early in the season disturbance of likely nesting fields by light rolling – before the grass is 6 in. (15 cm.) high – will often force pairs to nest elsewhere. Vulnerable fields can also be dogged regularly each day to make them unattractive to intending nest-builders.

Some casualties to sitting pheasants and partridges will nevertheless be inevitable, but if *late cuts for silage and early cuts for hay are avoided*, major losses will be averted. The time when the fields will be full of birds is between 21st May and 20th June.

Depending upon the seasonal conditions the date of a first silage cut may vary considerably, but in most years it should take place between the 1st and 20th May. An 'early' field once cut and cleared should be left undisturbed for as long as possible. If a silage cut is followed by a crop of hay, a field can be left considerably longer, allowing gamebirds a good chance of hatching their clutches and the chicks being able to flutter away from working machinery.

By selecting a suitable strain of grass which would normally be mature before the peak danger period to game, and where possible by ringing the changes between silage, hay and grazing (so that the grass will be too short or undisturbed during the peak danger period), a certain amount can be done to avoid the worst of the casualties. Incidentally although extra nitrogenous fertilisers provide greatly increased bulk, they do not advance the cutting date – except for a day or two. They can, however, be used to discourage birds from nesting in silage fields, when early and medium grass varieties are selected. The first technique is to give an early application of nitrogen, so that the crop will be *too thick* for the birds to nest in during the latter half of April. The alternative method is to graze the field as hard as possible with sheep or cattle until the end of April, so that *insufficient cover* for nesting remains. A fertiliser dressing immediately after grazing should produce sufficient growth for a grass cut at the end of June. Where the grazing stock is available the second alternative is more effective, and of course both methods are dependent on weather conditions.

Cutting precautions
From a game point of view it is always advantageous to start cutting in the centre of a field and work outwards, thus driving any birds towards the hedges. If diagonals are cut across the field to start with, to allow trailers easy access to the centre and to ease turning at the corners, cutting from the centre need not be any trouble and may save birds. Irregular fields, or those on a slope, will be more difficult, and even in these cases cutting should start from the centre, working towards the longest headlands.

26

Recently the strip method of cutting has been widely adopted as being the quickest and easiest way of clearing a field. Where this method is practised, it is important that the headland is no wider than 15 yds. (14 m.), for the birds are reluctant to leak out of a centre strip across a wider headland.

Where chicks are known to be in the crop, a preferable alternative from the game point of view is to leave an uncut grass headland of 15–20 yds. (14–18 m.) wide until last. The centre of the field is cut in strips in the normal fashion and broods from the centre will tend to filter into the uncut headland, which is cut from the inside towards the hedge. This method gradually drives broods towards safe cover.

Whatever method is used when grass cutting, if an area of standing grass is rapidly decreasing at the centre of the headlands, it is always worth walking through alone, or with a dog, to flush any birds concentrated in the remaining cover.

If the last little patch to be cut is in the centre of the field, it will materially help young pheasants in the crop if the final cutting can be left until the following morning, thereby enabling the birds to draw out at night.

In some areas, where a high dry-matter silage is produced, the freshly cut grass is allowed to remain in the swath for several hours – a practice known as wilting. This introduces yet another field operation likely to disturb game as the forage harvester is then driven up the rows of drying grass. Many farmers also use a machine called a crimper, which enables hay to be baled in a very short period compared with a decade ago. Unfortunately the crimper affords little chance of survival for the game chicks huddled under a swath of hay.

Flushing bars

Trials using different types of flushing bar have been going on for many years: the perfect model – indeed even a reasonably efficient and simple model – *has not yet been evolved.* Our experience has been that the spring steel tine clamped to a square bar is the most effective type in thick grass crops. Like any other implement, the flushing bar must be used correctly to gain maximum effect. The tines must touch the ground and the tractor driver encouraged (a tip for each nest saved is probably most effective) to drive at a reasonable speed. The keeper should also have broody bantams or an incubator running steadily for any salvaged eggs.

Grazing

Paddock-grazing is now well established and requires less labour than strip-grazing. Each paddock, made with semi-permanent electric fencing, is of such a size as to allow one or two days' grazing for the milking herd. The value of this for the gamekeeper is that it reduces the concentration of cattle in a confined area, giving partridges with very young chicks time to move away. When strip-grazing, cattle are on a very concentrated front, inevitably

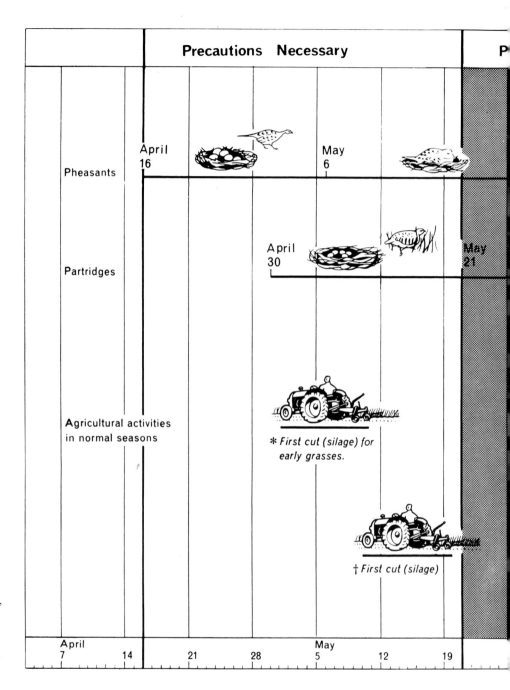

Precautions   Necessary

P

Pheasants	April 16	May 6
Partridges	April 30	May 21

Agricultural activities in normal seasons

* *First cut (silage) for early grasses.*

† *First cut (silage)*

6 *Italian ryegrass, perennial ryegrass except S.23

†For timothy, meadow fescue and lucerne

April 7   14   21   28   May 5   12   19

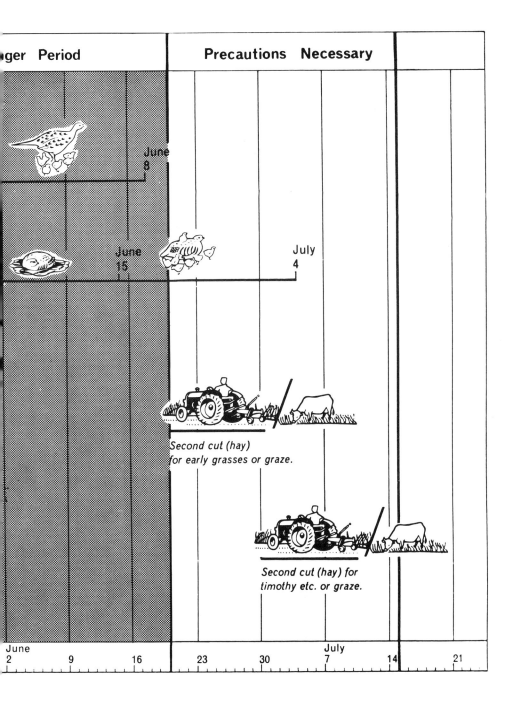

ger Period   **Precautions Necessary**

June
8

June   July
15   4

Second cut (hay)
for early grasses or graze.

Second cut (hay) for
timothy etc. or graze.

June
2   9   16   23   30   July   14   21
                                              7

29

trampling over nests and either smashing eggs or scattering the baby partridges. With both strip-grazing and paddock-grazing, it is desirable to put an electric fence along the hedgerows, thus preventing cattle eating out the hedge bottoms and destroying nests.

Straw burning

The continuing increase in the total cereal acreage coupled with a decrease in the agricultural labour force means that straw and stubble burning is always likely to be undertaken – particularly in the eastern counties. A decline in the traditional markets for straw (bedding for cattle and industrial paper- and board-making processes) has been partly offset by an increase in demand for straw to be cubed for feeding. The damaging effect on wildlife by burning straw and stubble has been considerable, especially when high winds fanned speeding flames and formed a ring of fire around a field. These fires were often started in the evening and left to burn out through the night. There is conflicting evidence about direct burning of pheasants and partridges. Although some burned bodies were found, the birds might have been killed during harvesting or have died naturally before the straw was burned.

Reared pheasants will sometimes panic and scatter if straw is burned anywhere near their release point or covert. More important is the fact that badly burned grain is unpalatable to pheasants and partridges, and even pigeons will not touch it. In past seasons, when conditions have not been so dry, straw has burned in swathes or windrows without setting alight to the actual stubbles. Some 6–8 weeks afterwards (especially in a wet autumn) weed growth has been observed along the burned swathes which can provide some food for partridges. However, in a very dry year this small benefit does not occur, and the countryside in predominantly arable areas presents a bleak prospect to gamebirds in search of food. The solution to the problem is not at all clear, and the fact will have to be accepted that straw burning is here at least for some time.

If straw is burned, precautions must be taken, and the N.F.U. has produced a code of practice. A short list of precautions with game in mind would be:

Never start fires in the evening and let them burn out overnight.

If possible, 'dog' the field before burning. Alternatively, a few fast runs across the field with a tractor or Land-Rover would help to flush any birds off the field.

Never start fires around the perimeter of the field, thus trapping wildlife in the middle.

Burn upwind whenever possible.

Careful supervision of any fires should always be undertaken, and changes of wind direction and strength must be carefully noted.

Always provide some sort of firebreak near hedges, shelter belts, and valuable grassy nesting cover.

7 Strip-grazing cattle often trample gamebird nests

8 Uncontrolled straw burning causes losses of birds and may destroy the habitat

31

9 Strips of mustard or kale alongside hedges and plantations provide a firebreak and give cover

The ideal firebreak would be a strip of kale (sown in April/May) along the edges of particularly valuable shelter belts, coverts or hedges. After harvest, a ploughed firebreak at least 10 furrows wide is a minimum precaution to take.

A Hampshire farmer who damaged some shelter belts and hedges while burning straw decided that in future he would encircle each of his arable fields with firebreaks of rape and turnips sown early in June. These firebreaks were very effective in preventing further damage and so provided excellent game-holding strips during the winter.

Where *stubble* burning is considered as a means of controlling cereal weeds and diseases, the alternative control methods using chemicals (e.g. 'Gramoxone') or cultivations might be preferable. Although stubbles will still disappear, there is less direct risk to permanent cover such as hedges, grass banks and spinneys.

Irrigation

Irrigation is an agricultural practice which has an economic value over a surprisingly large part of Britain, despite our seemingly damp climate. Some shooting men may not be conversant with the details involved or the possible effect of irrigation upon game.

The agricultural crops which are most economic to irrigate are sugar beet, potatoes, grass and kale. The minimum area for irrigation is reckoned to be 20 acres (8 h.).

32

Japanese Pheasant *lithograph from Gould 'Birds of Asia'*

Some Predators of Game 'Tooth and Claw' *C. F. Tunnicliffe*

An indirect effect of irrigation is the tendency towards block cropping; for example, 40–60 acres (16–24 h.) of potatoes in one block so that the maximum area can be covered with as little labour requirement as possible for moving pipes. With a smaller pump unit, an alternative effect will be that root crops are rotated around fields within close reach of the water source to cut down capital expenditure on a long header line, as well as loss of water pressure at the sprinklers.

The worst direct effect is probably caused by the portable main header line being laid along a hedge bank. This will cause disturbance to nesting birds, not only when the main line is being put down and taken up but also at each move (every 2 to 4 hours) of the lateral sprinkler line. Our recommendation is that the main header line is laid down along the headland *as far from the hedge bank as possible.*

A further direct effect will be spray falling on the hedge bank at nesting time. Wild pheasant nests will be susceptible between mid-April and early June when the hens will be sitting and hatching. Partridges, with their shorter sitting/hatching period, will be very vulnerable between 30th April and 20th June. The sitting hen may be forced to desert her hedgerow nest under heavy spray. If she does return, the eggs may be soaked and thus have a much reduced chance of hatching out successfully. After hatching, chicks may well become sodden and chilled in the first few days of life as they forage in the nearby crop, and this is a further hazard which can be avoided if care is taken in laying down the sprinkler line.

'Killer' crops

There are some farm crops which present particular dangers to wild game stocks, either because of their growth characteristics or because of harvesting methods.

Cocksfoot grass, grown for seed in 14-in. or 21-in. (36 cm. or 53 cm.) drills, falls in the first category. The crop produces a strong, bushy growth which provides a 'ridge and furrow' pattern of ground cover. Both pheasants and partridges have shown a preference for siting their nests in this crop even when good hedges around the field offer apparently ideal breeding cover. Birds choosing to nest in the middle of a large field of cocksfoot give their chicks little chance of survival. Young chicks can stray and get lost easily in such thick cover, and in a wet spell they will be chilled or even 'drowned' for lack of drying-out space. To discourage birds from nesting in the crop, the principal deterrent will be to cultivate between the rows (a normal weed-killing practice) as late as possible, with the intention of destroying early nests, in the hope that birds will re-nest in a safe hedge.

The experts at Fordingbridge have been trying to turn this attraction for cocksfoot to the benefit of game management by sowing cocksfoot nesting strips of only one drill wide (6–8 ft. [2–2½ m.]). This provides ideal nesting cover

33

alongside hedges, fences or stone walls, at the same time overcoming the disadvantages mentioned above.

Many varieties of *field peas* are grown for cattle feed, canning, freezing or hand-picking for direct retail sale. Peas for cattle feed are often dried on tripods and provide very attractive food and cover for the game where this practice is carried out. When grown for canning or freezing the harvesting methods provide a very different aspect. In order to harvest the peas at the correct stage, machinery carries on throughout the night with pea harvesters, lorries and tractors surrounded by spotlights, often moving at high speed. This activity leads to great disturbance and may lead to mortality among wild game broods, for unfortunately the pea-growing areas are centred in good wild game country in East Anglia and East Scotland. Very little can be done to protect birds apart from flushing them out of the peas with dogs early in the season to reduce the risk of broods being in the crop at harvest time.

10 Drills of cocksfoot alongside a fence or hedge give useful nesting cover at low cost

Farm chemicals

Some of the chemicals used on farms have proved poisonous to birds while others appear to have no directly harmful effects. Fortunately the general trend today is towards more selective chemicals which are poisonous only to certain

34

weeds or insect pests; and some of the more general 'killers' which were in use just after the last war are already obsolete. In recent years herbicides have rarely been connected with any losses to game and wildlife. However, their indirect effect in reducing the weeds on which many invertebrates feed has generally reduced the amount of food available to gamebird chicks during the critical first week or two after hatching. Some insecticides can be directly harmful to gamebirds and mammals, but their use is much more restricted than the ubiquitous herbicides. The countrywide scare resulting from the numerous bird deaths reported in the spring of 1961 led to the voluntary banning of the more poisonous and persistent seed dressings (e.g. aldrin, dieldrin, heptachlor) on spring-sown corn. Now that dressings containing these chemicals are used only when special circumstances exist (e.g. heavy wheat-bulb fly infestation) gamebird losses resulting from seed-dressing poisoning have rarely been reported. For insecticide dressing on spring-sown corn the less poisonous (and apparently repellent) BHC is generally acceptable. The dangers from the very persistent insecticide D.D.T.* are now widely recognised, and this chemical should *not* be used if an effective alternative is available that breaks down more quickly.

The other group of insecticides which may occasionally cause trouble are those designed to control the various green-fly that may infest sugar beet, beans and brussels sprouts. These insecticides may be either systemic (i.e. they are taken in by the plant and kill insects which suck plant juices) or act on contact. Systemic insecticides can be applied as a seed dressing (e.g. to field beans), scattered as granules on the soil surface between the growing plants, or applied as a spray on the vegetation. While insecticides of all these types have been suspected of causing damage to gamebirds or their chicks, little real evidence exists. But the farmer who is concerned about his gamebirds and wildlife should know that it is this group of farm chemicals which is most likely to be a threat to game chick survival and he should use them only when no other alternative exists.

'Gramoxone' and game

'Gramoxone' is one of the first chemicals to appear on the farming scene which promises to be of positive help in increasing gamebird stocks. There are three main ways in which 'Gramoxone' can be useful to the farmer who wishes to conserve his gamebirds. These are stubble cleaning, couch control and sod-seeding of game crops.

The low dosage rate (less than 2 pints of 'Gramoxone' per acre) on stubbles should encourage farmers to use this economical method of cleaning. The fields

---

*The law regarding the use of D.D.T. (the subject of a voluntary restriction at present) is soon likely to change.

can then be left unploughed through the winter – to the great benefit of wild gamebirds.

'Gramoxone' sprayed on headlands helps to suppress couch grass and, where combined with frequent cultivation, provides dusty drying-out strips for gamebird chicks which would otherwise perish in the thick corn crops and hedgerow banks during a wet summer. These strips are of particular importance since agricultural production has become more intensive. This has left fewer dusty tracks around fields. As we have said, present-day farm tracks are in such constant use by Land-Rovers, tractors and trailers, and sometimes lorries, that they present a considerable hazard to gamebirds.

The use of 'Gramoxone' in the normal way will make it much easier for farmers to plan strategically-sited patches of kale, fodder radish or mustard. These can be sod-seeded into a grass sward with a minimum amount of time, labour and disturbance.

Many farmers have found 'Gramoxone' a useful aid in keeping the farmyard tidy by spraying nettles, weeds and annual grasses alongside walls and in awkward corners. However, if this principle is extended to the farm as a whole and 'Gramoxone' is sprayed along fence-lines, under pylons, along every hedge bottom and every rough corner, the resulting loss of nesting cover to wild birds would be disastrous. If sprayed directly on to pheasant eggs it has been shown that hatchability can be adversely affected and, useful as 'Gramoxone' is for many purposes, moderation is suggested with regard to clinical tidiness on the farm – if the owner is interested in his game crop and the four or five months' sport that it can bring.

Safety precautions

Under modern farming conditions insecticidal sprays and other chemicals are recognised as very valuable aids to maximum crop production, but it may be worth noting some precautions which can be taken by any farmer to reduce the risks to wildlife.

(a) Always use the least toxic chemical which will do the job efficiently.

(b) If it is necessary to use a dangerous chemical, restrict it to the area (one crop, or part of a crop) where it is needed.

(c) Keep the sprayer away from field hedge banks, especially at nesting time, and do not contaminate any water which birds might drink.

(d) Complete any weedkilling with known poisonous sprays *as early in the season as possible*, before partridges hatch and before there are many pheasant chicks in the corn.

(e) If poisonous sprays have to be used on brassicas (cabbages, kale, rape, mustard, etc.), *spray before the cereal harvest* so that birds still have safe alternative cover in the standing corn.

(f) Do not leave in the fields any tins or receptacles which have contained poison, any puddles of concentrated spray, or heaps of dressed seed corn.

(g) Where toxic seed-dressed corn is concerned, make sure the seed is properly buried under the surface, and no heaps of corn are left as tempting food.

Shortage of insect life – the effect on partridges

Directly and indirectly modern agricultural methods have reduced the number of insects – both pest species and useful ones – on the average farm. This has affected the survival of partridge chicks, in some cases drastically. The subject is discussed in the next chapter.

Chapter 3
Wild Partridges: Some Reasons for the Decline

Before discussing the shortage of food insects that are so vital to the survival of partridge chicks, we must consider partridge (*Perdix perdix*) losses generally. A later chapter deals with the red-legged species.

Partridge numbers are limited by three main types of losses. Those that occur between August and March are termed 'winter losses'. Sitting hens and their clutches lost during the breeding season are referred to as 'nest losses', and the third and most important group is termed 'chick loss', due to mortality in young partridges usually less than six weeks old.

Much of the following information has been obtained from a lengthy study on twelve farms, comprising our West Sussex study area.

(i) Although termed 'winter losses' the weather itself is usually of little importance and over the period 1968–73 these losses averaged 50 per cent and showed little annual variation. Nearly three quarters of the variation that did occur within the study area, and in different years, could be explained in terms of the density and age and sex structure of the August population. Losses were greatest when densities were high, and among single old cocks and young birds. Of the two, the August density was slightly more important than age and sex structure.

Although in areas shot over, 28 per cent of the birds were killed, there was no significant increase in overall losses. This suggested that there was some compensation for mortality caused by shooting, aided by immigration from the periphery of the shot areas.

(ii) Nest losses showed considerable annual variation and averaged 57 per cent over the six years 1968–73. They generally increased with breeding density, but this was less marked on keepered areas. *Good keepering and management can nearly halve nest losses.*

Even in keepered areas most nest losses are due to predation – particularly foxes on our own study area: this is accentuated on unkeepered areas where magpies and crows may be serious egg thieves.

11 Biologist and insect-suction 'hoover'

(iii) Over the six-year period the chick loss averaged 64 per cent. Although only a small percentage of the total variation in chick survival could not be explained by differences in chick food availability, the modifying effects of weather and keepering were taken into consideration.

Weather, although by itself not very important, aggravates the effect of food shortages and predator attacks by increasing the time when chicks are exposed searching for food. It may also increase the incidence of disease, particularly 'gapes'. When, due to inclement weather, suitable insect food is scarce, partridge chicks may feed on other invertebrates which may be infested with gapeworm larvae. Such infestations are particularly liable to occur where reared pheasant density is high and concentrated. On both our present study area and on our earlier shoot in Hampshire the incidence of gapes in partridges increased with higher reared pheasant densities – particularly in the vicinity of release pens.

Good partridge management implies a knowledge of the breeding densities and chick survival rates to which any shooting programmes must be adjusted. (Obviously this is virtually impossible on unkeepered land or for a non-resident syndicate.) It can also improve nesting success and chick survival rates, but

39

may not significantly affect the level of winter loss. In recent decades – as mentioned earlier – the main limiting factor in partridge production has been a deterioration in the abundance of suitable partridge chick food.

Whereas in the past effective predator control was by itself sufficient to increase partridge abundance, this is no longer true. Nesting cover is often lacking or poorly distributed, and ameliorating measures such as avoiding further hedgerow destruction, filling in of dry pits or levelling of banks, coupled with the protection of hedge bottoms from grazing, should be taken. On the average farm it is surprising how many odd parcels of land – useless for cropping – can be turned into valuable partridge cover.

The most important limiting factor – the lack of adequate insect chick food – is more difficult to correct. While a return to a system similar to the Norfolk four course rotation – including most kinds of traditional ley farming – would do much to improve the situation, we realise that this is rarely practical at the present time.

12 The effects of bad weather. See p. 39.

Distribution of insects across a field of winter wheat

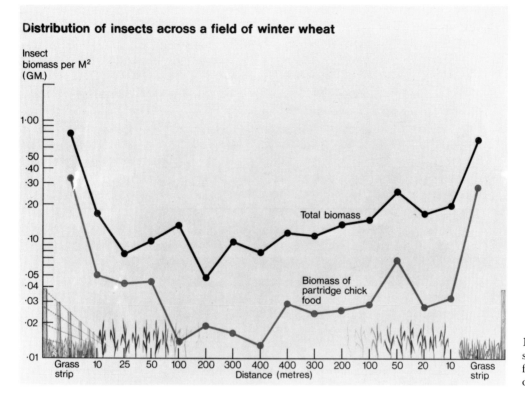

Insect biomass per M² (GM.)

Total biomass

Biomass of partridge chick food

Distance (metres)

Grass strip · 10 · 25 · 50 · 100 · 200 · 300 · 400 · 400 · 300 · 200 · 100 · 50 · 20 · 10 · Grass strip

13 'Insects suitable for partridge chicks . . .'

Availability of sawflies in relation to brood size of partridges

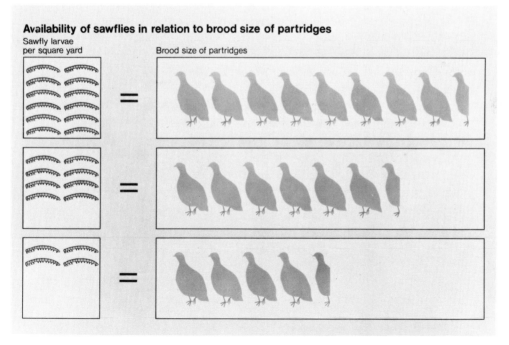

Sawfly larvae per square yard

Brood size of partridges

14 'Availability of sawflies . . .'

41

Systems in which 25 per cent of the cereals are undersown with grass and clovers are ideal, especially where the cereal/grass ratio is about 6:4. Undersowing allows the build-up of one of the partridge chick's most valuable sources of food – the larvae of species of sawfly (*Dolerus* spp.). These grubs, although harmless to the corn, are large enough and move sufficiently slowly to be readily taken by partridge chicks. A small number of these grubs can soon fill a young partridge's crop! The preservation of grass headlands, and the growing of winter corn (wheat or barley) are all steps in the right direction. Refraining from the use of pesticides would be irresponsible, although not infrequently these chemicals are over-used and insufficiently selective. There are good insects as well as bad ones! Straw burning may be necessary at the present time, but its ill-effects can be minimised. Certainly it destroys valuable insects in the stubble.

The effects of direct drilling have not yet been assessed, but any attempt to minimise cultivations (even by using herbicides) in arable systems may improve the chances of producing adequate chick food supplies without increasing the risk of any pest attack on the crops.

The selection of crops, such as lucerne, which can be rich in suitable insects, will help. It must, however, be appreciated that when 'cropping for insects' it can take time for them to build up, if the ground starts with a relatively low insect population.

The key to partridge chick survival is a sufficiency of insects of the right sort, in the right place, at the right time.

New information since the last edition

In the decade since the above was written, much more has been learned about the conservation of partridges on modern farms. Studies have also extended to other countries with very different farmland landscapes and game management policies.

As a result it must be emphasised that poor insect supplies set the upper limit to grey partridge numbers only where the nesting habitat is already suitably dispersed and of the right quality, and where nest predation is under control.*

Any insect conservation measure must not interfere with farming and so far only one method has been proven; restricting the use of herbicides along cereal headlands, the aim being to encourage certain broad-leaved weeds and therefore the insects which depend on them. Such reserved headlands amounting to only 2 per cent of the crop area have added an average of two or three chicks per brood to the August population. Even smaller percentages will suffice where there is a traditional system of undersowing. An important point is that partridge chicks like the cover of cereal crops – we have found it difficult

*Potts 1980, *Advances in Ecological Research* Vol. 11, 1–80.

to attract them on to special weedy patches. However on the reserved headlands great care is needed with the restriction of herbicides in order to prevent weed encroachment; precise details are still being worked out by the Cereals and Gamebirds Research Project.

Chapter 4
Enemies of Game: Part 1 Winged Predators

Good game country with carefully preserved habitat and sympathetic farming cannot produce a good yield of birds if the land is swarming with their enemies. And more prey – in the form of game – tends to mean more predators. Equally, on an estate which is well trapped, but devoid of cover and hammered by intensive agricultural practices, there can only be a very limited stock of game. The right environment coupled with some control of essential predators will produce results.

Trapping is one of the most important skills required of a good keeper. Planning and preserving the correct habitat should be the task of his employer.

In the old days a keeper had five main duties to perform: keeping poachers at bay, trapping 'vermin', nest management, feeding and sometimes rearing. The habitat was there, and rarely needed any improving.

With most game species predator control is still an essential task.

Why control is necessary

It is an accepted principle that weeds, insect pests, rodents and even predatory fish must be suppressed or restricted if maximum food and timber crops are to be harvested. The same applies to wild game.

Some old-fashioned keepers misguidedly try to eliminate every bird or animal which even looks as if it might be harmful to game. On the other hand, there are estate owners who will not have a trap on the place in the hopes that the 'balance of nature' will take care of everything. This is unrealistic. There is no known instance in this country of a completely 'natural' shoot which has produced a reasonable surplus of game over a period of years.

Predator control must be selective, not wanton. Only rarely is it necessary – as with rats – to aim at near-extermination. At other times, in the case of rooks for example, it is a question of reducing the population to reasonable levels. With some species such as badgers, it occasionally becomes necessary to put down the odd 'rogue' (but see footnote overleaf).

The law

A careful study should be made of the Wildlife and Countryside Act (1981), as well as any other relevant legislation, before embarking on any pest or predator control. This Act gives lists of species that are allowed to be controlled, either at all times or only at certain specific times, as well as lists showing those species that are fully protected.*

Winged predators and pests

Rook

In the last few decades the rook has greatly increased in numbers in most parts of the country. Its food habits have also changed to the detriment of the game population.

No gamekeeper doubts the damage and disturbance caused by this species during the nesting season, particularly where nests are exposed or are in open situations. During a six-year period on our Hampshire experimental estate, rooks and crows headed the list of nest destroyers for three seasons. Though, by contrast, one spring when there was an early growth of cover the losses to corvids were nil.

As to the intelligence of the crow family, they have been known to watch for partridges entering their nest runways. They will also go 'egging' along fences, hedgerows and stone walls, and are equally clever at raiding any nests in the uncut patches left by an observant tractor-driver when cutting hay.

At our former experimental gamefarm, the pheasant laying pens were for some time raided by birds from a rookery 3 miles away. At least 150 eggs were found in the pens, broken and sucked by the rooks, and hundreds of others were carried off. More than one gamefarmer has found it economic to buy laying-pen roof netting – the eggs saved from corvids have soon repaid the cost.

In most cases where nests are robbed by corvids, partridges and pheasants will lay again – but it is preferable for the game preserver to undertake the nest management, rather than leave it to the rooks.

The rook's egg-stealing habits are often shown up most noticeably on estates where the Euston system is practised. (Under this system partridge eggs are replaced by dummies, the real eggs being safely incubated by broodies or in incubators and returned to the nest when they start to chip.) There are innumerable records of dummy partridge eggs being found scattered about the fields or recovered at the foot of rookery trees in hundreds!

The table on page 47 shows the causes of losses among partridge nests found on the 4,000-acre (1,620 h.) experimental estate during 1948–59. The

*The law is fully explained in *Shooting and Stalking*, edited by Charles Coles, Chapter 4 'The Law and Shooting' by P. A. Gouldsbury (Stanley Paul, £12.95).

accompanying diagram (Figure 15) illustrates the proportion of these losses caused by various predators. It is seen at a glance how many are due to corvids. The table and diagram do not include pheasant nest losses which could quite easily be as high – or higher – since pheasants do not cover their eggs in the same way as partridges, making the nests more readily visible from above.

Beside the obvious crime of nest-robbing, rooks should be considered as potential hosts of gapeworms which could affect gamebirds. An examination of young rooks from Dorset and Hampshire estates showed that the birds each had an average of 10 pairs of gapeworms – with individual worm burdens of up to 30 pairs.

Control methods

The adult rook can be controlled in much the same way as the crow, and some suggestions for trapping, shooting and so on will be found under that heading. But as prevention is better than cure, the fundamental way is to go for the rookeries. A co-ordinated campaign with neighbours is preferable to a lone effort.

We have undertaken trials of 'Lepco' bird-scaring ropes, hung as high as possible in rookery trees, which give out loud reports every 20 minutes and cause the rooks to desert during a frosty night. The rope of 'bangers' should be hauled up into the treetops inside an oil drum from which the bottom has been removed. This will prevent rain from damping the fuse and also amplify the detonations.

During one trial, in early April, complete desertion of the rookery was obtained after 20 consecutive hours of explosions. Resistance to chilling varied with local conditions, weather, site and stage of incubation (the period of incubation is 16–18 days). Early embryos of 1–4 days died in a few hours as a result of exposure, but those of 7–10 days survived periods of chilling three or four times as long. The third week in March would probably be a satisfactory date for the first attack in a normal year. If the birds subsequently return to the rookery and start to lay again, it will be necessary to institute a second campaign with bird-scarers several days later.

Always check local by-laws before using bangers at night. Regulations may prevent their use during the hours of darkness.

Partridge nest losses on the 4,000-acre (1,620 h.) experimental shoot 1948–59

Total nests found	3,133
Total successful nests	1,812
Total unsuccessful nests	1,321

Causes of nest failure:

Predators		Farm activities		Various		Unknown	Picked up
Winged	142	Grass cutting	275	Human interference	39	258	94
Fox	110	Other farm work	87	Keeper	17		
Badger	39			Mole	17		
Rat	38			Pheasant	23		
Stoat	38			Disease	4		
Cat	33			Accidental death	11		
Hedgehog	33			Weather	16		
Dog	18			Fowl	1		
Grey Squirrel	4			Redleg partridge	1		
Unidentified	18			Other *Perdix*	2		
				Hedging	1		
				Rabbiting	2		
Total	473	Total	362	Total	134	Total 258	Total 94

Total destroyed or 'unsuccessful' nests: 1,321

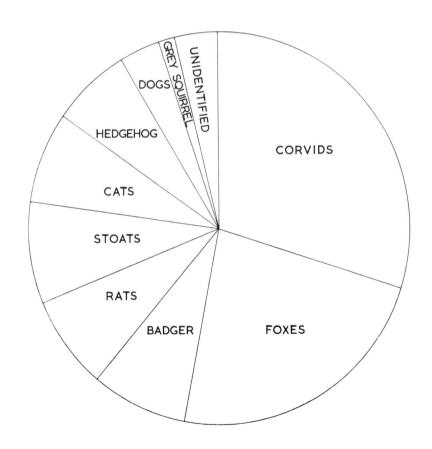

15 Proportion of nests lost to various predators (based on 473 nests on our experimental shoot, 1948–59)

47

The next move against rooks can be made in the second and third weeks of May, before foliage gets too dense, when the fledgling rooks or 'branchers' may be shot with a ·22 rifle. In this way a rookery can be thinned to reasonable proportions. Rook shooting used to be a traditional country sport in England and shooting the branchers' with a rifle and telescopic sight is a humane and inexpensive way of checking an increase in population. With hollow-point bullets it is 'hit or miss', with little chance of wounding. Rook pie is also a fair dish – always provided the pastry is good, and there is more egg and gammon than rook!

Once the rooks have flown, a good method of catching them is to build a rook cage trap. Successful types are described on pages 52–54.

From October onwards good bags of rooks, crows and jackdaws – up to 40 during an evening – can be made by shooting the birds as they flight in to their communal winter roosts at dusk.

Carrion and hooded crow

The above remarks about rooks as pests apply even more to crows. They are expert nest thieves and swift killers of young gamebirds. A single pair of carrion crows which nested on the boundary of our Sussex study area destroyed over 200 game eggs that we were able to count!

They can also cause havoc among wild duck nests and in mallard nesting baskets if the entrance is too large.

Control methods

The offensive against crows should start in the breeding season and a pair should never be allowed to nest on the shoot. If all old nests (and grey squirrel dreys) are destroyed, or poked down every year when the leaf is off the tree, the task of spotting new nests will be much easier.

Some keepers prefer to let a pair of crows build their nest, lay the clutch and start to sit. It is then usually quite easy to shoot first the male and then the female. Hides sometimes have to be employed.

If an unsuccessful attempt is made to shoot the birds as they leave the nest, they will become even more alert and suspicious. As soon as a person enters the field, they leave the nest. On such occasions, they can be dealt with at night by using a strong spotlight when the birds are at the nest. It requires two people to carry out the operation: one to handle the light and the other using the gun. Frequently both cock and hen can be shot in this way.

In spring, it can be useful to carry a dead crow in the game bag as a lure. When a crow is seen sitting in a tree and calling, it is often possible to attract the perching crow by first calling it and then throwing the dead crow high up in the air – as is done with woodpigeons. The crow invariably flies closer to investigate and comes within gunshot.

Other lures which will bring birds within shotgun range include white ferrets, stuffed or rubber crows and magpies; and on the Continent tame eagle owls.

In the United States, crow decoying or calling is a sport in its own right. In addition to decoys and inexpensive bird-calls, recorded sounds are often played on amplifiers to attract these wary birds within range. The fighting and feeding calls are the most tempting and the ones we have used very successfully.

Crow shooting is not to be despised – whether over decoys or using a crow-call. In this way, for example, the young shot can learn about woodcraft, camouflage and hide-building. For many townspeople and even country youngsters, crows and grey squirrels provide the only shooting readily obtainable – and give good training for those who will graduate to game shooting and stalking.

Several types of cage traps which can be used for rooks, jackdaws, etc., are illustrated on page 53. In Scotland, hooded crows have occasionally been caught in cages of this type using dead sheep as bait. Carrion is usually a better draw than freshly killed meat.

There is some doubt as to whether cage traps have ever been very successful in catching carrion crows, since young rooks are often mistakenly identified as crows. (Hoodies are equally, if not more, difficult to take than carrion crows.) There is no difficulty in distinguishing between *adult* rooks and crows: the bare skin around the base of the rook's beak, the purple sheen on the plumage and the narrow beak, lacking any suggestion of the crow's hooked tip, are all well-known distinguishing features.

However, the separation of *young* rooks and crows is another matter. There is a 'wing formula' which is clear-cut and infallible. In the rook the second primary (from the outside) is longer than the sixth, while in a crow the second is shorter than the sixth. Expressed in another way, this means that there are *four* primaries longer than the second in the crow and only *three* in the rook (see Figure 16).

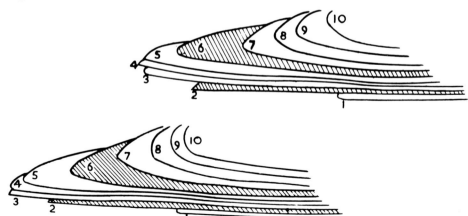

16 Crow. Second primary shorter than sixth primary
   Rook. Second primary longer than sixth primary

49

Baits to attract crows to spring traps, where these are permitted,* include such unsavoury items as rabbits' heads with an eye exposed, dead rats with paunch protruding, bad fish and, of course, eggs – particularly half-incubated ones. Pheasant and bantam eggs in artificial nests are very successful in attracting rooks, crows and jackdaws. Most gamebirds are, of course, drawn by eggs in the open and this danger must be borne in mind.

The baited trap should naturally be sited in a safe place such as inside an open wire-netting pen, on a small island or a raft.

The crow is an extremely wary, suspicious bird and trap-baits should be placed so as to make use of plough furrows, tree roots or tussocks of grass as natural-looking barriers to guide the crows over the concealed pan of the trap to the bait. A crow will invariably peck first at the eyes of its victim, and if the bait is a rabbit's or sheep's head, the position of the eye in relation to the pan of the trap should be carefully considered.

Jackdaw

No countryman would be without the friendly jackdaw: his clowning and 'clacking' is as much a part of a summer's day as the cawing of the rooks in the elm trees. But these birds often need to be controlled, and the shooter must be ready to do this speedily and humanely when necessary. Not only are jackdaws expert at stealing eggs from laying pens, but they will also rob wild nests with great perseverance.

Jackdaws can be cage-trapped to much the same baits as crows – rabbit paunches, stale bread and eggs being as good as any. Apart from shooting, cage-trapping is the only practical method of control: techniques are described on pages 52–53.

Magpie

In addition to robbing nests, magpies will kill gamebird chicks when they get the chance. An example of this happened at Fordingbridge when some pheasant chicks began to disappear from a batch of 90 being used for a nutrition trial in an unroofed pen, visible from the office windows. The secretaries could not believe that a pair of magpies were to blame – until they saw an actual attack on the chicks, then reduced to about 20.

Control methods for keeping the number of magpies at an acceptable level are much the same as those described for crows. In the winter they can be shot flighting in to their roosts. Sometimes as many as 200 birds will congregate at this time of the year. In April the nests can be thinned out, or the breeding birds and young can be destroyed later. Magpies are a good deal harder to cage trap than rooks, but using baits, such as carrion and eggs, they can sometimes be

*Illegal in the U.K.

taken. A live decoy magpie can be a very good draw. The best period for general trapping is during hard weather, though for egg baits the spring is the most successful time.

American game conservation workers use portable cage traps (letterbox type) and 'walk in' types with ground entrances, baited with dead sheep or carrion. These catch magpies very well, provided the trapped birds are not left in long enough to frighten away any newcomers. The trap should be moved to a new location frequently, and the bait changed from time to time.

Another method consists of using Black's Patent Cage Trap, containing a nest of dummy thrushes' eggs. (These are available from game equipment suppliers.) Foliage should be placed around the outside of the trap to camouflage it. This trap is most effective in the spring when song birds are laying.

Magpies have also been decoyed and shot, particularly during the breeding season, by setting up two stuffed magpies and some eggs near a hide.

Jay

A certain amount of enthusiasm is always shown when a jay is brought down on a shooting day, whereas the more destructive rat or crow is usually dispatched without comment. But the jay is one of the few creatures that is not as black as it is painted. The odd pair of jays here and there are useful sentries on a shoot, giving a keeper warning of undesirable visitors.

Though no one will deny that the jay is very fond of the eggs and chicks of game and song birds, in a five-year period on the experimental estate only one jay was caught redhanded – shot beside a pheasant's nest from which it had taken two eggs. We do, however, know of a Suffolk estate, bounded by what might be described as a vermin sanctuary, where large numbers of pheasant chicks were found dead – but not eaten – on the rearing field. This proved to be the work of jays, and after they had been 'trimmed out', the killings ceased. A Danish gamefarmer also reported that jays had caused a lot of trouble among his hand-reared mallard ducklings.

On the whole, though, the jay is not so adept as the crow at finding and robbing nests on the ground, and those that kill game chicks are probably exceptions.

When it becomes necessary to reduce the number of jays, an experienced keeper can account for a certain number by luring them to his gun, using calls or 'rabbit-squealers'.

Jays can sometimes be caught in large traps designed for jackdaws, though smaller ones on the pheasant-catcher principle, about 3 ft. (0·9 m.) square and 2 ft. (0·6 m.) high, are more effective. Good baits for jays are peas in the pod or, in the spring, an artificial nest of, say, starlings' eggs. Maize is very attractive to them, but unless the size of the sleeve entrance to the catcher type of trap is restricted, pheasants may be caught as well when grain is used.

One simple way of constructing a good cage trap for catching jays, particularly in the winter, is to make a semi-circular trap of wire netting, again similar to the pheasant catcher many keepers use. The wire netting should be 1-in. (2½ cm.) mesh and 6 ft. (2m.) wide. A half-circle is made 3 ft. (0·9 m.) long, 2 ft. (0·6 m.) wide – pegging down the sides – and the remaining 3 ft. (0·9 m.) is used for the funnels, tucking 1 ft. 6 in. (0·45 m.) in at each end. The entrance should be 2 ft. (0·6 m.) wide and 1 ft. (0·3 m.) high in the front and the inner entrance is 4 in. × 3 in. (10 cm. × 7½ cm.) high and baited with grain in the entrance and inside.

Large cage traps

The commonest type is the funnel cage, which has caught 250 jackdaws in one week. The disadvantage is that ground-level funnels – if used – *sometimes catch game*. A writer to *The Field* stated that he caught 892 jackdaws and 63 other pests – including rooks, crows, four magpies and a few grey squirrels – in two cages during June and July. In this case the cages had funnels at ground level as well as in the roof.

Funnel-entrance cage

The design of the funnel-cage will be seen from the illustration: the size is unimportant. A successful model in Suffolk, which caught about 250 birds (in two cages) in a year, measured 6 ft. × 6 ft. × 3 ft. 6 in. (2 m. × 2 m. × 1 m.) with the funnel going down to within a foot of the ground. Other successful sizes have been 8 ft. × 8 ft. × 6 ft. (2½ m. × 2½ m. × 2 m.), and 9 ft. × 9 ft. × 6 ft. (3 m. × 3 m. × 2 m.). Our own, which seems a convenient size and catches well, is 10 ft. × 6 ft. × 5 ft. (3 m. × 2 m. × 1½ m.). All cages should have a door about 2 ft. (0·6 m.) wide, and stout perches across the top of the entrance funnel. Two funnels may be fitted in the roof of a large cage trap. The funnels should be 18 in. to 20 in. (45 to 50 cm.) square at the top, tapering to about 8 in. (20 cm.) at the bottom, and they should come to within about 2 ft. (0·6 m.) of the ground. (Short funnels about 1 ft. [0·3 m.] long are also in use.) It is important that when constructing a cage trap of any kind, one should always use *natural* timber, such as larch trimmings, and not sawn timber, which may make the birds suspicious. The wire netting should be of 2-in. (5 cm.) mesh. If smaller mesh is used, a great number of small wild birds will be caught.

It will be of great assistance if the cages are made sectional and portable, as they sometimes have to be moved about a good deal. Permanent ones are often effective in a park, but on our experimental estate the cages were always moved as the birds changed their feeding quarters.

Another type of temporary cage trap which can be put up in an hour or so, is built on the lines of a wire-netting pheasant catcher. The cage looks rather like a Swiss-roll, with the tapering 'maze' entrance at the side. Unfortunately it will also catch game unless carefully sited. It should be remembered that it is essential to peg or stake the cage down firmly, or it may be knocked over by the occupants.

Letterbox cage trap

The letterbox, ladder or 'slot-entrance' cage is also a very good trap. As will be seen from Figure 17, the V-shaped roof slopes down to a slot 6 in. to 9 in. (15 cm. to 23 cm.) wide, which runs the entire length of the cage. The rungs across this slit are about 9 in. (23 cm.) apart, like a ladder. The trap seems to be equally effective with just two or three rungs for support, and to assist the birds to drop in. Another modification sometimes seen consists of two wire-netting 'curtains' hanging down from either side of the slot.

MAGPIE TRAP

ROOK PEN

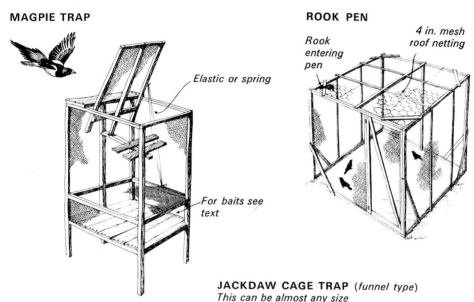

Elastic or spring

For baits see text

Rook entering pen

4 in. mesh roof netting

JACKDAW TRAP ('Letterbox' type). About 6 ft. high at corners and 8 ft. long (2 m. × 2·5 m.)

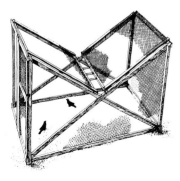

JACKDAW CAGE TRAP (funnel type)
This can be almost any size

A stout perch helps the crows to drop in

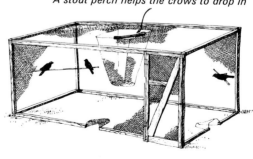

The ground-level funnels can be removed if it is found that they catch pheasants

17 Cage traps

53

These act as additional obstacles which prevent the birds from escaping. Wire netting should also be placed along the end of the ladder-entrance – a foot at either end, otherwise jackdaws will climb the sides and get out. If it is found that birds are escaping through the entrance, it is quite a simple matter to reduce the width of the entrance by laying a thin larch pole on one side of the rungs, securing it in position with wire.

Rook pen

The rook pen can be of any convenient dimensions and can be permanent or portable. The model used at Fordingbridge measures 10 ft. × 6 ft. × 5 ft. (3 m. × 2 m. × 1½ m.) and, being sectional, is easily dismantled and moved. This type of cage is very simple to make, having 2-in. (5 cm.) mesh wire-netting sides and a plain 4-in. (10 cm.) sheep-netting roof without any funnel. The rooks drop down into the cage through the large-mesh roof, but are unable to fly out.

Jackdaws also get inside the pens, but have been known to climb out again – funnel or letterbox cages are more certain.

Siting cage traps

The cages should be placed either where rooks are feeding, on flight lines, near poultry houses, rookeries, ricks, 'perching' trees, or in fields where pigs or sheep are run – using the troughs for bait. If one pitch fails to catch, the cage should be moved about until a good position is found, and when a successful pitch ceases to catch, it is time to move the cage.

Upon one occasion a new cage was erected on the study area at Fordingbridge and baited with soaked bread. The next morning 14 jackdaws had been caught. The following day there was no catch at all, and the cage continued to be empty for about a week. It was then moved 100 yds. (90 m.) and the next morning a further 16 birds were caught, but the following day it was again empty. It is of great importance to move the cage traps when necessary.

An excellent site for setting a cage trap during April and May, when the old birds are feeding their young, is to intercept their flight line by placing the cage trap in a prominent position in a field, using eggs or bread as bait.

Baits

When the cage is first put out, the bait may be scattered all round the cage, inside and out. If the roof is sectional it can be left off or the door propped open for a time.

Successful baits include white bread, eggs, dead rabbits – with paunch opened up – corn and chaff, and thick yellow cart grease! (One of the staff keepers observed the rooks eating such grease on railway lines, and adopted it as a successful bait.) The feeding habits of the birds should always be studied carefully, and the baits altered accordingly. For instance, early one season no

54

rooks at all were caught on bread or rabbit baits, but when eggs were used the trap began to be successful. After that, white bread came into its own again.

Decoys

A domestic fowl is often recommended as a decoy until the first jackdaws or rooks are caught. Certainly the small, portable crow trap, placed beside a poultry run so that it looked like part of it, caught very well indeed. It has been found, however, that except in the breeding season, a single decoy rook or crow can be more of a hindrance than a help, by running up and scaring the wild birds away. Three or four tame *young* decoys have proved very successful, but they must be properly looked after. Water, food and some shelter are required by law. Do not forget to ring the decoy so that it can be easily distinguished from the caught ones.

Management of cage traps

Corvids are quick to observe the effects of cage traps. One keeper, for instance, failed to remove a dead jackdaw from a cage. The corpse was evidently spotted by the free jackdaws outside and not a single bird was caught until he moved the trap to a new position. Another keeper had a cage trap which was catching birds well all the season, until one day someone released about 30 trapped birds. For the rest of that winter not one further bird was caught.

Hawks and owls

Some of the hawks and falcons kill game. But these birds are often rare and beautiful, and even where they are not protected by law – as in some countries overseas – the game preserver is urged to think twice before reducing their numbers unnecessarily. In a few areas abroad the goshawk may be building up problems for the future. In Britain *all hawks and owls are rightly protected*.

The inter-relationship of predators and game is a very complex subject, and there are, for instance, biologists who think that a few hawks are a good thing to keep gamebirds alert and watchful. While this is a rather doubtful argument, there is no evidence one way or the other to be dogmatic about it. Game Conservancy observers would *not* agree that hawks take only weakly birds, as is claimed by some naturalists. There are, however, two factors which are of great importance:

(*a*) The availability of alternative sources of food (i.e. other than gamebirds) for the hawks.

(*b*) The amount and disposition of escape cover for the game.

Identifying owl damage

In Britain we have five species of owl – the little owl, the long-eared owl, the short-eared owl, the brown or tawny owl and the barn owl – *all of which are now protected*.

On the whole, the British owls are beneficial to the farmer, on account of the large numbers of rodents and insects they eat – but at least three of them can cause local damage to game. It may be worth knowing what to look for when losses to owls are suspected.

The little owl was introduced to this country and became established in Northamptonshire about 1890. On our own rearing field, and occasionally on the estate, this species was observed killing pheasant, partridge and bantam chicks, usually at about 2–3 weeks old – their kills invariably being made at twilight. The legs and other remains of birds near little owls' nests were also examined, but only a limited number of young gamebird victims were found.

Tawny owls can be determined killers of chicks and poults. On the experimental estate penned adult partridges were lost to tawny owls in January, young hand-reared pheasants in late May and roosting poults in July and August. These were driven or knocked off their perches and killed on the ground. Some of the penned partridges were taken away over 6-ft. (2 m.) wire netting. A tawny owl kill is often characterised by the fact that the victim is decapitated.

Nevertheless this owl is among the farmer's friends because – as we have said – it kills many rats and mice.

The long-eared owl will certainly take reared pheasant chicks if the opportunity presents itself. The barn owl attacks game very exceptionally.

Moorhen

The moorhen or waterhen can be very troublesome on a shoot if allowed to become too numerous. These birds greedily eat the food put down for pheasants or duck; they will damage watercress beds and will sometimes take eggs, small game chicks and ducklings. Moorhens can be shot quite easily, or caught alive in baited cage traps with funnel entrances. Pheasant catchers are also suitable. Moorhens are protected from 1st February to 31st August in Great Britain.

Chapter 5
Enemies of Game: Part 2
Mammalian Predators

Harmful species

Rats and feral mink are the only species which must be rigorously controlled at every opportunity: other predators require more selective measures. Foxes may be the subject of all-out attack in some districts, but in areas where there is hunting the campaign needs to be balanced. The wild cat only rarely conflicts with low-ground game, while the badger* does so occasionally when an individual rogue animal develops a taste for gamebirds' eggs or poults.

The weasel and stoat can be controlled by tunnel-trapping, while the other pests on the shoot are of less significance: these include the hedgehog and an occasional mole. A very real predator can be the feral cat or domestic cat living wild.

The trapping network

The basic defence against ground predators (or 'vermin' for the reader who is really more at home with the term) consists of a strategic network of tunnel sites for trapping all over a shoot – particularly round the boundaries. On a beat of 1,000–1,200 acres (400–475 h.), where the fields are of normal size and where there are sufficient hedges, stone walls, banks, etc., a good keeper will be wise to operate 60 to 70 traps practically the whole year round, although he may have to spring some of them when he is busy with nesting, rearing fields, shooting and so on. In practice, 70 tunnels are about as much as a keeper can look after effectively, whatever the size of his beat, so one keeper will find it difficult to trap thoroughly over a beat of 2,000–3,000 acres (800–1,210 h.). In these circumstances it is all the more important to choose the best catching places for every trap and to cover the boundaries as well as possible.

---

* The badger is now protected and may only be controlled *under licence*, in the event of serious damage to crops, property, etc. – not game.

Types of traps

'Tunnel traps' are simply traps set in natural or artificial tunnels, attractively situated in the normal thoroughfares of ground predators. The gin trap was banned by law in 1958, and humane traps are now used.

For catching in tunnels, the little Fenn trap has proved itself. The cost is modest and it is obtainable from Mr A. Fenn, F.H.T. Works, High Street, Astwood Bank, Redditch, Worcs., or game appliance dealers. The new Sawyer and Lloyd traps are also very effective. When using these traps it is essential to build the tunnels fairly low and to stake the entrance with twigs so that the intruders are obliged to pass over the centre of the plate.

Tunnel-trapping

The tunnel can be made of a wooden frame covered with turf, or of large stones, bricks, drainpipes, bales of straw, faggot piles and so on. The tunnels should be about 18 in. to 2 ft. (45 cm. to 60 cm.) long, and just large enough to house the trap. Natural sites, such as the roots of trees, can equally well be used. Apart from the ordinary 'run-through' tunnel, one can also construct blind tunnels with no exit; these can be made in grass banks. In East Anglia the wellams – or pipes carrying ditches under gateways – make ideal trapping sites even when there is a little water running. The rough grass beside wire fences is also a good trapping place.

Useful portable tunnels can be made by nailing together three rough offcuts of timber about 2 ft. (60 cm.) long; inside measurements about 5 in. (13 cm.) high, and 6 in. (15 cm.) wide at base. (Earth base, with sides and top of wood camouflaged with turf, etc.)

Tunnels are usually unbaited, as ground predators are normally curious and will hunt almost any earthy hole. In the early spring it may pay to put a flesh bait in the tunnel – rabbits' guts used to be the favourite – or to use the urine from a trapped female stoat on all the traps in the vicinity. Bitch weasels are very light and may not spring a Fenn trap. A piece of hare or rabbit flesh or liver skewered to the ground at the tunnel entrance will almost certainly induce the weasel to have a tug-of-war over the trap and result in a catch. Pigeon flesh also makes a good bait, and a dead hedgehog placed on top of the tunnel will often draw other hedgehogs.

In a wide, unkempt hedge, 'wings' of turf, logs, small-meshed wire netting, etc., should be constructed to form a lead-in to the tunnel. Another similar – and very telling – practice is to make a short cut from the outside furrow in either field, leading to the centre of the hedge. If a weasel is travelling down this field furrow, as they often do, unless there is an intersecting furrow veering off to the centre of the hedge, it will pass the trap by. The turf dug out of this furrow should be banked on top to make it even more difficult to climb out of it.

In areas of rough, tussocky grass, where ground predators have no obvious travel lane such as a hedge or bank, a straight furrow may be ploughed right

18 Artificial pathways or runs should be created to lead small ground predators from the field furrow into the mouth of the trap tunnel

19 The Fenn trap is humane and efficient against small ground predators when placed in suitable tunnels with restricted height and width

59

across open ground in order to form an artificial run for stoats and weasels. Such a furrow will almost certainly become a regular runway if it is kept clear, and will be easy to trap.

A well-planned trap round should lead the keeper along almost every hedge and into every copse on his beat. Even if he is taking only an occasional grey squirrel or rat from six dozen traps, he will at the same time be covering his ground very thoroughly and should miss nothing of importance that may be going on. *This is almost as important as killing the pests.* He will see the farm workers and road-men almost daily; he will pass winter feeding stations or pheasant catchers according to the time of year; he will make a note of partridge pairs. If he is a young man gaining experience, this regular round will help him to become a first-class naturalist and field detective. He will learn to spot the presence of unwelcome killers, or even poachers, and take appropriate action before serious damage occurs.

Before being used new traps should be buried in the earth or weathered until they have lost their factory smell. Gloves need never be worn, but a trapper's hands should be free from any obviously unsuitable smells – soap, for instance! When setting the trap, the chain, peg and spring shaft (where one exists) should be buried and the soil made firm all round the tunnel entrance. The trap itself should be placed sufficiently far back inside – the trigger pan about the centre of the tunnel – to avoid danger to dogs or game investigating the entrance. It is a matter of personal preference whether the plate is covered or not: it is certainly not necessary for stoats or weasels. If the tunnel opening is too large, it should be made smaller by sinking two sticks firmly in the ground across the entrance – leaving a gap just large enough for stoats, hedgehogs, etc., to enter.

Traps should be examined daily and reset frequently, whether they have caught or not. If this is not done, the working parts may get blocked by mud, leaves and so on, and they will fail to catch.

Among the predators which can be *continuously* controlled by a good coverage of tunnel traps are rats, stoats, weasels, hedgehogs, grey squirrels and feral mink. *It cannot be too strongly emphasised that one can never build up a first-class shoot – particularly for partridges – if all their natural enemies are allowed a free run.* The tunnel trap is working while the keeper is asleep, and it also costs nothing to feed!

Box traps

The same can be said of the Continental box trap – the wooden tunnel with a see-saw in it – which is employed much like a tunnel trap. Trials at Fordingbridge were carried out for some years with these little portable wooden tunnels, and excellent results were eventually obtained. Comments were also invited from some very experienced trappers in France, Holland, Denmark and Germany – which countries have used these traps for generations – and the combined suggestions are set down briefly in these notes.

60

There are basically three sizes of box traps, varying from ones over 3 ft. (1 m.) in length designed to catch poaching cats, etc., to the smallest ones, 1 ft. 8 in. (50 cm.) long, for rats, stoats and weasels. The entrance end of the tunnel is usually about $3\frac{1}{2}$ in. $\times$ $4\frac{1}{2}$ in. (9 cm. $\times$ 11 cm.) with the roof sloping up to 5 in. or 6 in. (13 cm. or 15 cm.) at the far end. Some box traps are made the same height at either end. Inside is a see-saw, pivoting on a metal spindle, which tips up as the animal runs into the box – the see-saw remaining locked in the 'closed' position behind the animal. At the far end the tunnel is covered with a metal grille, toughened glass or Perspex.

It is important that the wood is properly seasoned and does not swell, or the see-saw will jam in wet weather. Creosote should not be used as a preservative, as it is likely to keep predators away for a long time until the smell has completely worn off. New white wood is also a disadvantage.

20 Box traps in stone walls are used in pairs so that they catch from either side

How to use box traps.

Small ground predators enter these box traps for exactly the same reason that they enter tunnel traps, i.e. in search of prey, and to take shelter quickly in what looks like a convenient bolt hole.

Normally the traps are not baited – and in any case they soon acquire the smell of the many mice they are always catching – but, as in tunnel-trapping, refinements (if one may use such an inappropriate word) such as the contents of a weasel's bladder are often used with advantage.

Box traps can be used singly, but are also effective if used in pairs, side by side, with an entrance facing either way. They can be put in exactly the same sort of place as a conventional tunnel. A certain degree of camouflage around the entrance may be advisable to prevent curious people from pulling them out

61

and possibly stealing them. The box should, however, slide easily in and out of its tunnel – if it is being used in that way – and not have too many flints or turves placed directly on top of it, otherwise the tunnel will have to be reconstructed every time it catches.

Some of the best places include the following: on small, used paths in spinneys and copses (blocking the path on either side with brushwood or a similar obstruction so that the animal is forced to go through the middle); on a plank over a stream; in the boundary furrow of a field, often used by stoats when the hedge bank is very wet; in the field ditch or the hedge; between two farm crops, if separated by a track; in a pile of flints in the corner of a field; beside a barn or a wall, and on rafters in old farm buildings; in hay and corn ricks; alongside a wire-netting fence or a pheasant pen; in the centre of the rough grass under a downland wire fence; beside hen coops; half hidden in a pile of cut logs in covert; or in a dry drain or culvert.

As a result of experience at Fordingbridge with these traps, it is suggested that the keeper makes a more or less permanent network of, say 40 or 50 of the old-type tunnels on each beat to house Fenn traps, with a further two or three dozen box traps to be kept on the move as furrows are ploughed, ditches become dry and so on.

It is advisable to carry a small stout bag on the trapping round in which to tip the captive, so that it can be killed humanely and without risk of escaping or biting.

The shotgun and other methods

Some years ago the proportion of predators, both furred and feathered, that were *trapped* was compared with those that were *shot* on the experimental estate. The results were roughly 60 per cent trapped to 40 per cent shot, which brings home the fact that, wherever possible, the keeper should have his gun handy. On the unkeepered shoot, where it may be difficult to run a big number of tunnel traps owing to the impossibility of making a daily visit, the gun comes into its own even more.

Foxes and badgers

In Britain the three major field sports are shooting, fishing and foxhunting. There is still plenty of scope for all three, and there must be few countrymen who would not wish to see them survive and flourish side by side – in fact, many shooting men are equally devoted to hunting and fishing. While, in this book, the authors are solely concerned with the protection of gamebirds, they would not like to advocate measures which might interfere with the sister sport of hunting, any more than they would suggest spoiling a salmon river to create better conditions for duck. Although there is no doubt that the fox is one of the most important enemies of game, especially at nesting time, its control in relation to hunting and other local conditions is a matter which must be left to the landowners and farmers to evolve a satisfactory compromise: indeed, such a compromise already exists in many areas where hunting and shooting are both important amenities of the countryside.

Foxes are, however, increasing in number in many places where hunting is impossible – ranging from commons in the suburbs to Highland glens. In these districts it may be necessary to control their populations by methods such as snaring. While the Game Conservancy does not approve of snaring, it is at present the only control method that is at all effective and until a better technique is available people will continue to use it.

The loop of a snare should be pear-shaped and measure 8 in. long by 6 in. deep (20 cm. by 15 cm.). The height above the ground is variable, depending on the site, but a hand's width (4–5 in. [10–13 cm.]) is normal, although in open runs it may need to be set up to 8 in. (20 cm.) above the ground to catch successfully. Sometimes it will be an advantage for the snare to have two prop sticks or 'tealers' to hold it in position.

Deer occasionally get caught up in snares set for foxes. This can be prevented quite simply by placing a 'deer leap' a few inches in front of the snare where the latter is sited in an open run. This consists of a thin branch of willow wand placed across the run at a height of about 18 in. (46 cm.) and held up by forked sticks pushed into the ground on either side of the path. Deer almost invariably jump over the obvious obstacle, while they might blunder into the less visible snare. The presence of the branch over the run does not deter foxes, which still pass underneath and into the snare in the normal way.

Commercial snares are available with non-return slides which prevent the noose from slipping open after catching. Those supplied by A. Fenn are good, also another type sold by Gilbertson & Page Ltd, Hertford, Herts.

Cyanide gassing powder – such as 'Cymag', marketed by Plant Protection Ltd – is an effective method of killing foxes, especially in the spring when cubs and vixens are in the earths.

Badgers are not usually harmful to game interests, though on one occasion 18 partridge nests on the study area were lost to one rogue animal.* The normal badger is an asset to the countryside, and should be left in peace.

Feral cats, rats, hedgehogs and moles
The half-wild or feral poaching cat ranks very high as a destroyer of nesting game, and often young chicks as well. If there is any doubt as to whether an animal is a wild-living creature or merely a wandering pet, a cat trap will take it alive and unharmed; this enables it to be returned to its owner with a suitable comment!

* See footnote on page 57.

A recent working party on the control of predatory mammals, with representatives of all shades of opinion from conservation, agriculture and game management groups, described the feral cat as 'a menace to wildlife'.

Cage traps should be baited with fish. Suitable types are made by Young's of Misterton, Somerset, and the Martin Humane Trap retailed by Lincolnshire Pheasantries Ltd, Tumby, Mareham-le-Fen, Boston, Lincolnshire.

Rats it would seem hardly necessary to list, except that there still appear to be some people who do not realise how much damage the common rat can cause. One has only to manage a partridge beat for a single season, or rear a few broods of pheasants or mallard, to see what a killer the rat is. Tunnel traps and baiting points (for poisoned meal) at all strategic places will keep them under control, but the anti-rat campaign is one that can never be really relaxed. No sooner has the ground been thoroughly cleared than they seem to draw in gradually from over the boundaries. As long as the shoot owner has game food in store, stacks in the coverts or winter feeding points, there is always a chance of attracting rats. One of the simplest methods of using 'Warfarin'* is to put down individual baits in small paper envelopes (about the size of pay packets). Even better is the polythene envelope. Rats seem to go for anything that is wrapped up. This has the advantage of keeping the meal reasonably dry and 'in one piece' until the rat starts to eat into it; and it also makes it easy to lift the baits if and when necessary. It is particularly successful in hedgerows. If by chance the rats should develop a resistance to 'Warfarin', as has happened in a few areas, zinc phosphide, 'Raticate' poison or 'Sorexa C.R.' should be used instead.

The recommended pre-bait is 15 parts finely ground barley meal to one part caster sugar, and this should be used on two alternate days prior to adding the poison (5oz. [140 g.] of zinc phosphide to 6 lb. [3 kg.] of barley meal).

Hedgehogs can do considerable damage to nests on a partridge beat. Drop-pits baited with bad fish or rabbit paunches are a safe, humane method of capturing them alive if there really are too many. Others will be taken in the tunnels.

From time to time moles accidentally disturb partridge nests. In one year on the trial ground 10 nests were upset by moles, though 6 were rebuilt by the watchful keeper. On another occasion 14 partridge eggs were recovered from a mole run. Second attempts at undermining nests can be discouraged by putting such things as mothballs or knobs of calcium carbide (provided the tunnel is sealed) down the runs.

Trapping with the barrel and half-barrel traps requires a rather special touch, but there is also available a patent double-ended steel trap (sometimes

---

* Warfarin poison can kill dogs, whether taken in a large single dose or in small doses over a long period. Dogs are particularly likely to be fatally affected when they eat the poison and later take violent exercise. Pregnant animals are also very susceptible.

Pheasants *Alex Jardine*

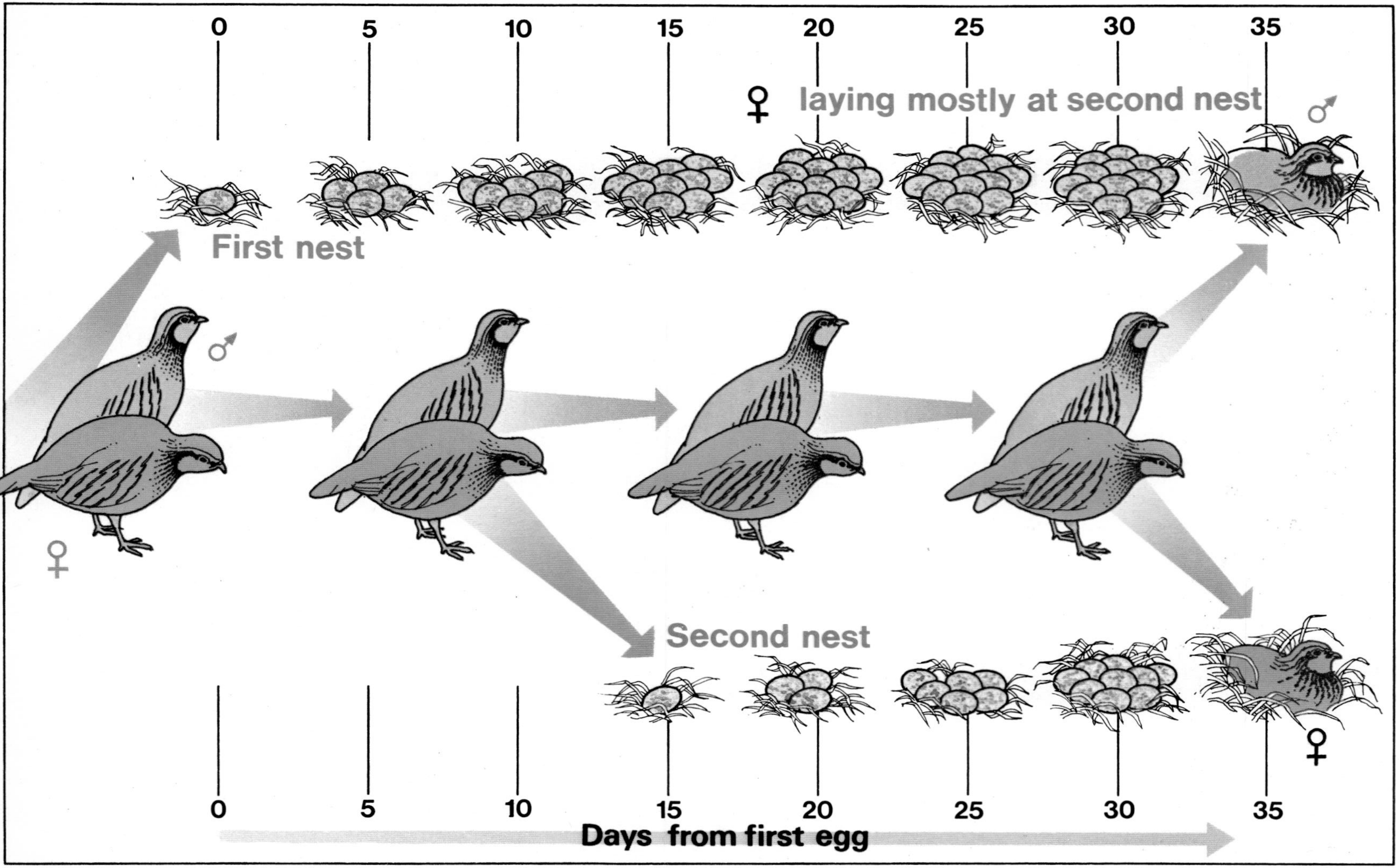

0
5
10
15
20
25
30
35
♀ laying mostly at second nest
♂
First nest
♂
♀
Second nest
♀
0
5
10
15
20
25
30
35
Days from first egg

Double nesting in the Red-legged Partridge *Game Conservancy*

called the Duffus) with a strong spiral spring, which is much easier to set. (This is available from Young's of Misterton, Somerset, or Gilbertson & Page Ltd, Hertford, Herts.)

Poisoning with strychnine, using good-sized worms as bait, is probably the most effective method available for killing moles. But to learn how to do it a personal demonstration by an expert is essential. The poison can only be obtained by applying to the Ministry of Agriculture and proving evidence of mole damage.

Feral mink

In recent years feral mink – the descendants of escaped fur-farm animals – have become quite a problem to poultry keepers, game rearers and others.

In the Hampshire Avon Valley about 300 of these animals have been trapped in three seasons. Mink will swim well, but although they have a liking for river banks and will eat fish, crustaceans and so on, they are also found well away from water. As many as 300 pheasant poults were killed in one night by one mink. About 40 counties in the United Kingdom have a mink problem and they could become as common as stoats.

21 Cage traps on riverside sites are ideal for catching mink

65

22 Ferret in Martin trap. The most recent models of this trap have metal cladding

Mink can be caught quite easily in tunnel or cage traps. They do not appear to be trap-shy, and 'catch-'em-alive' models designed for rats and cats are very successful. These are effective when baited with fish, offal, chickens' heads or gamebird 'kills'. The traps can be sited on river banks – preferably on a stretch of mud at the water's edge – or under the bank itself. A light covering of water weeds can help to make the set look more natural. Old willow stumps, in which mink often take up residence, also make good trapping sites. A watch should always be kept for their tracks, and trapping started immediately any are observed.

Grey squirrels

These imported rodents are normally not a serious menace to game. They will destroy both eggs and young of song birds: they will frequently steal a large proportion of the food put down for pheasants in covert they are experts at pilfering grain from hoppers. They are, however, a serious pest to the forester, being extremely destructive in young plantations, eating the buds, shoots and bark of trees.

Drey-poking, live-trapping and tunnel-trapping are the three main methods of control.

With a set of light alloy poles and a gun, drey-poking can provide good sport. A wet and windy day early in the year, or a very cold one, will confine most squirrels to their dreys and ensure the best results. A useful team consists of three or more men – one with the drey-poking pole, one or two persons with shotguns for moving squirrels, and perhaps a rifleman (with a ·22 weapon) for the occasional static shot when an evicted squirrel 'freezes' on a tree trunk. Bags of over seventy have been made in a day by experienced shots.

The grey squirrel's drey can be recognised by its use of twigs in leaf, whereas the red squirrel constructs a drey of leafless twigs.

66

Drey-poking operations will be made very much easier if in a selected area all – except for one decoy drey – are prodded out. This single drey, preferably fairly accessible, may yield many squirrels throughout the year. And with all other dreys destroyed, operations in the following season will be very much quicker.

Live-trapping in either single-catch or multiple cages is the most economic and efficient method of squirrel control. The peak cage-trapping period is April to July.

The Forestry Commission has found that a wire-netting cage trap (up to $\frac{3}{4}$-in. [2 cm.] mesh) with dimensions of 25 in. × 16 in. × 4 in. (60 cm. × 40 cm. × 10 cm.) is a suitable size. They can have either a sleeve entrance, as are used in crow cages, or a light metal door, hinged at 45°, which is pushed open by the squirrel and drops down after it has entered.

Most of the bait – maize, acorns, wheat and so on – should be placed sufficiently far back from the swing door, so that it cannot rest half open on the squirrel's back. A small amount should be displayed at the entrance. Pre-baiting for about five days will be necessary.

The Legg P.B. (permanently baited) trap can catch up to six squirrels at one time, and has a metal screen which prevents a trapped squirrel from frightening another one about to enter. An exit door or sliding hatch should be made in one corner of the cage so that the captives can be bolted out into a sack or other container.

Traps should be set 150–200 yds. (135–180 m.) apart on clear ground at the base of large trees. Marauding foxes, badgers or dogs may upset them and where this possibility exists it will be necessary to peg them down.

Tunnel-trapping, which has already been discussed, is another very good method of catching grey squirrels.

Identifying nest predators

As it may be useful for the spare-time keeper to know which particular nest robber is at work, a brief description is included of how nests are raided.

The shells of eggs which have been eaten by the crow family often have an irregular-shaped hole on one side or in the end, with shell particles adhering to the egg membrane and hanging down in the cavity of the shell. On the opposite side of the egg a small 'star' or even a hole may show where a heavy thrust of the corvine beak 'came out the other side'. Although many keepers have their own ideas concerning the typiical sins of the work of crows, rooks and magpies, it is usually impossible to distinguish with any certainty between the three species. One spring in the grounds of the research station a mallard egg was seen to have been taken by a jackdaw and the bird had stabbed a remarkably neat hole in the end of the egg, while nearby a clutch of pheasant eggs was descended upon by a flock of rooks which reduced them to very small pieces of 'confetti' in a few minutes.

Usually there is little evidence left at the nest whether the eggs have been taken by rook, crow or magpie. Sometimes the nest lining may be scratched out, as if the thief was unwilling to believe that the last egg had been taken, but most frequently the nest lining or egg covering is left intact and the eggs have disappeared as if removed by hand. Nor is any trace of the eggs usually found in the vicinity of the nest.

Losses to foxes, while numerically second in importance in our experimental estate records, are much more serious due to the fact that almost invariably the nest is destroyed during the incubation period and the hen is killed.

Frequently the eggs are not touched, although if the sitting hen should escape the fox may 'make do' with an egg diet. Although a sitting partridge may fall a victim at any stage of the incubation period, there does seem to be considerable evidence that predation by foxes is most likely to occur when the partridge first goes down on the eggs and again during the last night or two before hatching. At this period the hen becomes more restless, and probably this releases scent which guides the fox to the nest.

The signs left by a fox are usually surprisingly few, even at a nest that is naturally well protected by thorn or bramble stems. Indeed, there may be practically no disturbance at the nest itself: not even a feather will betray where the fox pounced on the sitting hen. But almost invariably a search around within a five-yard radius will show where the fox gave the final 'crunch' and wiped a wisp of the saliva-covered feathers from its mouth on a clump of grass. Perhaps these few feathers, looking as if they had been crawled over by a large slug, are really the hall-mark of a fox's work. If the night has been a warm one and the keeper is early on his rounds, the eggs may be salvaged to be hatched under a broody. Occasionally a vixen that has lost her litter may eat the partridge where she killed it or it will be half buried rather untidily.

But most often, apart from the cold eggs in the early morning and, perhaps, a trace of rusty hair on a bramble stem, the saliva-smeared flank feathers of the partridge wiped against a grass tussock is the evidence to look for.

Cats, on the other hand, are most untidy killers and not infrequently eat the partridge on the nest or drag it only a few yards. Feathers are often widely scattered and wings, legs, head and gizzard are usually left – as characteristic a trade mark as the skull and crossbones of the pirate. Eggs are almost invariably left intact, and if the partridge is more than the cat can eat at one time, it will usually return to finish off its meal the following night. If the cat is feeding kittens it may carry or drag the partridge a considerable distance, and the trail of feathers will give some useful information concerning the direction from which the trouble has originated.

Dogs tend to chase off the sitting bird rather than kill it, but when they do get hold of the sitting hen there are usually a lot of feathers in the nest and the bird is crushed across the back. It is often left uneaten and the eggs are not touched.

Fortunately, it is only the occasional badger that develops a strong liking for

23 'Warfarin' in paper packets or polythene bags will keep rats under control

24 Crushed partridge eggshells left by a badger

69

partridge eggs. When this does occur, however, several clutches of eggs may disappear in one night. Usually the keeper is left in little doubt about the identity of the marauder: if there is much cover around the nest, there will be obvious signs of the passage of a large heavy body. Nearly always the badger frightens off the hen and then eats the eggs just outside the nest, 'champing' up the eggs with its broad molars and dropping the crushed eggshells, with the shell particles still attached to the egg membrane. The nest may be completely raked out. Although the hen partridge is seldom molested, the majority of clutches taken by badgers have usually been incubated for more than a fortnight and are rarely followed by repeat nests.

Hedgehogs, also very fond of partridge eggs, can sometimes leave a relatively broad trail into a nest, particularly if the vegetation is lush. But the hedgehog is a much more messy feeder, and it crunches up the eggs over the nest. Its sharp teeth cut through the egg membrane as well as the shell. The contents of smashed eggs, pieces of shell and the nesting materials are all mixed together. In contrast to the badger, the hedgehog obtains most of its eggs during the partridge's laying period, and there is usually a good chance that re-nesting will occur.

Both rats and stoats may take a few eggs or the whole clutch. They may also, on occasion, kill and eat the sitting hen partridge, although this usually occurs only during the later stages of incubation, when the partridge is very reluctant to leave her eggs without putting up a struggle. Eggs may be carried considerable distances, and we have known a female stoat to carry a number of partridge eggs (one at a time, of course) a distance of over 100 yds. (90 m.).

If the eggs have been eaten near the nest it may not be easy to distinguish between the work of a rat, stoat or fox. In all cases the egg will retain its shape, but a rat usually eats away a larger proportion of the shell, and its incisor teeth leave a characteristic 'scalloped' outline.

The weasel leaves traces similar to those of the rat, but it is not an important nest predator. Sometimes a weasel will pull out the tail feathers of a hen partridge as she leaves the nest.

Moles are often an accidental cause of egg loss during the laying stage when the eggs are still lying on the floor of the 'scrape' and before the materials covering the eggs have been worked into a loose lining to protect the eggs. If the mole happens to tunnel under the nest at this stage and the tunnel 'breaks surface' on the floor of the nest, eggs may drop through and be pushed some distance along the tunnel by the burrowing mole. During the incubation period, when the egg-covering materials have been worked into a firmer platform, such disturbance is less likely, but occasionally a mole 'surfacing' immediately beneath a partridge nest will cause actual desertion.

Chapter 6
Hedgerow Keepering and Nest Management

A good partridge keeper will spend a lot of time walking his beat, particularly inspecting his hedgerows. Tunnel traps, feeding sites and – during the most vital time of the year – nesting birds, will be his main concern. The way he manipulates the eggs in the nests is properly called 'nest management' and can result in many more clutches hatching successfully, than if left to chance.

Although both red-legged and grey partridges may occasionally start to lay in mid-April, the usual time to find eggs is about 30th April. There is little annual variation, since length of daylight is the most important factor in determining the onset of egg laying. The average clutch of 15 eggs (*Perdix*) takes about 22 days to lay, so most partridges begin to sit in the latter half of May and hatch about the middle of June. With pheasants, the main events are about a fortnight earlier than with partridges – but the laying, sitting and hatching dates are spread out over a much longer period.

'Look after the partridge and the pheasant will look after itself' has long been an axiom in East Anglia, where wild birds of both species occur on the same estates. And looking after the wild partridges entails finding their nests, protecting them in various ways, identifying the causes of nest losses and generally managing them so that the maximum number of partridge chicks are hatched.

Nest-finding begins in late April, when a large number of bare earth 'scrapes' (distinguished from the pheasant's 'scrape' by the deeper depression) are most easily located. Not all the 'scrapes' will eventually be used, but if they are noted by the keeper a lot of time will be saved later on. When a few eggs have been laid in the 'scrape' and covered with dead leaves and other material, nest-finding can become a very time-absorbing occupation. In the last week of April and the first ten days of May a general search of the most likely hedgerows should have been carried out. A knowledge of the distribution of the partridge pairs – acquired during the keeper's rounds – is a considerable help to nest-finding, as well as knowing the nest sites in previous seasons. The rapid growth of the vegetation at this time of the year and the beginning of incubation by some of the earlier partridges in mid-May, makes nest-searching inadvisable after the end of the second week in May. Nor is it prudent for a novice to search for partridge nests without skilled supervision, since much damage may inadvertently be done. Partridges will sometimes put up with a great deal of disturbance during the later stages of incubation, but any interference in the first day or two is liable to result in the clutch being abandoned.

The experienced partridge keeper will visit his nests – which will usually be recorded on a map – daily if possible. In most cases a close approach is not necessary – the judicious use of a hazel stick to part the covering vegetation is often all that is needed to see that the nest is progressing satisfactorily. Any displaced leaves are carefully restored so that discovery is not made any easier for potential nest-robbers.

Some early nests will be made in particularly dangerous situations and the keeper may decide to pick up the eggs and make the partridge re-nest, hoping that she will choose a safer place the second time. These picked-up eggs will be placed under broody bantams or in incubators to provide the keeper with early clutches of 'chipping' eggs which he can exchange with later clutches from nests where impending dangers may make it necessary to advance the hatching date. In hedges surrounding grazed fields nests may have to be temporarily fenced off to prevent trampling by cattle, while as an added insurance the partridge eggs are substituted with artificial eggs. If no harm befalls the sitting hen, her own eggs, which have been incubated safely elsewhere, are returned to her as soon as they begin to chip. In a few cases it may be advisable to delay the hatching date (e.g. to avoid hatching immediately before grass cutting is due) and this can be done by exchanging with a later-hatching clutch. Sitting partridges will quite readily accept a reduction or extension of the incubation period of 7–10 days. Most partridge beat keepers will keep a number of broodies sitting on artificial eggs ready for use in emergencies, and chicks from clutches which cannot be returned (due to the loss of the sitting partridge) will be reared by the keeper.

On private ground, where the co-operation of the farm workers is assumed, it is often an advantage to mark the vicinity of nests clearly so that they are not accidentally disturbed by farm machinery. Where the public have access, however, it would be dangerous to draw attention to a nest site, and less obtrusive methods of nest marking – and protection – have to be used.

Although the incubating partridge apparently gives off little scent (except perhaps when she is 'fidgeting' in the early stages of hatching), barrier smells are sometimes used to protect the sitting bird from her enemies. Each keeper will have his own recipe – often simply urine, or a mixture of ammonia, creosote and other strong-smelling fluids – which he will decant into a small container in the vicinity of a nest. It is extremely unwise to spread these fluids on the ground since some animals, like foxes, may learn to connect a certain smell with a nest. Containers (e.g. empty cartridge cases) can be removed, and new smells quickly substituted, if trouble arises. Pieces of old machinery, metal objects, a suspended tobacco tin or almost any strange-looking article may have some *temporary* deterrent effect against would-be predators. But no device remains 'strange' for very long and the keeper must be ready to ring the changes frequently.

Sometimes, particularly in unusually dry springs, the vegetation will be slow to provide the necessary natural cover and a little judicious 'bushing' with twigs, bramble stems, etc., may provide sufficient protection from sharp-eyed winged predators. In areas where bryony is common, it can be dug up and transplanted to the vicinity of the exposed nest – the thick fleshy root of the bryony preventing the wilting of its large five-pointed leaves.

In an average year on a well-keepered beat, about one third of the nests will fail to hatch. The two main causes will usually be predators and agricultural activities such as grass cutting. (This has been illustrated by the table on page 47.) Unless the keeper locates a large proportion of his nests and visits them regularly, losses from predation may be considerably higher.

Although the average number of eggs in a partridge's clutch is 15, individual clutches show considerable variation. It is common practice to standardise partridge clutches to 15 eggs – reducing the larger clutches and adding to the smaller ones. At the same time, any pheasant eggs which may have been laid in the partridge's nest are removed. With the rapid deterioration in the partridge's breeding habitat which has occurred on farmland, the decrease in invertebrate food supply and the unfavourable June weather, it may be that an adjustment of clutch size to only 10 eggs would result in a larger number of surviving young partridges – particularly if the picked-up eggs were hatched and reared by broodies.

Nest management can mean almost anything from operating the full-scale Euston system – in which all the partridge eggs are temporarily replaced by artificial eggs – to adjusting only for clutch-size and manipulating the more dangerously situated nests. Whichever method is adopted will depend on how much time the keeper can spend on his partridges, but inevitably for his wild stock, hedgerow keepering will remain his most important commitment.

Chapter 7
Red-legged Partridges

Not so long ago one hardly ever met a keeper who devoted much time to red-legged partridges. Pheasants and grey partridges had special attention, but redlegs were virtually ignored. In fact, in the old days they were actually discouraged – being unsuitable for walking-up. As a table bird their darker flesh no doubt further contributed to their unpopularity.

Now all this has changed, for without too much difficulty the redleg can give us excellent October shooting – provided it is shown properly. Anyone who has shot driven redlegs in Spain or Portugal, fizzing over deep rocky gullies or appearing suddenly from the tops of scrub-covered hills, will be enthusiastic about their flying qualities. Obviously shooting them in England on a muggy day in a flat countryside presents problems, but the birds *are* worth taking trouble over. Indeed, in the eastern countries, their increase in the post-war years has done something to offset the decline in grey partridges.

We are frequently asked why the wild redleg has succeeded while the grey partridge has been declining. A recent four-year project by the Game Conservancy (1978–82) has clarified details of the population ecology of this species – including breeding and nesting behaviour, as well as chick food requirements. The study also explains some of the differences between the two species.

When the grey partridge began to decline (1952–1962), fewer in numbers *and* a smaller proportion were shot, so that the reduced shooting pressure on greys helped the redlegs to build up. The ratio of redlegs to greys shot is double that in birds going over the same Guns. Since about 1974, however, redlegs – largely reared – have been shot in their own right and as a result in many areas the wild stocks have declined, production rates being insufficient to offset the substantial harvesting.

Reared redlegs – in contrast to grey partridges – have also shown that, when released and shot the same year, the return in the bag can be as high as that for pheasants. A 40 per cent recovery rate is not unusual if the birds are liberated carefully into a suitable habitat.

No wonder that, in recent seasons, shooting men have taken a much greater interest in the red-legged partridge. The numbers now being reared are often restricted only by the difficulties of obtaining adequate supplies of eggs or chicks from a good hardy strain.

25 Distribution of the red-legged partridge

In southern Europe the bird thrives in a wide variety of habitats, from well-tended arable land to olive groves, vineyards and the scrub-covered sides of high rocky hills. It has shown an equal ability to make use of very varied habitat in England, though it appears to be more at home in the drier arable eastern part of the country. In Suffolk, where the redleg was first successfully introduced in about 1770 – this was the second attempt – it rapidly established itself. It still far outnumbers the grey partridge on the dry heathland of east and north-west Suffolk. Rather surprisingly redlegs do well on the clay soil of central and south Suffolk and parts of Essex – surprisingly, because their pedestrian habits sometimes result in crippling balls of clay adhering to the toes of both young and adult birds.

Coupled with the spectacular decrease in the numbers of grey partridges in the later sixties, the increase in redleg pairs is somewhat surprising and as yet by no means fully explained. It can, however, be said that the grey partridge is not decreasing *because* the redleg is increasing. In fact on our study area, where the greys approach 1 pair to 7 acres (3 h.) or better, the wild redlegs tended to move off.

The breeding season

Covey break-up starts later and is spread over a longer period than in the greys, with small coveys sometimes occurring into April.

Compared with the grey partridge the redleg lays a relatively small clutch of eggs – the average number being about 11–12, compared with approximately 15 from the grey partridge.

Unfortunately, comparable data for redleg clutch size from their homelands in S. Europe is not available, though the clutch size in Spain is generally reported to be larger. Here very large clutches known to be laid by a single hen occasionally occur. It may be that the smaller clutch size in England is an adaptation to our less suitable climate.

As with the grey partridge, repeat nests will frequently replace nests lost in the early stages. Loss rates are higher than with the grey, mostly because the eggs are not covered with leaves.

One of the main questions answered by our recent study of the redleg concerned the question of double-clutching, in which the hen lays two clutches, one of which is incubated by the cock and reared as a separate brood. By catching birds in the breeding season, and fitting them with back-tabs or radio tracking devices, the behaviour of individuals was closely observed.

There were often long delays – averaging 15 days and up to 37 – between clutch completion and the beginning of incubation. The first (delayed) clutch was the one invariably incubated by the male – a good system even though the delay exposes the eggs to more destruction by predators than is the case with grey partridges.

There are perhaps two important points to note from this study for those interested in the practical aspects of game conservation rather than the mysteries of bird behaviour. The most obvious is that red-legged partridge eggs left unattended for weeks will probably be incubated eventually by the cock and do not need picking up and putting in an incubator. Eggs from delayed nests have the same hatchability as those incubated immediately. The second point is that, while both partridges benefit from the control of nest predators, red-legged partridges do so more than greys, because their potential productivity is higher due to double nesting, and their susceptibility to egg predators is greater.

The study also showed that, when necessary, the redleg chicks could survive on a largely vegetarian diet – unlike the greys.

After the breeding season the sex ratio of the two species is very different. An examination of the bag on our study area during October shows that in relation to the number of hens, many more cock grey partridges were shot than redlegs. This may be explained by the fact that most of the losses occur during incubation affecting both cock and hen redleg, but only hen grey.

The peak hatching period appears to be less well pronounced in the redleg and is about ten days later partly because of the delays caused by the double clutches.

In Spain and Portugal one commonly sees the first broods about 10th May, though the main hatch would not occur until the first two weeks of June. There is some evidence to suggest that there are two quite distinct hatching peaks, probably as a result of so many repeat nests being made, after the first attempts have been destroyed by predation.

Throughout the species range the eggs themselves are notoriously 'tough'. Every year reports are received of stained and discoloured clutches of eggs through which the vegetation has grown up, being successfully incubated after a delay of several weeks, as explained.

Production of young

Brood counts in August show that in most years the survival rates for the young of the two species are similar. Most variation is due to the later hatching of the redleg. Perhaps in a year of good survival, when the post-hatching weather has been unusually dry and warm, the production of the young redlegs is slightly higher, while in a wet summer, when young/old ratios may be down to 1/1, the redleg may fare worse than the grey partridge.

In low survival years when more broods are lost, the unsuccessful adults of either sex either join up with other adults to form 'coveys' of old birds or associate with a true family covey. Spanish keepers avow that there are groups composed solely of cocks, sometimes up to 30 in number. Incidentally, at this time of year sex identification is not always easy for the non-expert, as cocks which have gone broody and are 'mothering' chicks often develop feminine characteristics and to the casual observer look much like hens.

Winter losses

In the autumn and winter, differences in apparent survival rates between the two species become most noticeable. When shooting occurs on estates where both species are present, the redleg, as we have stated, is shot out of proportion to its true numbers. Even in good partridge years it is most unusual with formal shooting to kill more than a third of the grey partridges present in September. Of the redlegs, however, as many as two thirds of the total number may be shot. The reasons for this are the ease with which redleg coveys are broken up once they have been driven into a suitable cover crop, and their habit of flushing singly or in twos and threes. The grey partridge has a stronger covey discipline and groups are less easily scattered.

Deaths from a wide variety of causes constituted the main losses up to the time of covey break-up in January, and from then until the middle of March movement off the estate (particularly by the young hens) caused the reduction in numbers of breeding partridges. Even where large blocks of land are keepered, there are usually some areas of unkeepered land – e.g. for some depth around each village – which to the partridge appears to be suitable territory. In fact, in such places the chances of successful breeding are extremely small and mortality among the adult birds is often very high. Although no one ever appears to gain from this spring movement of partridges, this is mainly because the areas 'colonised' during this spring emigration are unkeepered areas where no one takes enough interest to record or even notice the temporary increase.

On the average, between 30 per cent and 40 per cent of the grey partridges present after shooting 'disappear' from recorded shoots before the following March, but on some East Anglian estates the comparable figure for redlegs is little over 20 per cent.

Yearling redleg females that dispersed from our study areas were largely replaced by others from outside which paired with locally bred young males. These pairs would take up territories close to the natal area. The older birds tend to pair with each other rather than with yearlings.

Rearing and releasing

As stated earlier, not so long ago the possibilities of rearing the redlegs were rarely explored, rather due to prejudice or to some unhappy experience with badly shown birds in very flat country. Now, the driven redleg is appreciated!

Incidentally, redlegs will hold obligingly on comparatively bare ground – such as rough fallow or cultivated stubbles – and can be driven over the guns at intervals and in twos and threes. Grey partridges would rarely utilise such inhospitable surroundings and in any case would be more likely to flush all together. The Frenchmen will also use scrub cover – rather like pheasants – so hedgerows, thorns and rough corners, adjacent to any fields being driven, should also be walked through.

The red-legged partridges reared at Fordingbridge are raised with the same equipment as we use for pheasants and grey partridges. A 5 ft. × 5 ft. ($1\frac{1}{2}$ m. × $1\frac{1}{2}$ m.) brooder house with an electric 400-watt Wrenn infra-red or a propane gas brooder, will house 70–100 birds.

For the first two weeks a special partridge starter crumb with a relatively high and easily digested protein content is recommended. Failing this a turkey starter crumb is quite suitable. The food should be scattered on papiermâché egg trays for the first few days – the movement of food particles caused by the chicks running over the trays seems to encourage active feeding.

At two weeks a pheasant rearing crumb can be used and the changeover to this food can be completed within the third week. During the following week cut wheat can be gradually introduced. Penning space (10 ft. × 5 ft. [3 m. × 1½ m.] sections) should be similar to that used for pheasants; at 6 weeks of age the birds should have a 40 ft. × 10 ft. (12 m. × 3 m.) pen.

A form of 'hysteria', in which all the birds will run or fly from one end of the pen to the other, very occasionally occurs at this stage. Some cover in the pen will help to prevent this. Spraying the poults with water from a hosepipe for a minute or two on a warm day has given good results, but at other times it has been necessary to divide a large unit into a number of small ones (15–20) in movable pens.

Unlike grey partridges, redlegs rarely suffer from moniliasis. They are however particularly susceptible to 'blackhead', and if this disease is diagnosed 'Emtryl' – obtainable from a chemist – should be given in the drinking water.

Redlegs are more lively than grey partridges in the early stages and the two species are better reared separately.

Details of partridge rearing will be found in Chapter 16.

Although they can be moved to release pens out on the shoot at six weeks, the best recovery rates have been obtained from birds taken out at 8–9 weeks.

Releasing can be carried out in one of two ways. Where the numbers reared are relatively small, a 10 ft. × 6 ft. (3 m. × 2 m.) movable pen – containing 15 birds – can be strategically sited at the junction of a cover crop and stubble. A cultivated stubble is ideal and remains attractive to the redlegs for a very long time. Root crops, such as sugar beet, provide ideal cover, as well as being useful later in the season for driving. A piece of bare ground next to or near the release site is an advantage, and helps to hold them. They do not like thick cover all round them. Ideally birds should be in pens with some wire netting at the sides – low enough to enable them to look out. Box-type pens that only give a view of the sky are less satisfactory.

After a week's confinement half the birds may be quietly released from a sliding hatch – the remainder being kept inside the pen for another week. Alternatively, one end of the pen can be raised for a short while to allow half the poults to walk out.

Food and water should be provided both inside and outside the pen.

A second method of release which has proved equally successful where larger numbers have been reared, is to construct a temporary pen from a 50-yd. (45 m.) roll of 6-ft. (2 m.), 1-in. (2½ cm.) mesh, wire netting. Ideally a piece of rough grass, including some sunning and dusting areas, should be chosen for the site.

Up to 50 poults (temporarily immobilised by having the five outer wing feathers or primaries 'pulled') can be released into the pen. In 2–3 weeks the birds will be flying out of the release pen, which can then be used for a second release group.

Orthodox pheasant release pens have also been used for redlegs with success (temporarily immobilising the birds as above), the birds later feeding and holding with the pheasants and in some places coming over the Guns with them! As a general rule, however, from a disease control point of view we would not advocate mixing the species in a pen *if there were any degree of overcrowding*.

If some reared birds are to be retained for egg production the following year they can be overwintered in units of 12 in 10 ft. × 6 ft. (3 m. × 2 m.) movable pens, or larger aviaries. Towards the end of February the birds should be paired off and placed in special wire-floored laying pens supported on a stand above the grass. This prevents gapes.

It is usually very difficult to sex the birds before January.

Penned pairs should be given breeders pellets. Red-legged partridges can be kept for a second breeding season, when their egg production will exceed that of the first-year birds. About 30 to 35 eggs per pair would be the normal yield, but where a selection programme is carried out 45 eggs per pair can be expected from two- and three-year-old birds.

Pairing is not always easy. Although most young hen redlegs are smaller than the cocks, and do not have the knobbly 'spurs' which distinguish the male, some mistakes in sexing young birds may occur. Young cocks have not always developed easily recognisable protrusions by February.

There is also a method of sex determination based on examination of the cloaca. Used by an expert from late March onwards this method can be very reliable but the small differences in the appearance of the genitalia would not be sufficiently obvious for the method to be of any practical value in February.

With old birds the cocks are easy enough to identify, but some of the old hens may also develop fairly large nodules (on either one or both legs) and a little experience is then necessary to differentiate cock from hen.

Flock mating may be resorted to for those birds of indeterminate sex. About 20 birds can be placed in a covered pen, each side consisting of four 10 ft. × 5 ft. (3 m. × 1½ m.) sections. If rough grass is left for a yard (1 m.) inside the perimeter of the pen, nest finding and egg collections will be less difficult. The central area should consist of short herbage.

In the shooting season young birds can be distinguished from old by the cream tips* on each of the two outermost flight feathers or primaries. However, in pen-reared birds the tips of these feathers are often abraded, and juvenile primaries that have been pulled will in a short time be replaced by *adult*

---

* In red-legged partridges in Spain, this cream tip is much smaller and fainter, or even absent.

feathers. Accurate determination of such reared birds when subsequently shot (and required by game dealers) can only be guaranteed by wing-tagging.

Redlegs in the North of England

We are often asked whether it is worth while trying to encourage a wild breeding stock in the north. The answer is that – although the redleg is always surprising us – it is not very likely that they could be established in any number much further north than, say, the Doncaster area of Yorkshire. The number of pairs reduce rapidly as one travels north. Five years of partridge counts at Boroughbridge have shown little variation, 4 to 6 pairs of redlegs compared with the grey partridge population which fluctuated in these years between 100 and 170 pairs.

In Spain the range of this species extends from areas with 10 in. (25 cm.) of rainfall to 35 in. (90 cm.). They are affected by prolonged snow and cold weather.

If a Frenchman had been asked in 1769 – the year before the successful release in Suffolk – whether they would have had any chance of breeding and establishing themselves in England, he would have certainly replied that as their natural range did not extend much beyond the Loire, how then could they thrive over 300 miles further north?

But he would have been wrong, so it may be that we shall again find odd pockets in surprising places which will suit the redlegs.

Releasing birds for shooting is another matter, as winter conditions and the vagaries of the weather at nesting time are not involved.

Some released reared redlegs which survived the shooting season have nested and reared broods as far north as Banffshire, but they have then often disappeared.

Regarding crosses between redlegs and chukhar, recent legislation has made it illegal to release into the wild crosses between these two species, as well as pure chukhar.

Partridge management in Spain and Portugal

In contrast to England, on most Iberian estates there is usually no shortage of insect foods for the young partridges: cover is generally abundant, and agricultural pressures from toxic chemicals and machinery are in many areas minimal, but they are increasing. Grass cutting and barley harvesting can cause losses locally.

The weather is normally kinder to the young chicks than in our own country, but bad thunderstorms or even hail in May can sometimes destroy a great number of nests.

In good areas two wild birds per hectare (2·5 acres) can be shot. With such good natural conditions it is curious that some owners are more keen to release reared birds – often from intensively bred stock – rather than manage their own wild partridge crop in order to produce better shooting. Where reared birds have been released, recoveries in the bag have been generally poor – unlike results in England.

The main problems regarding wild birds are that a very large proportion of the nests – well over half – are deserted early in the season, the keepers being ignorant or unaware of the reasons. We are not discussing the 'delayed' nets, although these can cause confusion. Certainly predation can be extremely heavy, and for the most part old, heavy, inhumane traps are in use, which are not conducive to a practical and well-planned campaign of control. In spite of the lack of hedges and ditches that make trapping easier by providing good sites for tunnels and the travel lanes, predator control could be made much more efficient. Weasels and polecats are present, though not stoats: box traps could be useful.

In some places traps and shotguns (as opposed to the traditional carbine) are not permitted – it being feared that the keepers might use them to take partridges and rabbits! This may be true, but it lets the partridges' natural enemies off very lightly.

In many areas eyed lizards (*Lacertus lepidus*) and magpies are a serious problem; also foxes, feral cats and semi-wild dogs. The large Montpelier snake (*Malpolon monspessulanus*) – sometimes 6 ft. (2 m.) in length – will eat partridge eggs and chicks, and take animals as large as leverets. On the credit side, it preys on the eyed lizards, which themselves can grow to 2 ft. (0·6 m.) in length. Such specimens will take small birds and field mice with ease, as well as eggs.

On many estates there is a system of rewarding farm workers for nests found. As we have said earlier: much disturbance can result – the redleg is far more nervous than the grey partridge. A better system is to pay a reward *only for nests that hatch* – explaining the damaging effect of too much nosing about while the hens are sitting.

On the whole the co-operation of the shepherds is invaluable on partridge ground and should be encouraged – not forgetting their over-enthusiasm at nest-watching. They are often better naturalists and keepers than some of the 'guards'.

The use of dummy eggs is virtually unknown, and the maintenance of a small flock of broody bantams for saving 'hot' eggs is rare.

Where there are vast tracts of scrub or *monte* composed of trees and plants like scrub evergreen oak, broom, heaths, juniper, rock rose (*Cistus* sp.), *Lavandula* sp., rosemary, etc., which are for the most part useless to the birds, some clearing should be considered. This can be done by cutting, swiping or – *where it can be safely undertaken* – by burning open tracts through the undergrowth, so that wild grasses and plants, with their ant and other insect communities, can take over. On stony ground the swipe chains can be set high. Clovers and vetches can sometimes be established on cleared areas.

In certain terrains – for example where olives are grown and the rows in between the trees cultivated and kept weed-free – the nesting cover can be insufficient. It is *not* a sound practice to leave the trimmings from the olive trees on the ground as nesting cover, as this encourages the olive fly – a serious pest – to breed in the dead wood. A better plan is to plant a game crop in every sixth row, leaving the other five rows fallow. This green strip can be rotated to the adjacent row the following year. A mixture of vetches and wheat, thinly sown, will provide food and cover, but there are many other possibilities.

It is also helpful to the breeding birds *not* to hand-weed around the base of every olive tree. This island of grass is useful as nesting cover. Such patches will, of course, have to be clear by harvesting time, when, in any case, their usefulness is over.

Redlegs often sit under the trees when they need shade, and perch in the branches when rain is threatening!

Winter wheat provides safe nesting cover, but in some areas barley can be cut while the birds are sitting. Harvesting can start around 10th June.

Aridity can be a problem, and where practical, water-fountains or shallow pools should be provided in shady sites or under home-made foliage or reed canopies. Partridges have often been observed drinking from irrigation ditches, low cattle troughs and natural pools. A water supply – or adequate moisture in some form – is absolutely necessary to the young chicks.

Any cement pools should have well roughened, non-slippery sides, and not slope too steeply. The centre can be partially filled with stones and boulders. Temporary drinking pools can be made by lining a hollow with heavy-duty polythene, covered to a shallow depth with soil on gravel.

Though covert or winter feeding, as we understand it, is rarely necessary, at certain times of the year – August and perhaps January – the partridges may be short of natural food. Hoppers filled with wheat or other grains will be useful. Small food patches, left unharvested, will also help where the ground is not too poor to grow them. Vetches, buckwheat, chickpeas, lentils and clover are among the most valuable. The leaves and seeds of the carob bean are also favourite foods.

Of the cereals wheat is the partridges' favourite. In addition barley, oats and rye are also taken, as well as many agricultural seeds, and large quantities of greenstuff from mid-November to mid-March.

In the autumn the birds will also eat olives, and acorns of the evergreen oaks. The birds' beaks are strong enough to peck into the hard acorns themselves, though sometimes pigs and wild boars will crush them partially first. From June to September grapes are eaten, occasionally in large enough numbers to incur the wrath of the vineyard owners!

Chapter 8
Stocking a Pheasant Shoot

Reared or wild birds

It is sometimes assumed by inexperienced shooting men that to have a really good pheasant shoot it is necessary to rear large numbers of birds every year. In fact, there are a great many shoots where natural conditions are so suited to *wild* pheasants that it is more profitable to devote available labour and money to keepering for the birds of hedgerow and copse rather than rearing.

Equally, there are many shoots where wild pheasants will not thrive naturally, but where a very good show can be made with reared birds. Reared pheasants are in some ways less of a gamble than wild birds: one is not so dependent on having a good nesting season. A bad hatch can often be counteracted by setting a second lot of eggs, and in any case the hatches can be staggered to prevent them from coinciding with a bad weather peak. Nesting losses of all kinds and casualties due to such hazards as poisonous farm chemicals, grass cutting and so on, are avoided.

Incidentally, many pheasant shoots where birds are liberated would better succeed if more time was spent in preparing the ground before putting pheasants to covert. It is quite useless to devote a great deal of energy to the hatching and rearing programme if work on maintaining the coverts and release pens is neglected, and predators are allowed to thrive unchecked. There is no easier target for predator or poacher than a reared pheasant, particularly where there is wire netting round plantations.

One must also consider that a large stock of pheasants may, to some extent, be in competition with the native wild partridges. Unless carefully watched, pheasants will often spoil partridge nests by laying in them. Where, for instance, nesting cover and natural food are not too plentiful, it may be wise to let the partridges have first priority. If the pheasant stock is shot hard every year, the partridges can have it all their own way during the late winter and spring – the months of 'competition'. A yearly rearing and restocking programme for the pheasants would mean that they would only be on the ground in any number from August to December.

84

Different methods of restocking

A shoot can be restocked by obtaining pheasant eggs, day-old chicks, poults or adults.

Hatching eggs and day-old chicks

In the long run the cheapest method is to obtain eggs, hatch them out under broodies or in incubators, rear the chicks and put them to covert at about 6 weeks of age. Such birds will quickly learn to regard the covert as 'home' and those anchored by foster-mothers will become acclimatised without difficulty.

This system, of course, means that reasonably skilled labour and quite a lot of equipment must be available.

Eggs can either be obtained by catching-up and penning wild hens from the estate or they can be bought from professional gamefarmers. There are also invariably a number of eggs which have to be picked up for one reason or another from wild nests.

Most gamefarmers guarantee 90 per cent fertility, but usually the fertility is over 95 per cent. A number of estates which find it too expensive to get all their eggs from a gamefarm often compromise by setting a proportion of their own eggs and buying the remainder from outside.

When estimating how many eggs are needed to produce a required number of poults, one can reckon that an experienced man with only a few sittings to look after ought to get a hatch of nearly 80 per cent with good broodies, though with a large number of eggs to set he may average 75 per cent or less. From the chicks he hatches he ought to put about 70–75 per cent to covert from an open rearing field, and 80–90 per cent from predator-proof movable pens or brooders. In very rough figures, therefore, he would want 1,500–1,750 eggs to produce 1,000 poults. While an experienced man might think he could do far better than this, the average keeper will be grateful for extra eggs as a margin of safety. Accidents will happen.

Using artificial incubation methods, at least 10 per cent more eggs will be required. Commercial pheasant hatcheries usually work on a figure of a 50 per cent hatch – for safety's sake. Private estates using incubators would probably average 60–65 per cent over the whole season.

Buying day-old chicks is an increasingly popular way of restocking and may save the busy keeper a considerable amount of time – and therefore money. It is not very much more expensive than hatching out the eggs at home.

Buying poults

A number of shoots which do not have labour and equipment to do the rearing themselves prefer to buy 'ready-made' poults, usually at 6 weeks old.

Poults with broodies will settle down well in covert, but older birds that have left their foster-mother, or poults that have been brooder reared, must be conditioned in a release pen before being allowed their liberty. It is almost always useless to release brooder-reared birds to the four winds and expect them to be there when the shooting season comes along. The releasing technique is fully discussed in a later chapter.

Buying adults

Adult pheasants are sometimes available from gamefarms after they have done a tour of duty in the laying pens. They may or may not lay a small clutch in the wild – much depends on age, ancestry and method of penning. Few properly controlled experiments have been conducted, but from Conservancy trials with marked birds it is not economic to buy hens which have been taped or brailed all their lives. Many gamefarms, however, sell birds which have been full-winged.

A period of acclimatisation in a release pen will certainly increase the chances of survival and limit the degree of straying.

Catching-up pheasants

It is essential for plans to be completed by Christmas at the latest, otherwise it may not be possible for the catchers to be put out and baited for a sufficient period to enable enough hens to be caught up in time. *Reared* birds from the coverts (easily identified by wing-tags from a previous season) will settle down quickly in their laying pens and need not be brought in until 1st March. Wild birds will benefit by being penned up about a month earlier.

Sometimes stock hens are caught up before the shooting season so as to avoid unwittingly penning any 'pricked' or injured birds which might produce infertile eggs or no eggs at all. This is, however, an expensive way of setting about it, and nowadays it is usual to start catching up when the shooting of hen pheasants is over.

It is advisable to put out and bait the catchers some time before they are to be set, so that the pheasants can get used to feeding around them. According to the type of catcher used, the number of hens required and the skill of the keeper, it may take anything from a few days to a month to catch up the birds. A lot also depends on the weather, for obviously birds will come to feed more readily in hard weather.

How to catch up the birds

There are two types of catcher – multiple and individual catchers. The former are constructed on the lines of jackdaw cages, usually with ground-level funnels, and they will catch half a dozen or more birds at a time. Catchers made of wire netting are not recommended, as the trapped birds will often crash about and damage themselves.

26 Hen pheasants, both wild and reared birds, are caught up at Fordingbridge and penned for egg production. After laying their quota of eggs in pens, some are tabbed and released in mid-May to nest in the wild

27 Multiple pheasant catcher made of slatted timber

87

A reliable catcher is the slatted timber type illustrated on p. 87. The cage can be of any suitable size, the slats having spaces between them which are wide enough to allow pheasants to put their heads through without damaging themselves.

At each end an opening about 1 ft. (25 cm.) high should be left so that the pheasants can walk in and out quite easily. This catcher can be left on a feeding ride permanently so that the birds become quite used to it.

When the time comes to operate the catcher, wire-netting funnels should be slipped into the open space at either end. The catchers will hold up to half a dozen birds or so and make a quick job of getting the hens. A sliding door at the side gives access to the catcher.

Another multiple catcher, which is used in Scandinavia, consists of a wooden cage of similar construction, about 4 ft. 6in. ($1\frac{1}{2}$ m.) square, and 18 in. (46 cm.) high, roofed with netting. At either end there are openings about 8 in. (20 cm.) square, on which are hung doors made from three or four pieces of rigid steel wire, as in a pigeon loft. The doors are hinged from above and can only open inwards. The bird pushes its way in and the door closes behind it.

Individual catchers are more like traps, in that once the trip wire or tripping stick has been touched and the bird confined, no other bird can be caught until the catcher has been emptied and re-set.

If most of the pheasants to be caught up are from stock previously reared under broodies, a familiar coop will make a good catcher. For wild pheasants, an alternative is a 'basket' which can be made very easily from a few hazel rods (see photograph 28). Both types are propped up on trip sticks, just high enough to allow a pheasant to walk underneath. 'Sieve' catchers made from wooden hoops and netting (similar to those used by small boys for catching sparrows) are also quite efficient.

Tripping devices can consist either of a springy wire or a pliant hazel bow, set so as to release the lid, coop or basket the moment the bird touches it. A strong wind will bring the catcher down if it is too lightly set. There are a number of ways of making and setting these tripping devices, and most keepers will have their own favourites. The photograph shows one method of setting up a catcher with trip sticks. Note the wedge-shaped ends and the notches cut in the hazel sticks, which allow the two sticks and the half-hoop to be held together under tension.

Good baits include wheat, barley, maize, peas and beans.

All birds should be carefully examined for signs of disease or injury, and only birds in first-class condition should be penned.

Laying pens

There are three types of laying pens: fixed pens built in rows such as those commonly used on gamefarms; movable laying pens, some of which are

28 'Basket' catcher. Note that there is a notch on the bottom bar of the catcher (not visible in the photograph), and also a horizontal notch on the bottom of the vertical stick to take the wire

29 Hen pheasant in catcher. A coop can be used as a catcher in the same way

dual-purpose and can also be used for rearing; and large communal (or flock-mating) pens. There are advantages and disadvantages to each system.

Fixed pens

Each pen to hold one cock and six or seven hens is 8 yds. (7 m.) square (though 5-yds. [4½ m.] square pens are quite common) and made of 6-ft. (2 m.) wire netting (2-in. [5 cm.] mesh) nailed to 12 larch posts, each 8 ft. (2½ m.) in length. At the top of the wire there should be a floppy, 'anti-fox' fringe, which is made from a strip of wire netting about 1 ft. (0·3 m.) wide, held parallel to the ground by means of stiff wires. It should not be too rigid – this will only help the fox.

Corrugated iron sheets (2 ft. [0·6 m.] high), boarding or sacking is used to surround the pen and give protection from wind and weather. The more sheltered the birds are, the more reliable will be the egg production.

30 Section of a fixed laying pen, showing clumps of conifer branches which provide essential privacy and cover for the birds. The anti-fox fringe is a wise precaution

The birds should have one wing brailed or taped to prevent them from flying out, so no roof netting is necessary. Although this is a saving in expense, in some seasons we have had a lot of eggs stolen by rooks and jackdaws. Game food will also be taken from open pens by scavengers such as starlings. If only a few hens are to be penned it will be worth while to put an 'Ulstron' net roof on the pen.

90

Each pen should be furnished with a shelter of bark timber against the back wall (about 3 ft. × 1 ft. 6 in. [90 cm. × 46 cm.]) and two clumps of cut evergreens (not yew) in the corners. Alternatively, a tunnel of evergreens can be made against two sides. The more privacy the birds have, the better. In hot countries they will furnish necessary shade.

Unit pens of this size are not as simple and cheap to construct as a communal pen of equivalent holding capacity, and when it becomes necessary to move them to fresh ground the job will take longer and be more costly. Unless disease appears in the pens, however, they can remain standing for four or five laying seasons. Up to the present, no cheap, safe way of sterilising the soil in pens to kill off disease organisms is known.

A disadvantage is that if a cock turns out to be a failure it may not be discovered until hatching day, and all the eggs from half a dozen hens or so will be infertile. This is, however, rare. It cannot of course happen in a communal pen. A sample of early eggs can always be candled at 10 days so that any impotent cocks can be removed. The fertility in small pens, however, is normally a little better than in communal pens.

Sectional pens
Many people now rearing pheasants in 100-unit brooders use 10 ft. × 5 ft. (3 m. × 1½ m.) sections for their brooder runs. These can also be employed before they are required for the rearing season to make up temporary pens for breeding stock, for example 30 ft. × 10 ft. (9 m. × 3 m.) or 20 ft. × 20 ft. (6 m. × 6 m.) pens for six hens and a cock. A suitable roof covering can be made with 'Ulstron' netting.

Communal pens
This system is still quite commonly used and for large numbers of birds is satisfactory. From the point of view of materials required it is the cheapest. One hundred birds in a communal pen require an area of between 1,000 and 1,200 sq. yds. (836 and 1,003 sq. m.) (i.e. a pen between 32 and 34 yds. [29 and 31 m.] square). *The pen can with advantage be larger*, much depending on how long the birds are to be penned and how good the vegetation is. The pens should contain one or two low feed-stacks, or clumps of brushwood and fir branches. Permanent shelters can be made of bark timber or corrugated iron. If it is convenient to include a few bushes or small trees in the pen they will be appreciated by the birds. They should not be near the netting, or the birds may succeed in using them as a means of escape.

In a communal pen, one cock will usually try to assert his supremacy over the others and there may be a certain amount of fighting. It may also mean that the 'master' cock will try to serve too many hens and fail, causing a slight drop in fertility. It is, however, surprising how many hens a vigorous cock can look after. Trials in America showed that a cock penned with 12 hens produced eggs with a fertility of 93 per cent; penned with 15 hens, a fertility of 91 per cent; and penned with 20 hens, a fertility of 83 per cent. Notwithstanding these figures, it is safest to pen one cock to every 6 or 7 hens. Wild cocks may also fly in over the top of the pen and serve the hens.

If the pen is large and the grass is long, it may be difficult for the keeper to be sure of clearing the pen of eggs every day. As a result stale eggs may be brought in from time to time.

Movable laying pens

In the standard 10 ft. × 6 ft. × 4 ft. (3 m. × 2 m. × 1 m.) movable pens, the output and quality of the eggs are good, though the birds themselves are inclined to be rather cramped. During the course of the season one or two of the hens usually injure themselves slightly in the confined space, and some of the cock pheasants lose their tail feathers.

Such pens are not recommended for true *wild* hens – they are too small and the birds never settle.

Another difficulty experienced with any of the smaller types of pens is that the hens find it practically impossible to escape from the attentions of a vigorous cock, and a number of minor injuries result. In bad weather the ground may get very muddy owing to trampling, and it is therefore advisable to use a rainproof feeding trough or to feed under a shelter.

In spite of the above limitations, many people use them with success and obtain excellent eggs.

They can also be used for holding *laying* pheasants until such time as the pens are required for rearing the chicks, thereby economising on equipment.

No more than five hens should be put into each pen, or they will be overcrowded. The pens should normally be moved about once a week, but the frequency will depend on the weather and state of the vegetation.

In addition to the dual-purpose (10 ft. × 6 ft. [3 m. × 2 m.]) pen, another type of movable laying ark is also in use which, though considerably lower, is much roomier. The birds come through the laying season very well, and the eggs produced are of excellent fertility. An advantage of this larger type of ark is that the eggs are disturbed and trodden on less than in the smaller pen. The measurements of one model are about 15 ft. × 9 ft. ($4\frac{1}{2}$ m. × 3 m.) at the base of the pen, the sides sloping inwards towards the top. This gives the birds good protection in rainy weather. The height is 3 ft. (0·9 m.).

The pen is divided into two compartments (one large and one small), with a pop-hole in the movable partition: this arrangement seems to make it easier for hens to get away from the cock when they want to. The small compartment can also be used for catching up. A low perch is fitted to each pen. Each unit houses one cock and five or six hens and is moved approximately once a week, depending on the weather. The low roof discourages the birds from flying

92

upwards, but in case they do the wire netting should be kept floppy rather than taut so as to soften the blow.

The cost of construction of these large pens is high, but with proper maintenance they should last 20 years or more. They are more cumbersome to move than the lighter pens and, unless they are sectional, storage may be a problem.

The management of laying pens

Where possible the position of the pens should be sheltered and have a southern aspect; the land should be light and well drained, and if movable pens are to be used the surface should be reasonably smooth and level. Good herbage is also to be desired, although in hot countries excellent eggs are produced from aviaries bedded on pure sand. Greenstuff is usually provided as an extra.

Ground where poultry or turkeys have been running should be avoided.

An open wood can be quite a suitable place for a pheasant aviary, but pens should not be sited in plantations where there is lack of sun.

At the end of the season the grass should be cut and the ground scarified. Although there is no safe or economic treatment which kills off all disease organisms in the soil, there is some evidence that altering the acidity of the soil water may reduce the incidence of gapes. This can be achieved by the addition of lime to slightly alkaline soils, or ammonium sulphate to soils with an acid tendency – while with neutral soils either chemical may be used.

Selecting breeding birds

If the eggs are to be hatched under broodies it will be sufficient to pen healthy birds of all breeds. With incubator hatching, however, it is advisable to select the wild or hybrid type of pheasant that tends to lay a smaller egg. The larger eggs of the heavier varieties (e.g. Blackneck) are usually more difficult to hatch in most incubators.

The most prolific egg-laying breed on the experimental gamefarm at Fordingbridge was always the Old English Blackneck (*Phasianus c. colchicus*). In April and May alone they would average at least 40 eggs per hen.

The Mongolian (*Phasianus c. mongolicus*) is a slightly heavier bird with many fine qualities: although rather nervous and not quite such a prolific layer as the Blackneck, this breed nevertheless has a very good record of fertility and hatchability. A first cross between these two breeds produces as good a bird as can be obtained.

Chinese (*Phasianus c. torquatus*) and Melanistic Mutant (*Phasianus c.* mut. *tenebrosus*) pheasants also have their devotees and make another good cross. Pure Chinese are somewhat lacking in natural camouflage, being so very light

93

in colour, but otherwise they are a good breed. The Melanistic Mutant (a sport that breeds true) is hardy, slightly smaller than the others and not such a good layer.

At Fordingbridge a strain of wild hybrid pheasants is maintained which have a number of fine qualities. Although they are not as large as some pure breeds, and inclined not to lay really well until their second or third year of domestication, they are excellent for restocking projects. Their hatchability is the highest of all the breeds penned.

Japanese green pheasants (*Phasianus versicolor*) are smaller and more active than the *colchicus* type. They do not usually come into lay until the end of April, and although first crosses are fertile their progeny when 'selfed' produces a large number of infertile eggs.

The above findings are the result of many years of pheasant study on the gamefarm. In other countries, however, some of these breeds of pheasants behave rather differently. For example, in the Balkans the Melanistic Mutant is recorded as being a prolific layer, which suggests that the *strain* of the local pheasants is far more important than the actual breed.

No one breed of pheasant is more prone to straying than any other. Some are more easily noticed than others.

How many birds should be penned?

Hatching with incubators may necessitate setting eggs at weekly intervals and the number of pheasants penned should be geared to the incubator capacity. During the peak laying period of approximately 6 weeks (from mid-April to the end of May or the first week in June) about 65 per cent of the hens will be laying each day. This means that if the weekly capacity of the incubator is 500 eggs, 120 hen pheasants will need to be penned. With broody hatching, one can allow the eggs to accumulate for a fortnight without any fall-off in hatchability.

Approaching the problem from another point of view, if it were intended to rear 1,000 poults and anticipate a 60 per cent hatch and 80 per cent rearing success, 2,000 eggs would be needed. This number could be produced by 60–70 hens by the end of May.

Fertility is at its peak around the second and third week of May, and not in April as is often supposed. Where birds are maintained in *small* pens, the longer they are confined the more they will lose condition: the lack of fresh greenstuff over a long period may also check them slightly. Some shooting men prefer to collect only 15–20 eggs per hen, and then release the birds to make wild nests in the woods. By releasing the laying stock about the second week in May it is almost certain that caught-up hens will lay a reasonable clutch in the wild. If they are kept penned until June the chances of this wild 'supplement' are not so good.

Egg production will be noticeably affected by the weather and by diseases such as gapes.

Late eggs

Another alternative is to go for some late eggs. There are two sound reasons for this. On the average shoot the longer the time between releasing poults and shooting the coverts, the greater the wastage due to straying, accidents, death from predators and so on. Early produced birds will also require covert feeding for 6–8 weeks *more* than late-hatched birds.

A pheasant is actually mature at 17–18 weeks, though it may not attain its full first-year weight by, say, 2 oz. (57 g.) for a further month. This means that birds hatched as late as 20th July (set 25th June) will be fully mature on 30th November.

The shoot owner will obviously try to keep these later birds for December days.

Egg production increases by light stimulus and special feeding

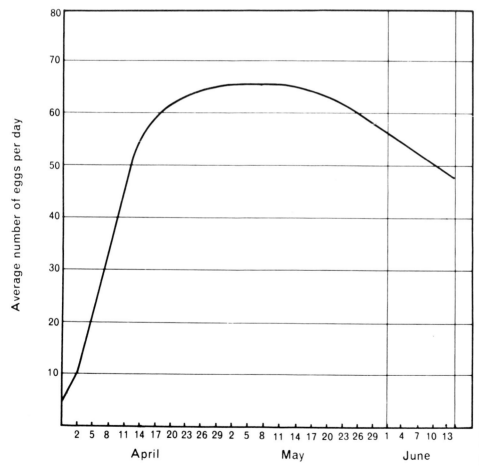

31 Average production per 100 hens, over six years, on our experimental gamefarm

Hen pheasants can be made to lay earlier than normal by giving them artificial light stimulus. A number of such trials have been carried out at Fordingbridge, and pheasant eggs have been produced in December. The hatchability, however, was a good deal below standard, and this practice is not recommended to ordinary breeders. Trials on the Continent, whereby the penned birds had about 2 hours' U.V. light included with the ordinary artificial lighting, greatly improved the hatchability.

Egg-eating

Egg-eating occurs to some extent during most seasons. Sometimes it will stop of its own accord, and at other times it will grow into a habit which becomes difficult to check. Most first-year hens are inclined to peck at an egg once or twice out of curiosity, but this rarely develops into anything serious. Soft-shelled eggs and eggs broken by crows will tempt pheasants to peck at them and perhaps acquire the habit. An old-fashioned precaution is to leave one or two dummy eggs about the pen before the start of egg-laying to blunt the ardour of any would-be egg-eater. If egg-eating has started, a sham egg or a stale egg (kept specially from the previous year) can be substituted for a real one and left in a prominent position in the pen.

Culprits can usually be identified by filling an egg with dye. Alternatively, they can be discouraged by filling 'bait' eggs with noxious substances such as red pepper mixed with the yolk, and turpentine or soft soap. If the habit becomes bad it may be necessary to collect the eggs two or three times a day. Debeaking is usually, but not always, successful in preventing trouble.

Steps which may be helpful in preventing egg-eating include the provision of shell-forming material such as oyster shell, limestone and grit, as well as fresh greenstuff and roots to peck at. The oyster shell is not strictly necessary, except to prevent boredom, since a high level of calcium is incorporated in the recommended diet of breeders' pellets. Grit is also something of a luxury when the birds are fed on soft foods, but one of which the Fordingbridge breeders approve.

Feeding

The importance of giving laying stock a high-quality feeding ration cannot be over-emphasised. If they have to put up with an inferior diet, the hatchability will suffer and the growth of the chicks may also be affected.

A well-known and tried brand of pheasant (or poultry) *breeder's* – not layer's – pellets is essential. These should contain all the necessary vitamins, minerals and other nutrients; 18–19 per cent is adequate for a breeder's diet: too high a proportion of protein will depress the hatchability.

96

Satisfactory results can be obtained without the addition of maize or other fattening foods. The change from maintenance pellets should take place about 1st March and any extra greenstuff will be a welcome addition when the grass or clover is eaten down. Fresh water should be provided regularly and the drinking fountains kept clean.

The pellets should be fed as at least three quarters of the daily ration, with wheat or mixed grain for the other quarter. It is a wise precaution to check that the grain has not been dressed with any harmful chemical.

Chapter 9
Incubation of Gamebird Eggs

Fertility

The fertility of penned pheasants' eggs is usually very high – higher than hens' eggs – and does not normally drop below 90 per cent until well into June. Very early eggs can be affected by abnormal weather.

Unfortunately, not everyone who buys pheasant eggs knows the difference between a fertile and an infertile egg, and many people blame gamefarmers for supplying infertiles. If a germ dies soon after it is laid it will undergo no further development as a result of incubation. Upon examination, no recognisable embryo will be visible: these eggs sometimes contain putrefied matter, and are called 'rotten' or 'addled'. They are not infertile.

An infertile egg will certainly look and smell good enough to use for cooking purposes after a full period of incubation, providing it does not become contaminated.

Hatchability

Obviously an infertile egg cannot produce a chick, but there are also many reasons why a fertile egg fails to hatch. For example, rough handling or transport, chilling due to weather, lack of broody heat, incorrect humidity, faulty storage, staleness and so on. It is possible that an egg is quite fertile but – in everyday language – not very 'hatchable'. Poor hatchability can also be an inherited characteristic.

Eggs for incubation

The first requirement for successful hatching – particularly using an incubator – is a uniform egg. There are many breeds, varieties and crosses of pheasants, all of which produce eggs with slightly different characteristics. For example, there can be at least 6 hours' difference in the normal incubation period of different breeds. Long-stored eggs take longer to hatch than fresh ones. The size, shape, shell texture and nutritive properties of eggs will vary according to the parent stock and how they were fed. There will be differences between aviary stock and picked-up wild eggs. It is easy to understand that an incubator

98

working constantly with a fixed set of values in temperature, humidity and air movement (unfortunately not always true in practice) cannot provide the ideal conditions for more than one type of egg. If it is exactly right for a 35-gramme Blackneck egg set two days after laying, it will be wrong for a 28-gramme Melanistic stored for a fortnight before setting.

It is therefore well worth while taking every possible precaution to ensure uniformity in any one batch of eggs intended for the incubator. In practice, this standardisation of eggs is easier for the man dealing with thousands than for the small-scale rearer who wants to make use of every egg, often derived from a variety of sources; but the following are some of the steps which should be considered:

(a) All unduly large or small eggs, and those with chalky or otherwise abnormal shells, should be ruthlessly culled.

(b) Keep picked-up wild eggs separate from gamefarm or aviary produce.

(c) Where it is necessary to incubate eggs from several different sources, try to keep each source separate by making up complete incubator trays (usually about 180–200 eggs) from each source. In many cases it is possible to treat each trayful as a separate incubation unit, e.g. when hatching in still-air machines. When buying or collecting eggs it is useful to keep in mind the number of eggs needed to fill a tray in the incubator concerned. For instance, it may be best to order 400 or 600 (to fill two or three trays) rather than 500 in any one batch.

(d) This 'tray-unit' principle can also be applied with advantage to different-aged eggs collected from penned laying stock. For example, if you are getting 100 eggs per day, earmark each two consecutive days' production to set in one tray rather than mix six or eight days' production among three or four trays.

(e) Uniformity in eggs suitable for incubation can be improved by careful culling and selection of breeding stock. By 'standardising' an experimental strain of pheasant over several years, particularly by setting only regular sized and shaped eggs and discarding bad layers, it was found that the eggs became very uniform and the hatchability in incubators progressively better. The incubator itself is a good selector of suitable breeding stock from which eggs will result that are especially suitable for machine-hatching.

(f) Another suggestion for the keeper who has a very mixed sample of eggs is to keep a few sitting boxes handy with broody hens. A lot of the quite good-quality eggs which are not sufficiently uniform for incubators can be set under broodies at the same time, any chicks hatched being added to the incubator chicks when transferred to the electric or other brooders for rearing.

99

Storage and transport of eggs

In addition to careful selection of uniform, good-quality eggs for incubation there are several important points in the care of the eggs between laying and setting in the incubator. Good hatches cannot be expected from eggs which are stale, have been subjected to extremes of temperature, or jolted and possibly cracked by careless handling or transporting. Fine hair cracks may be invisible. When eggs have travelled for even a short journey it is best to rest them for a day before setting. This steadies the yolk and its supporting strands which may have become strained by movement. If eggs are 'home produced' from penned laying stock they should be collected *at least* once a day, or twice a day (late morning and evening) in very hot or frosty weather. They should always be handled carefully and collected in a receptacle with a soft lining. Jolting about in an iron bucket is an easy way of producing hair cracks and internal damage to the eggs. If necessary dirty eggs may first be dry-cleaned with wire-wool. Eggs require washing with warm water (100°F. [38°C.]) to which an egg sanitant has been added (EWP 250 and other proprietary brands of egg

32 Hatching pheasants' eggs under coops

100

sanitant should be used according to the manufacturer's instructions), before being rapidly dried and transferred to the cool, damp storage place (preferably 50–55°F. [10–13°C.]). A cellar, old dairy or north-facing stone building is often a good storage place.

The temperature in a wooden hut (especially with a corrugated iron roof) on a hot day in April or May can easily be enough to start some of the eggs developing. The germ then dies when it cools down, and there is no possibility of it hatching. This development can start at anything over 70°F.(21°C.) if kept up for several hours.

Eggs can be conveniently stored on easily obtainable plastic or papiermâché egg trays, provided they can be kept in a damp, cool place. These trays are very useful for ensuring easy turning without handling the eggs. Placed in these trays, blunt end up, with the trays stacked in boxes, any necessary turning can be done simply by tilting the box at an angle of 30–40° and reversing the tilt daily. Turning during storage is unnecessary if the eggs are stored for less than a week, but if they have to be kept longer it is wise to turn daily – only a small alteration of the storage angle will suffice. *Pheasant eggs destined for the incubator should be incubated within a week of laying.* Trials showed that the percentage of fertile eggs hatched may decrease by 8 per cent in eggs stored for 7–14 days and by 23 per cent if the eggs are stored for 14–21 days.

Of course, there are plenty of contradictory facts in wild birds on most of these points: for example, why do red-legged partridges often hatch a clutch which has been left for 3 weeks – some of the eggs must be 5 or 6 weeks old before incubation starts! How do plovers' eggs stand continual exposure to full sun, often alternating with frosty nights on a bare, dry fallow or chalk down?

Hatching under broodies

Few people who hatch and rear gamebirds under broodies realise how very greatly the ultimate success or failure of their rearing season depends upon their hens. Few, likewise, appreciate how far more often a bad hatch is due to lack of care and consideration for the broody than it is to infertility of the eggs. The whole secret of success with broodies is patience.

Selection of the sitting hen

The best of all broodies for pheasants are mongrels or 'barnyard' hens, which are hard to come by in these days of pure-bred fowls and battery hens, but Light Sussex, Buff Orpington, Rhode Island Red and crosses of these breeds are usually good. Dorkings and Wyandottes were at one time widely and successfully used by keepers. Hens from deep-litter houses and batteries should be avoided if possible.

For partridges, a bantam is a better proposition than a full-sized fowl, and a number of breeds were tested on the experimental gamefarm. For many years a mixed strain of Jungle Fowl, Old English Game and Silkie was used, but, owing to the difficulty of maintaining a three-way cross, pure breeds of 'sitters' and their first crosses are now employed: the keynote of the trials being selective breeding for the specific purpose of incubating the brooding and gamebird chicks. The favourite breeds are Cochins (Pekins) and Orpingtons. Birds should be obtained from a healthy 'working' strain. Pullets of broody strains have been used quite successfully, but it is safer to use 2- or 3-year-old hens if available.

The surest way to determine whether a hen is broody or not is to place your hand beneath her with the fingertips upwards. If broody, she will squeeze your fingers with her wings and ruffle her hackles, and you will feel her breast warm and bare. Contrary to popular belief, there is no rise in temperature, the heat applied to the eggs being in the region of 103°F.(39·4°C.).

Other points to look for are thighs and abdomen well feathered, small feet and, above all, clean legs. A scaly-legged hen should never be used, as she will pass infection to her chicks. (Scaly leg can be cured by immersing the hen's legs in a mixture of two parts linseed oil to one part paraffin for about a minute.)

The hen must be in good condition, otherwise she will lack the necessary stamina for the long job ahead of her. The incubation period takes a lot out of a hen, and it is useless to select one that does not start in first-class order. The eyes should be clear, the breath sweet and the comb 'broody' looking. Hens which are moulting, or hens which have had their wings clipped, should

33 Hatching pheasants' eggs in nest-boxes

naturally be avoided. A bantam or hen that is known to be a good 'caller' will be an advantage after her chicks have hatched.

Breeds with heavily feathered legs, such as Pekins, should have these feathers trimmed before being used.

Disinfection

Having selected the broodies, be sure to disinfest them before putting them on the eggs. There are several suitable insecticides on the market known as louse powders, and a good dusting implement can be made from a tin pepper-pot. A bellows or aerosol is perhaps more efficient but costs more. The essential parts to powder are those under the tail, round the vent, inside the thighs and under the wings. Repeat the process, 'blowing' both broody and nest, on the twentieth day of incubation.

Dummy eggs

All broodies should be put down on dummy eggs – pheasant or partridge size – in the nesting boxes for three days to enable them to settle down before being given the eggs that they are to hatch.

Spare broodies

Spare broodies should be at hand, at the rate of one for every 10 nest-boxes. Hens get chills or colds in spite of every care, while some lose their broodiness before incubation is completed. If possible a hen should be earmarked for duty when she has been broody for only a short time. If she has already been sitting for a long period, she may not continue to sit for a further 24 days.

The nest-box

The best type of box has a base measuring about 16 in. (40 cm.) square. Most nest-boxes are much too small, and in consequence the hen is apt to smash eggs when getting on the nest. In any case she has no room to move her position on the eggs, which she wants to do frequently during incubation. Broodies vary in size, particularly if large fowls and little bantams are to be used in the same type of nest-box. It is safer, therefore, to have a nest-box which is on the large side. Much will also depend on the way the nest is shaped. Some gamefarmers prefer coops to nest-boxes, which will mean a saving in equipment. An advantage of the ∧-shaped coops is that the chicks can get under the sloping sides and avoid being trampled.

The siting of the nest-boxes must be carefully considered. They should not be in full sun, nor should they be under the drip of trees. Half sun and half shade is the right place, and screens of sacking and wire netting can sometimes be used effectively. An ideal place is beside a tall hedge or belt of trees. Wild pheasant eggs get a good deal of fresh air during the incubation period, and the proper ventilation of nest-boxes must not be forgotten. Holes may be bored in the side of the box, or a small panel of perforated zinc may be fitted. If necessary in very hot weather the lid should be propped open an inch or so.

Finely sifted leaf-mould, earth or turves should be used for making up the saucer-shaped nest, which should be thinly lined with moss, fine hay or dried grass. It is important to shape the nest properly. If it is too deep or bowl-shaped, the hen will have difficulty in turning the eggs in the centre; if it is too flat, eggs which have inadvertently been pushed away from the clutch will not roll gently back under her again. Similarly, newly hatched chicks may escape to corners of the nest-box – perhaps during a very cold night – and get chilled and die. This can be avoided, particularly when small bantams are used in large nest-boxes, if a 'collar' of tin or roofing felt is put round the hen 48 hours before the eggs hatch. The nest-boxes or coops should be placed on level ground – much as they would be in the wild state – so that they can take up the natural moisture from the ground. Some keepers make their nests by merely cutting out a round sod of turf, shaping the hollow and lining it with hay. If, however, there is any danger from flooding, the nest-boxes can be sited on a low bank of soil. Fresh-cut turves under the hay lining will keep the nest humid. When the sitting boxes are finished with, all the nest materials should be burned at once and the boxes scrubbed out and disinfected.

Number of eggs per nest

Sixteen or seventeen pheasant eggs is a good number to give a broody hen of normal size. If a hen is large enough to take more than this, then she is almost certainly too heavy and will crush eggs in the box and trample chicks in the coop. Similarly, 12–15 partridge eggs for a medium-sized bantam is about the right number. When setting pheasant eggs under a bantam *it is essential not to give the hen more than she can safely cover.* One is sometimes inclined to forget how small some bantams are. The danger in placing too many eggs under a broody arises from the way a sitting bird turns and shifts her eggs, which she does very frequently. If the number is too great the outside eggs will get chilled; or if they do hatch, the chicks from them will be weak and should be culled.

Food and feeding times

Ordinary poultry pellets, with a little maize or wheat, are as good as anything. One meal a day is sufficient, to be given in the morning. When the broodies are taken to the rearing field, it is safest to discontinue any grain and give the hens the same crumb food as the chicks.

Grit and clean drinking water should always be before the broodies at feeding time; if they can enjoy a dust bath occasionally, so much the better.

Daily routine

More eggs are spoiled by the hen being allowed to stay too long off her eggs than from any other cause. No hard-and-fast rule can be laid down; the temperature of the day must be the guide, but the hen must always be put back while the eggs are still warm. The temperature of the eggs can best be judged with the back of the hand, which is very sensitive. As a very general rule, however, about 10 minutes would be about right during the first week, 15 minutes at the end of the second, and finally 20 minutes or more according to the weather.

Often one sees hens allowed off for the same period of time each day, irrespective of whether the day is a cold or a warm one. It is sometimes argued that putting them back quickly leads to dirty nests. No bird, of course, should be put back until she has evacuated, but it is perfectly simple to persuade her to do so. Gently push her about for a few moments, and the desired result will be achieved.

Between 10 a.m. and noon is a good time to take the broodies off: this should be done *at the same time every day*.

Tethering broodies

Tethering the broodies probably has advantages over letting the hens wander about the yard, and the normal method of tethering the broody to a Y stick with a short cord and a slip knot or spring clip leg fastener is quite satisfactory. Overcrowding should be avoided, as broodies will sometimes start to fight, particularly during the first three or four days. If possible, the tethering sticks should be moved to fresh grass at the end of 7–10 days to prevent the ground becoming foul. All droppings should be removed daily.

Handling broodies

Many eggs are smashed by carelessness in placing the hen on her eggs and taking her off. This can be avoided if you treat her gently. A hen that is broody is just as keen to get back on her eggs as you are to put her there. As good a way as any to take a hen off is to put the open hand beneath her and gently lift her up, making sure no eggs are being held under her wings. In our opinion it is easier to manage a broody in a sitting box with a lid than with a drop-front, but this is probably a matter of personal preference. The lid should slope from back to front, and not the other way round.

The management of broodies undoubtedly takes up a lot of time and comes at a season when keepers have many other important jobs to do. It is here that the danger lies. A man who has a full day's work before him will often try to save time over the broodies by taking off *too many at a time* – with the inevitable result that the last birds are put back on chilled eggs. Thousands of eggs are spoiled every season in this way, and the ignorant pheasant rearer puts the bad hatch down to that bogey – 'infertility'.

Humidity

Under normal conditions the eggs will require damping slightly on alternate days from 9 days onwards, and in exceptionally hot weather more moisture may be required. On the 18–19th day of incubation the eggs should be well sprinkled with tepid water. If, as a result of a dry spell, the ground starts to bake, the soil at the back and front of the sitting boxes can be given a soaking with a hose or watering can. When one thinks of all the dew and rain that fall around a wild nest one is inclined to suspect that nest-boxes often lack sufficient humidity. In a dry season a bad hatch will surely result from eggs that have been incubated in too dry an atmosphere.

When the eggs are actually chipping they need a high humidity, but damping the eggs themselves may result in excessive cooling. Indirect humidity from the ground is safer.

Artificial incubation

Until now little *fundamental* research has been done to ascertain the exact requirements of a pheasant egg during incubation. As a result most trials have been directed towards trying out existing incubators (designed for poultry and turkey eggs), using somewhat modified techniques.

It is unfortunate that pheasant eggs appear to have certain features, such as a thick membrane, which do not respond well to the normal machine-hatching conditions used for poultry. The most common practical trouble is failure of the fully developed chick to complete the break-out of the shell. Unless temperature, humidity and air movement are exactly right from the chipping stage onwards it seems that the membrane either goes dry, hard and tough, almost cementing the chick in the shell, or becomes soft and 'rubbery' so that the chick cannot split it readily. Many other things can go wrong, of course, but the real obstacle seems to be this failure of the chick to get out of the shell after otherwise successful incubation. This is most noticeable when attempts are made to complete the hatch in large cabinet, moving-air machines – indicating that the *drying power* of fast-moving air, even at a high humidity, causes too rapid hardening of the membrane before the chick can get out. Strangely enough, the much smaller partridge eggs hatch much better than pheasant eggs under normal incubation conditions.

Choice of incubator

Apart from gamefarms and a few very large estates, most pheasant rearers' hatching requirements fall in the 200–5,000 chick range and the choice of incubator will be largely determined by its weekly egg intake. Where the total number of pheasant chicks required is 400 or less, one of the small so-called still-air incubators would be chosen, but for larger numbers a cabinet 'force-draught' incubator will be needed with a weekly intake of from 500 eggs. One medium-size cabinet incubator can be used for both setting and hatching pheasant eggs, but with others it is recommended that the eggs should be transferred to still-air incubators on the twenty-first day and hatched in these.

106

34 Examining an unhatched egg: the malpositioning of the embryo is only one of the causes of failure to hatch

Under optimum conditions the results obtained from still-air incubators, some cabinet incubators which set and hatch, and others which are used in combination with still-air incubators, are similar, and an average hatch of a little over 60 per cent of eggs set can be expected. With experience, up to 70 per cent of eggs set might be obtained, and in the U.S.A., where medium-size, highly uniform eggs are set in huge incubators in which both temperature and humidity are accurately controlled, an average hatch of over 75 per cent of eggs set is consistently obtained. In the smaller incubators mostly used for hatching pheasant eggs in Great Britain, humidity is seldom accurately controlled and the notoriously variable weather must sometimes influence the hatch. For this reason alone some difference in results must be expected. When the variation in eggs set is considered and the wide range of buildings in which incubators are sited, it will be realised that artificial incubation of pheasant eggs is still almost as much an art as a science.

Cabinet incubators that are designed to give good hatches from poultry or turkey eggs will not necessarily give good hatches from pheasant eggs, although they are quite satisfactory for setting pheasant eggs for the first 21 days. With most of these machines, although they appear to give perfectly good development of the chicks throughout the main period of incubation, there seems to be too much air movement and drying of the membrane at the final hatching stage. The chicks are fully formed but unable to get out of their shells. Rapidly moving air, even with a very high humidity, can dry the membrane very quickly when the chick first breaks into the air space and starts to 'chip' – which seems to be just the moment when moisture is essential to keep the membrane in the right condition for easy splitting. This 'drying power' of the agitated air is very difficult to reduce, since it is essential to keep the air moving fast enough to maintain a constant temperature in the machine: otherwise there will be pockets of very hot and quite cool air.

Good results are obtained using the 'transfer-system', setting the eggs in a Western Turkeybator Gamesetter and transferring them on the twenty-first day to still-air Glevum, Bristol, Eyles or Ironclad incubators. Of the medium-size cabinet machines claiming both to set and hatch pheasant eggs successfully, the Game Conservancy technicians tested the Hamer P21 and found it to be quite satisfactory.

Incubation in still-air machines

These types depend very much on correct conditions in the room in which they stand. A reasonable place is usually a cool, north-facing stone or brick building, with thatch or tile roof (*not* corrugated iron) and concrete or stone floor. Cellars or rooms below ground level, which appear suitable because their temperature is fairly constant, are not always right owing to lack of ventilation and air movement. For best results a room temperature of 60–70°F. (16–21°C.) is advised, but it is better to be rather too cool than too hot. The really important

108

thing is to avoid violent *changes* of temperature either way. If the room gets very cold more air will pass through the incubator and, of course, the temperature of the eggs will drop, despite the thermostatic control mechanism, which is only designed to control small changes. This makes it necessary to adjust the lamp flame repeatedly. Secondly, the humidity will be affected as the temperature varies and more air movement will increase the drying of the eggs.

If the room is too hot there will not be sufficient difference in temperature between bottom and top, inside the incubator, to keep a gentle flow of air moving. To correct this it may be necessary to reduce or remove baffles such as bottom felts. Actually, the accepted term 'still-air machine' is a bad misnomer – slow air movement by convection is a vital feature of these machines, and most of their troubles arise from the difficulty of keeping this movement at a constant rate. If the movement slows down too much the eggs can easily overheat, as their temperature will then be nearly the same as that registered by the thermometer above the eggs.

The makers of still-air incubators allow a wider range of room temperature than suggested above, but it must be remembered that these machines were designed for hens' eggs; pheasants' eggs demand closer temperature control than those of poultry.

Siting the incubator

The incubator should be sited so as to give plenty of space, both around and above it. Free ventilation, especially plenty of incoming air at floor level, provides the best conditions, the minimum requirements being eight complete air changes per hour. (This can be checked by igniting a smoke pellet and observing the time the smoke takes to disperse.) Daylight is not a necessity, and machines should never be placed where direct sunlight can fall on or near them. If not provided with stands, frame trestles should be erected to raise the machines to a convenient level for the operator.

All types of still-air machines should stand absolutely level, and this should be carefully done with a spirit level. If oil-burning types are used, the burners must be cleaned and trimmed regularly. Smoky burners will foul the atmosphere and reduce the efficiency of the machines. Machines must be on roughly the same level as one another and not too close together.

Temperature

Every attempt must be made to obtain a steady temperature (as specified by the makers, but see page 113) before setting. It often happens that after setting the eggs in the incubator the temperature alters from its original setting, due to the presence of the eggs. However, *it is best not to readjust the thermostat at this stage*. No harm will come by running the incubator a degree above or below the correct setting, but the hatch can be ruined by the fluctuations which are inevitable if you fiddle with the controls. It is best to counteract minor changes by adjusting the lamp flame. Any adjustment necessary to the controls can be made at about the fourth day. Do not make such adjustments early in the morning or late at night. Although the correct temperature should be obtained and held if possible over the whole period of incubation, a slightly inaccurate setting over short periods is less dangerous than rapid fluctuations.

Humidity

The second important factor is humidity. In the process of incubation an egg loses water by evaporation through the porous shell. This is necessary in order to give the embryo space to manoeuvre when it breaks out of the shell. If it loses too much water, the process of development will be interfered with and the embryo will die. Humidity is extremely difficult to measure in a space where the air movement is sluggish, and the best guide is the size of the air space. This is quite small in a newly laid egg, but increases in size during incubation. By observing its growth in size, the amount of evaporation can be very accurately assessed. Weight loss (12 per cent by 21 days) is another way of following the development of the air space. Figure 35 shows the extent of the air space found in successful hatches.

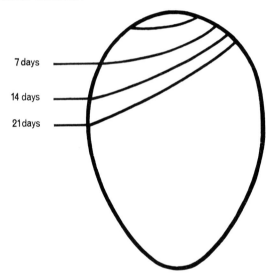

35 Pheasant egg. Development of air cell in an incubating egg

A sample of the eggs can be candled at 7 and 14 days, the space observed and marked with a pencil. If the space is too small, reduce the humidity; if too large, increase it, aiming at the standard size at 21 days. In any case it is advisable to increase the humidity when eggs have reached the 'chipping' stage.

Stinking or bad eggs should always be removed at once.

Turning eggs

Turning is most important. They should be turned at least twice a day (at 12-hour intervals) from the morning after setting to the twenty-first day, and

110

the method adopted is important. Have the eggs in neat rows to start with, then with the tip of a clean moistened finger, roll each egg a half-roll to the right in the morning and a half-turn to the left in the evening, working along the rows. By this method the eggs will be rotated in opposite directions alternately. It has been found that if eggs are rotated in one direction continually, the strands which hold the yolk become strained and the hatch percentage falls.

This method is shown in Figure 36, and it is still easier if all the eggs are marked with a pencil before setting. As one often wants to mark eggs with numbers or letters for other purposes, e.g. pen numbers, breed, source of eggs, etc., it is a good plan to put any such numbers midway on the side of the egg so that they act as a guide to turning instead of separate turning marks – one doesn't want to scribble all over the eggs. When dealing with large numbers regularly a small rubber printing stamp for marking saves a lot of time. In any case identity marks should always be on the side of the egg rather than the blunt end, to facilitate checking the empty shells after hatching.

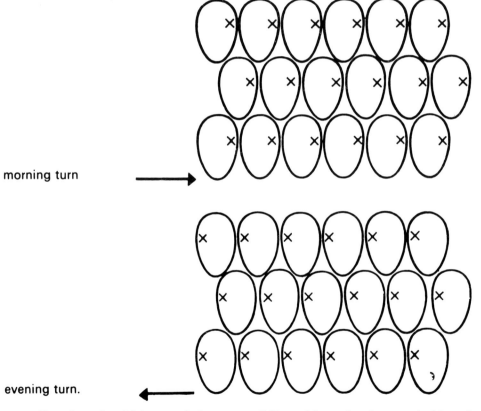

morning turn

evening turn.

36 Turning eggs in still-air incubator trays

Turning should be carried out carefully, without jarring or shaking, but stopped after the twenty-first day. It is best to have the egg tray loaded to full capacity. Detailed instructions for operating still-air incubators can be found in the Game Conservancy booklet no. 5 – 'Pheasant and Partridge Eggs – Production and Incubation'.

Incubation in cabinet machines

With cabinet incubators from which the eggs are transferred to still-air incubators on the twenty-first day, the following considerations must be borne in mind; but in the Hamer P21 three trays each containing approximately 180 pheasant eggs can be set each week. On the twenty-first day the eggs are moved from the setting trays to the hatching trays incorporated in the same cabinet.

Planning incubation

The necessary equipment depends, naturally, on the numbers of eggs to be dealt with and it is most economic to spread the total, whether home produced or bought from gamefarms, over three or four weeks in approximately equal weekly batches, rather than have one or two big settings. This is usually more economic in brooder equipment also, as some of the brooders can be used twice. For example, if 4,000 eggs are to be dealt with, 1,000 each week for four weeks, a 3,000 capacity cabinet and five still-airs (of 150 hen egg size) would do the work. Actually for most batches of 1,000 eggs, unless they were of exceptionally good quality, four still-airs would be enough to take the 'hatchable' eggs on the twenty-first day. The timing for the whole operation would be as follows:

Day 1	Set batch A (1,000 eggs) in cabinet
Day 8	Set batch B
Day 15	Set batch C
Day 22	Transfer A to still-airs, Set D
Day 25	A hatches
Day 29	Transfer B to still-airs
Day 32	B hatches

and so on, C and D being transferred on the thirty-sixth and forty-third days. If an early start is made there could be time for still another batch (E) set on the twenty-ninth day. It is convenient to make Friday setting day, bringing the hatch on Monday/Tuesday, but this can be adjusted to suit the individual concerned.

Packing trays

Packing pheasant eggs neatly and firmly in cabinet trays needs a little practice as, in most open trays, they must all be point downwards and support each other firmly; the more uniform the egg size the easier they are to pack. Remember that in a machine with automatic tilting trays (for turning) the eggs can easily roll or jog each other if not firmly packed. Plastic inserts to hold the eggs individually are now easy to obtain and have many advantages.

Candling

Under this transfer system it has been found simplest to candle all the eggs at the time of transfer on the twenty-first day rather than on the fourteenth day, removing all infertiles and early dead embryos, so that all the eggs transferred to the still-airs are ones which – as far as can be seen – are capable of hatching (see section on candling on page 114).

Operation

Each cabinet machine will have precise instructions from the maker for normal operation for hens' eggs, and these are usually suitable for pheasants: temperature 99·75–100°F. (37·7–37·8°C.): relative humidity about 50 per cent (or a wet-bulb thermometer reading of about 83°F. [28·5°C]). The temperature in a cabinet is lower than the figure given for still-air machines because the cabinet temperature is uniform; air, eggs and everything inside being kept at the same temperature. In a still-air machine temperature recorded *above* the eggs by the thermometer is two or three degrees higher than that of the centre of the eggs, as there is a sharp gradient of heat from bottom to top. The only other adjustment needed is to the vents controlling the incoming and outgoing air. The maker's instruction for hens' eggs sometimes gives too much air flow, resulting in excessive drying of the eggs. The only way to make sure of the correct drying rate to give the final correct air space is by candling or weighing a good sample of eggs at 7, 14 and 21 days as described on page 114. If they are drying too fast, slightly reduce the air inlet and increase the humidity, or reverse this if the air spaces are not expanding sufficiently. This, of course, needs to be done only on the first two or three batches put through a new machine, until the correct settings have been obtained. A good cabinet machine is an accurate scientific instrument and will produce the same conditions time after time once its controls have been correctly set. It is much more independent of outside conditions than a still-air but should still be carefully housed in a building with no direct sun, plenty of ventilation and no violent fluctuations in temperature.

Maker's instructions

Incidentally, anyone purchasing a secondhand incubator, either cabinet or still-air, is strongly advised to write to the maker, asking for an instruction booklet for that particular model. Some of these booklets contain a mine of valuable information and will save a lot of mistakes in setting up and in operation by an inexperienced man. Also there are various new gadgets, concerned with temperature and humidity control, turning trays, air movement, etc., which may be applied to an old machine – the manufacturer will know and advise.

Transfer to still-airs

After candling and discarding the dud eggs and packing the good ones into trays of the still-air machines, which must be done as quickly as possible to avoid chilling, the hatching routine and treatment of the still-airs is exactly the same as described in the previous section. While being 'candled' and transferred to the still-air incubators, and until humidity is increased by the filling of water trays and the insertion of damp rolls of cotton wool on the twenty-second day, the eggs will be subjected to a short 'drying down' period. This should coincide with the embryo's breaking through to the air space and the commencement of normal lung-respiration. As soon as 'chipping' takes place and air has no longer to pass through the eggshell pores, then high humidity is necessary while the escape from the shell is completed. It is a great advantage if the setting trays of the cabinet are of suitable size to yield, on the average, a full tray of 'hatchable' eggs for the still-air hatcher as this enables the contents of each setting tray to be dealt with as a unit from start to finish. For this purpose cabinet trays holding up to 200–220 pheasant eggs are usually about right, from which one can hope for something between 170 and 190 for transfer after candling, producing about 130–150 chicks. However, different cabinets have various tray sizes, sometimes two sizes in the same machine, so one has to work out the most convenient allocation of eggs according to the trays. It is best to have the hatcher tray full of eggs, but, if this is not possible, lay some *little* rolls of felt or other soft material on the parts of the tray not covered by eggs, placed so that there are plenty of gaps to allow the air to circulate as it would if the tray was full of eggs. These rolls should be damped (not soaked) with hot water and will then help to bring up the humidity – in addition to the soaked cotton wool roll along the front. It is certainly a bad plan to have a small number of eggs loose on the hatching tray so that they roll about as the chicks begin to hatch.

Maintaining hatchers

On a regular once-a-week hatching programme it will be seen that the still-air hatchers are normally in use for four days each week. If the transfer day is always on Friday, this gives time for clearing out trays, cleaning and checking heaters, etc., on Wednesday and Thursday. It is not worth stopping the heaters for this short period, as each machine should be in perfect running order by the Thursday evening ready for the next batch of eggs on Friday. It has been found best to make the candling and transfer a Friday morning job, then fill the emptied cabinet trays again with the next batch of new eggs in the afternoon.

Candling eggs

'Candling' is simply a method of seeing how the development of an incubating egg is progressing by holding it in front of a light, so that solid matter shows up

114

as shadows compared with fairly transparent liquid parts. It serves two important purposes. First, to show whether the egg is infertile or the embryo has died at an early stage: this is fairly easy at any time after 10 days and enables the useless eggs to be discarded before the hatching phase. Secondly, it shows the air space (see page 110) and therefore indicates whether the correct humidity has been applied.

It is well worth while for anyone hatching pheasant eggs to make or buy a contrivance for rapid and efficient candling. There are various types sold by incubator firms, but they are usually intended for hen or turkey eggs so may be rather large for pheasants. Pheasant eggs have much denser shells than poultry so need quite a strong light to show through them. Two simple ways of making an effective candler are shown in Figure 37.

The stronger the light the better, providing the container does not get too hot: an electric lamp of at least 100 watts. It is also important to use a *thick* black strip or circle of soft material to line the rim of the hole so that the egg can be pressed against it and seal any bright light round the outside of the egg, which dazzles the viewer and makes it difficult to see the contents of the egg. A short piece of one of the adhesive plastic strips, commonly used nowadays for draught excluders on windows and doors, makes a good seal.

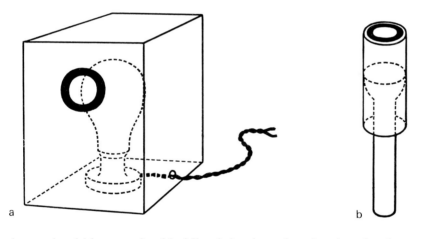

37a Egg candlers. Plywood or metal box covering electric lamp 1¼ in. (3 cm.) diameter circular hole with black cloth or braid edge

b Card tube or tin with hole braided. Strong battery electric torch inside tube

Each egg should be examined holding it by the pointed end so that it can be twisted in the fingers when held sideways on to the light hole. When transferring eggs from one tray to another (e.g. cabinet to still-air) have the candler between the two trays or held in one hand, so that the egg is picked up, candled and placed in its new position or discarded with one easy movement: speed is essential in this operation. Poultry hatchers often use a candling device which passes a strong light to and fro under the rows of eggs in the tray so that they are tested without taking them out individually. Unfortunately, pheasant eggs have such dark shells that this method does not work very well – and few pheasant hatchers will be likely to have such elaborate equipment.

115

At the fourteenth day, which is a good time to candle eggs in a still-air incubator, the embryo is clearly visible as a dark body occupying at least a third of the egg space. Infertiles show as clear fresh eggs, while eggs with 'dead germs', or stopped after a few days' development, are also clear but rather more cloudy than an infertile. Anything which does *not* have an obvious dark patch should be thrown out. At 21 days, when transferring from cabinets to still-airs, no mistake can be made, as three parts of the egg is solid chick and shows dark against the light. There may, of course, be some dead chicks at this stage which are nearly fully developed, and these cannot be distinguished from the live ones by candling.

Even when previous experience has shown that humidity and air movement are giving the correct air space, this normal candling to discard dud eggs gives a regular chance to check the air space carefully in the good eggs. The drying rate can vary considerably in still-air machines in fluctuating summer weather, and there is always some individual variation.

After hatching

Active, strong chicks are essential for brooder rearing, and it is never worth while going to a lot of trouble to 'help out' chicks which cannot hatch by themselves or to include any obviously deformed ones, such as curly toes, straddles or screw-necks: these should be culled as the incubator is cleared and another culling made after about two days in the brooder to eliminate obviously weak chicks.

It is a great advantage to keep the chicks in poultry chick boxes for several hours in a warm place after removal from the incubator rather than putting them straight into the brooder. This seems to get them well on their feet and able to compete with each other. They are quite all right in such boxes for at least 24 hours if necessary and can travel at this time under the same conditions as poultry chicks.

It is a mistake to have chicks of even slightly different ages in the same brooder. Chicks 24 hours older are very much stronger and will stand on top of the younger ones, often smothering them at night. It pays to start with a uniform, even-aged batch of chicks. When dealing with a big hatch – enough to fill several brooders – it is a good plan to 'grade' the chicks into two groups when putting them into chick boxes and allocating them to brooders; the strong and the not so strong. The latter will be mostly chicks which hatched a few hours later than the strong ones, and they will do best if given their own brooder instead of being mixed with the earlier-hatched ones.

Hygiene

At all stages of artificial incubation cleanliness is of great importance. Hatching compartments of incubators should be cleaned with a vacuum cleaner after each hatch, and trays washed with a warm solution of 4 per cent washing soda

116

(a double handful in $2\frac{1}{2}$ gallons [$11\frac{1}{2}$ l.] of water), or a Ministry Approved detergent type disinfectant. At the beginning of the season, and whenever the incubator is empty, fumigating with formaldehyde gas should be carried out for 30 minutes with all ports closed. This may be done by adding formalin to potassium permanganate crystals in a large dish. For every 100 cu. ft. (4·47 cu. m.) of incubator space use 3 oz. (85 g.) of potassium permanganate and $4\frac{1}{2}$ fluid oz. (128 ml.) of formalin (40 per cent formaldehyde). The formaldehyde gas is rapidly evolved, and care must be taken not to let the gas come in contact with eyes and nostrils.

Even when the incubator is loaded with eggs, fumigation at the above strength may be safely carried out except when it contains eggs at the 24–96-hour stage after setting or when chicks are present.

Hatching other species

Partridges: Both grey and red-legged partridges usually hatch well in still-air incubators, or where the transfer system is used. With fertile eggs, hatches of over 80 per cent are normal, using the same technique as for pheasant eggs. The smaller size of the eggs means that very careful packing is necessary in those cabinet incubators in which the trays themselves turn. Although the setting period is a day longer than for the pheasant, less time elapses between chipping and final hatching – a point to be remembered if the chipped eggs are being replaced in partridge nests.

Mallard: Mallard eggs are often laid under rather dirty conditions and washing is necessary. Eggs should be dipped in a proprietary egg sanitant, such as 'Nusan', or a 2 per cent caustic soda solution at 130°F. (54·4°C.) for about 30 seconds. Where initial dry-cleaning is carried out, eggs may be fumigated in the incubator using similar strengths (and precautions) as for pheasant eggs. It is also unwise to set mallard and pheasant eggs in the same machine (due to salmonella infection), and if they are set consecutively it is essential to fumigate between settings. The incubation period is from 26 to 28 days. With the same temperature settings as for pheasant eggs, a higher relative humidity (70 per cent) is recommended for the first 24 days followed by a temporary reduction to 60–65 per cent until chipping commences. At this stage, relative humidity is increased to 70 per cent until the ducklings are ready for 'drying off'. The transfer from cabinets to still-air incubators should take place on the twenty-fourth day. In still-air incubators, without any means of measuring humidity, spraying mallard eggs daily with warm water from the tenth to the twenty-fourth day has given good results when atmospheric humidity is low, but where conditions are naturally humid *this procedure may reduce hatching success*.

Of the cabinet incubators, we have found the Hamer P21 most satisfactory for incubating mallard eggs.

Candling is relatively easy and if carried out at the 10- and 24-day stages, bad eggs can be removed and humidity requirements gauged.

Chapter 10
Pheasant Rearing and Releasing

Let no beginner be deterred from trying to rear pheasants – the procedure is not complicated. An experienced man will obviously get better results than a novice, but many a learner has been successful – often using food and methods which would make a professional game breeder blush!

Inflation has made the food bill rise enormously and the Game Conservancy has spent a lot of time devising ways of keeping these expenses to a minimum. Expenses, other than those for food, vary so much from one shoot to another that it is quite impossible to work out a figure that would be of any use to the *average* shooter. For example, an owner-farmer will have a rearing field at his disposal for nothing, part of the equipment may be 'on loan' from the farm and some of the labour is also likely to be available without charge. A syndicate, particularly if they rent a shoot some distance from home, naturally has to 'shop' more expensively.

Young pheasants hatched under broodies or in incubators are normally hardy and will grow well, provided reasonable care is taken in selecting eggs or chicks from strong, healthy stock.

Reared birds make bold fliers and can usually be shown more easily according to plan than their crafty wild cousins. If there is a successful wild stock established it may be an error to divert precious keeping time to rearing a few poults for restocking. It may be better to concentrate limited resources on predator control and habitat improvement. However, in the wetter west and on grassland farms and other places where the wild stock cannot thrive, it may be essential to restock annually to produce shooting. In a year when wild broods have fared badly, the reared birds will ensure that the Guns can still enjoy reasonable covert shooting without detriment to the breeding stock.

There is absolutely no need for shoots stocked by reared birds to appear in any way 'artificial' if they are properly managed.

Every shoot has a different pattern – size, shape, scale of operation, available finance and so on. Choosing the correct system, the numbers to be reared and where they are to be released, cannot be set out in print. Game Conservancy advisory staff have the advantage of experience on a great many shoots of every size, shape and economic circumstance. We strongly suggest that you arrange for a visit from one of the field consultants before you make these vital decisions.

There are four basic ways of rearing pheasants:

1. The open rearing field – with coops and broodies.
2. Movable pens – with coops and broodies.
3. Brooder units, with grass runs.
4. Intensive rearing systems.

Open rearing field

This well-tried and understood system has been superceded by more modern and less time-consuming techniques. However, we include a description of what is involved as it still provides useful general information.

Preparing the field

A good site for rearing is a dry, well-drained, sheltered grass field – having a southern aspect if possible. A stubble field undersown with grass is a good choice; old pasture or parkland is also a favourite. A variety of weeds and wild white clover will be appreciated by the birds. A lush, rank growth should be avoided, and most fields will be better if grazed beforehand. Sheep are excellent for this purpose, though casualties to young chicks will sometimes occur if they are permitted to pick up wool.

All rearing fields should be reasonably level so that the coops can bed down well. Any moles should be trapped and the field then harrowed and rolled. A field which has been dressed with fertiliser early in the year is perfectly all right to use, but *no rearing fields should have been contaminated by poultry or turkeys*, however healthy they appeared to be.

Rides about 10 ft. (3 m.) wide should be cut where the lines of coops are to stand, and the coops – about fifteen to the acre – should be put out a few days before the hatch is due, to ensure that the ground under them will be dry. The grass inside the coop should be trimmed short. Placing the coops on sacks or boards is not advised, though a shovelful of dry sand may be spread inside for the first few days.

Some keepers place the rows of coops east to west and face the coops east so as to get the sun in the early morning and the shade in the afternoon.

Management

The best foster-mothers for pheasant chicks are medium sized bantams, but where these are not available, carefully selected fowls may be used – crossbreds or mongrels usually being better than purebreds. About eighteen chicks are enough for a broody hen, and twelve to fifteen for a bantam, according to her size.

After the chicks have hatched they should be thoroughly dried off before being taken to the field, and on no account must they be chilled during this move. When it has been ascertained that the broody is contentedly mothering them, the coop can be closed for about 12 hours, depending on the time of day when they are hatched. The chicks need not be fed for about 24 hours after hatching, as the remains of the yolk sac will be providing food.

For the first three days the chicks should be kept near to the coop in a nursery run about 3 ft. × 2 ft. (0·9 m. × 0·6 m.), made with wide boards fastened together by metal or leather hinges. If the weather is bad during the first week, the coop-front can be used as a lean-to to prevent the wind and rain from driving in. The coops need not be moved for 3 or 4 days, but thereafter should be moved one yard sideways every day or every other day, when the grass is dry.

Coops can be either box-like in design – preferably with a sliding roof, so that poults can be taken out one by one for weighing, wing-tagging, disease treatment, etc. – or triangular in shape. Although the latter are considered old-fashioned by some people, there is less chance of very young chicks being trampled by the broody. If 'pop-holes' are made at either side the chicks will learn to use them rather than run in and out between the broody's feet.

Coops must also be properly ventilated. There is nothing worse for gamebird chicks than to be enclosed in a hot, stuffy coop all night and then allowed out in the cold air on soaking wet grass. Very young chicks should *not* be let out at the same time every day regardless of the weather, or they may get chilled. Year after year, post-mortem examinations of reared pheasant chicks show that an extremely high percentage of the deaths are caused by chills and a congested condition of the lungs.

There is a certain amount of controversy about shutting up young pheasants at night as they get older and stronger, and if it were not for attacks by their natural enemies it would probably be healthier to let them jug out when they felt inclined. As things are, the coop is the lesser of the two evils, but let it be well ventilated.

The trouble is avoided by the use of movable pens in which the chicks are *not* shut up at night.

A few branches, preferably fir or other evergreen – not yew – should be placed nearby to give the chicks shade, and protection from winged predators.

Attacks by predators

'Vermin' will be attracted to a pheasant rearing field like flies to a jam pot, and a most careful watch must be kept for predators. Some suggestions for dealing with those that are *not* on the protected list have been mentioned in an earlier chapter. Ground vermin such as rats, stoats, weasels, mink, poaching cats, foxes and occasionally hedgehogs may also cause trouble. A good tunnel-trapping campaign, using the Fenn Mark IV humane trap both before and during the rearing season, is the best answer to the smaller ground vermin. Box traps, which are particularly good for weasels, can conveniently be placed alongside any wire-netting fences or enclosures. Rats should be methodically poisoned and a few baiting points kept in operation round the field until the poults are in covert.

At all times the rearing field keeper should be prepared to use his gun, his wits and his woodcraft.

When the young pheasants are permitted to jug out at night, one or two swinging hurricane lanterns, white paper sacks or road repair flashing lights manufactured by Dorman and Smith (Hazard Lighting Division), Preston, Lancashire, will often keep foxes away *for a time*: they are also useful in the rides when poults are first put to covert. They should be moved to a different position every day. Electric fences, probably the most effective deterrent to larger ground predators, are discussed later.

Tainting fluids, such as a mixture of Jeyes fluid, paraffin and ammonia, creosote or sump oil, and turpentine, have a limited use.

Putting to covert from the open field

The time to take the young pheasants to covert varies, but it is normally when they are somewhere around 6 to 7 weeks old, when it becomes difficult to shut them up at night and when the coop will in any case be becoming overcrowded.

Should the breeder wish to keep back any poults for stock it should be possible to distinguish most cocks from hens (except Melanistics) at 6 to 7 weeks.

Every keeper will have his own way of getting the young pheasants into the coops and shutting them in at night: it is certainly a job which requires patience, and much depends on the design of the coop, and having a shutter which will slide easily and silently.

When 'moving day' comes, after the poults have been shut in for the night a sack should be drawn gently underneath the coop and lightly tacked in position, so as to make it escape-proof. The move should not be attempted in very bad weather, even though it is easier to get the birds to go into the coops. The coops may either be taken to covert and left closed all night, or moved early in the morning, in which case the poults should be left quiet for an hour before release. The coop shutter should be opened just enough to allow the poults to walk out quietly – one at a time. A little food should be thrown down in front of the coop beforehand and the birds called or whistled in the accustomed way at every subsequent feed.

When first put to covert it will be convenient to keep the poults together as a unit, but as they grow they can be dispersed to other coverts by feeding. It may be better to do this than to put a dozen coops here and there all over the estate, but the layout of the coverts will obviously govern this decision.

Sites should be carefully selected – damp, shady places being avoided. If the rides are in poor condition they will be improved by harrowing and rolling, and if the grass is mown the birds will later have the benefit of young, fresh herbage. Wide rides can have *half* the ride mown, so that some taller herbage remains as cover and to provide natural food.

It is a good practice to release about one broody in every six, so that they can range about in the woods with the young poults, and teach them to roost at night. When the pheasants are going up to roost well the broodies can be removed, though it is a sound idea to leave one or two behind to 'anchor' the birds. For the same reason one or two empty coops may also be left about the rides until late in the season.

Movable pens

For many years the movable pen method of pheasant rearing has given very good results, and the percentage of chicks successfully reared to the poult stage is often 90 per cent in pens, compared with an average of 70 per cent on the open rearing field. The advantages are numerous and almost certainly outweigh the few disadvantages. Birds grow quickly and evenly; diseases can be isolated at once; losses from feathered predators are nil, and from ground predators negligible. Both rats and weasels sometimes squeeze in under the pens, but the occurrence has been rare. A further advantage of the folding system is that there are no losses from young birds straying away from the coops, and scavengers such as starlings or rooks cannot steal the chicks' food – and incidentally spread disease. Compared with the open rearing field, a smaller acreage is needed for movable pens. About twenty-four pens to the acre allows sufficient moves up to 6 weeks.

Perhaps the main benefit of the pen system is the saving in labour. If a keeper is tied to his bird field all day, his wild stock – pheasants and partridges – will undoubtedly suffer, and the predators will go unchecked. With the movable pens, however, he is able to leave the birds between feeding times and put in valuable hours on his beat. The keeper himself will also appreciate being freed from the task of 'shutting up' late on a summer's evening.

The initial cost of the pen is fairly heavy, but the capital outlay should be repaid within two or three seasons in higher survival of birds and lower labour costs.

There are a number of different types in use. Most of them are simply wire-covered runs ($\frac{3}{4}$-in.[2 cm.] mesh) about 4 ft. (1·2 m.) high, enclosing a ground area of about 10 ft. × 6 ft. (3 m. × 2 m.) or slightly less. An entrance door (about 2 ft. × 2 ft. 8 in. [60 cm. × 80 cm.]), starting about 14 in. (36 cm.) from the ground, should be built in one side of the pen within reach of the coop. A skirting of wood, hardboard or metal sheet (12–24 in. [30–60 cm.] high) gives

122

38 A 5-gallon drum converted to a drinking fountain

39 Shallow drinking pool on a Continental shoot

123

protection from the weather. At a slight extra cost – and most people find it is well worth it – the pens can be made in sectional form so that they can be dismantled and packed flat during the winter months. Butterfly nuts will make it possible to do this job very quickly, and dipping the threads of the bolts in grease will avoid the frustration of finding half the nuts rusted solid at the end of the rearing season. It is also advisable to number the sides and tops of all pens, as they are not always interchangeable when made by amateur labour.

40 Typical movable pen (usually 10 ft. × 6 ft. [3 m. × 2 m.])

Perches across the four corners (which also strengthen the pen and act as handles) are much used by the young pheasants and teach them to roost.

As many as possible of the battens, frames, etc., should be on the *outside* of the pen so that stale food and droppings cannot collect on them.

A hinged or sliding 'trapdoor' at the end of the pen, which can be used for releasing poults at the covert side (in case the rearing field should be adjacent to the wood) is a useful refinement.

If the pen itself is of rigid construction, Netlon synthetic netting (1⅛-in. [3 cm.] mesh) makes an excellent roof, which is very convenient to store. The heavier weight (60P) is recommended.

A simple pen can also be made by placing together two 10 ft. × 5 ft. (3 m. × 1·5 m.) sections to form a ∧. Wire netting is used to close off each end. In this way rearing equipment can be used to produce many more pens than can be made up by using standard square or oblong units. However, problems may arise if they are used for partridges because the triangular roof of wire netting – rather than the softer, plastic material – can cause injury if the partridges are disturbed and panic inside the pen.

Trials using both fixed and free coops have shown that the coop fastened to the framework of the pen is more convenient. Admittedly the ground under a fixed coop becomes rather dirty, but this can be overcome by pulling the pen forward just enough to clear the dirty patch, say, every other day.

Although a large fowl will comfortably brood eighteen chicks, fifteen chicks are quite enough for the limited space of a movable pen.

There are points for and against confining the broody to her coop as opposed to letting her free range within the pen, *but on balance it is preferable to keep the broody shut in all the time.*

Lice may become troublesome unless facilities for dust bathing are provided for the young pheasants. Dusting the broody with a safe insecticide such as ICI Insect and Louse Powder 3 or 4 days before she is given the chicks is recommended, but the preparation is not suitable for the chicks themselves.

The rearing field for movable pens

Extra care should be taken in choosing a good rearing field, for the penned-up chicks have less chance to range and find what they want in the way of natural plant and insect food. In order that there should not be too much herbage when the chicks are first put out, the field should be grazed until a few days before the chicks hatch. Sheep are best for this purpose (but see previous remarks on sheep) because cattle will sometimes churn up the ground if the weather is wet. If the herbage is dense and the field cannot be grazed or mown beforehand, a small open patch should be cut inside the pen so that the chicks cannot get lost or chilled in wet, rank grass: the grass should grow up with the chicks. Mown grass should not be left on the field (and this applies to all rearing fields), as young chicks will occasionally choke and die from trying to eat the dry, stringy stalks. Fungicidal diseases such as aspergillosis and moniliasis may also be encouraged to develop within the heaps of mouldy herbage. Deaths can occur from eating dried cocksfoot, and very young pheasants may die as a result of their gizzards becoming blocked by strands of wild white clover in a very dry season. Young pheasants can also die from choking as a result of picking up beech nuts, although this crop is excellent in other respects.

The rearing field should be free from depressions which might fill with water after severe rain and drown the young chicks. Any holes under the sides of the pens should be blocked with turves, to prevent the escape of chicks or the entry of rats.

Should the sun become unduly hot, shady branches, other than yew, can be placed on the roof.

During the moves great care must be taken to avoid crushing the chicks – particularly when they are very small.

If there should be a narrow space between the back of the coop and the pen, it should be blocked up otherwise stray chicks may lodge there and get 'lost'.

If the weather is fine, the coop need not be shut up at night after the first three days. At the end of the first week the pen must be moved to fresh ground; during

125

the second week it should be moved twice, during the third week three times, and after that it should be moved daily.

If the birds are reared on a field adjacent to the covert in which they are to be released, the pens should be started about a hundred yards away from the wood. (Fifty yards will suffice if the pens are moved once forwards, then once sideways, and so on.) This allows for the requisite number of moves up to the age of 6 weeks. When the pens are near the wood they can be propped up on bricks – or the end door opened – so that the poults can work back and forth from the pens to the wood.

At 6 weeks of age the birds will normally be taken to covert, but if they are being held back for breeding – as on a gamefarm – it will be as well to reduce the number of poults to eight per pen. If this is not done, feather-picking may occur. At 8 weeks of age the stock poults can be taped or temporarily brailed and put in an open run. The final brailing will have to be done when the wings are nearly full grown, i.e. at approximately 16–17 weeks.

With stock poults the broodies can be taken away at 6 weeks.

Putting to covert from movable pens

It is usual to leave the pens behind when moving to covert at 6 weeks – taking only the coops and broodies along.

As with birds reared on free range, the 'feeding' whistle or the tapping on a bucket to which the birds have been used should be continued in covert.

We recommend that poults purchased from a gamefarm which have been reared in movable pens are released by the conventional open-top pen as for brooder-reared birds discussed later. Putting out a few 'decoy' broodies before the poults arrive is sometimes successful in helping the new arrivals to settle down. Quiet, sunny rides or clearings should be selected as release points – if possible sheltered and shut in.

Needless to say, coverts that are to be restocked with reared birds must be free from the pheasants' enemies: foxes will mean failure from the start.

Feather-picking

Feather-picking on open rearing fields has never been experienced at Fordingbridge, though one or two cases are occasionally reported during very dry seasons.

In pens or brooders if the trouble can be spotted early, and attackers *and victims* removed at once, there is every chance that the habit may not spread, but once feather-picking has really got going it is practically impossible to stop it. *Basically the right thing to do is to debeak or bit the birds at once* – and at the same time find ways in which the management can be improved to prevent a recurrence.

In standard movable pens the trouble can usually be avoided by ensuring that the pens are moved daily so as to provide an adequate amount of fresh

126

herbage. In a very dry spell lettuces, root vegetables and so on can be given. Apart from satisfying an actual want, they will also help to keep the young birds occupied. The diet must obviously be properly balanced – a nutritional deficiency will almost certainly contribute to feather-picking. However, the two most obvious causes of this vice are overcrowding and boredom. The first is very much a problem in intensive systems and may be unavoidable without considerable extension to the penning layout. Boredom can often be overcome by a little extra work by the person in charge. The provision of 'toys' such as bundles of green stuff hung up so that the young birds have to jump up to reach them is a valuable exercise. Frequent changes of the position of the drinkers and feeders can also be useful since it gives the birds something new to occupy them. In any case it is not good management practice to keep drinkers and feeders on the same ground which becomes bare, wet and fouled with droppings.

One Scottish shoot reported that a portable radio kept their birds contented and this is also used with success in intensive farming systems for pigs and chickens. In this case, however, it may be the poor gamekeeper who has to suffer!

In very small runs, such as those made of two coops joined by 6 or 7 ft. ($1\frac{3}{4}$ or 2 m.) of corrugated iron, feather-picking may occur at about 3 weeks of age. It is evidently fairly common in dry seasons judging by the number of letters received on the subject. Unfortunately one cannot be sure how much is due solely to the small size of the pen and how much to the management and food, for numbers of excellent birds have been reared in these small pens without a sign of feather-picking.

If the vice starts in covert, the coops or feeding points should be dispersed as widely as possible. There is really very little else one can do: in time the birds seem to get over it, and do not appear to show any ill effects.

Quite often reared pheasants will lose their tails between 5 and 8 weeks of age – usually soon after being taken to the woods. At first it appeared that the loss of the tail feathers was a form of ordinary feather-picking – but this may not be so. It is possible that the sprouting feathers break off and start to bleed, and this condition then *leads* to feather-picking. It has been suggested that the initial tail shedding may be associated with a stress factor, resulting perhaps from the shock of catching up the birds clumsily when moving them to the woods. There have been reports that disturbance by a cat, and a severe thunderstorm, have also caused tail-shedding.

Debeaking

This is a very simple operation which consists of removing the tip of the upper mandible either with a pair of nail clippers or a debeaker which is heated electrically so as to cauterise the beak. It is preferable not to undertake this on birds younger than 10 days of age. Although the effect of *severe* debeaking has

127

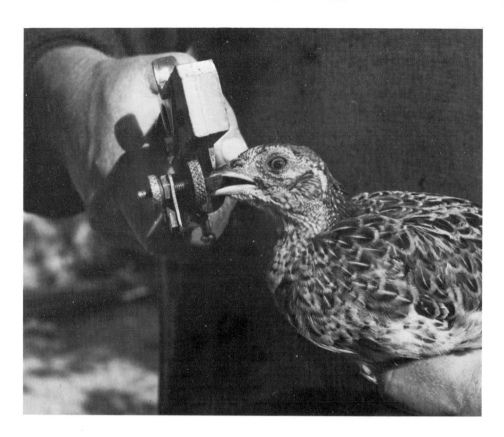

41a A battery-operated debeaker being used on a 5-week-old poult

been known to last for some considerable time, normally the beak grows again quite soon, and the bird is in no way inconvenienced.

American pheasant farmers sometimes debeak intensively reared birds three or four times up to the age of 16 weeks, on account of the quick regrowth of the beak, and there are apparently no ill effects.

After debeaking, the lids of the feeding troughs – if used – should be removed so that the birds can scoop up their food if they find it awkward to peck in the normal vertical position.

A portable debeaker which can be operated from a car battery is obtainable from the Game Conservancy.

Bitting

As an alternative to debeaking, 'bits' have proved very effective. There are 3 sizes of bits: size A up to 3 weeks; size B 3–7 weeks (most commonly used); size C 7 weeks onward.

They are available in three different materials – plastic, alloy and steel. The latter (steel) should not be used since they require more force to apply and are even more difficult to remove.

128

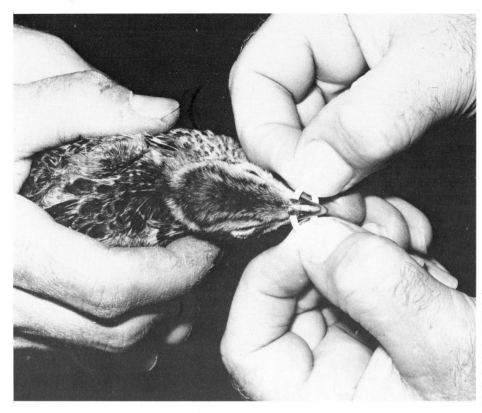

41b The ends of the plastic bit are slipped into the nostrils of a three-week-old pheasant. If a soft metal bit is used the ends of the bit are closed with a pair of pliers

Plastic bits can be applied – and removed – with the fingers, although a day's bitting will result in sore fingers. Circlip removing pliers can be used as applicators to overcome this difficulty. About 5–10 per cent of plastic bits may be lost during the three to four week period – possibly partly due to inaccurate application. With poults reared in units of 100 on grass-floored pens we have not found these accidentally de-bitted birds cause any trouble.

Alloy metal bits are easily applied with ordinary pliers and can be removed with a pair of pointed electrician's wire cutters. They can be applied at least as quickly as plastic bits and there is no risk of lost bits. Where rearing is intensive, particularly when birds are kept indoors to 5 or 6 weeks, alloy metal bits may be advantageous since we have had reports of severe feather-picking occurring when plastic bits have been used under these conditions.

As with debeaking, care must be taken to ensure that the chicks can feed easily after bits have been fitted. They may be unable to pick up the same-sized crumb to which they have been accustomed. It is important to keep the troughs well filled to allow the chicks to scoop their food.

129

Chapter 11
Pheasant Brooder Rearing

With reliable high-quality foods available the development of artificial brooding systems was logical, and a satisfactory system was designed and used at Fordingbridge in the early 1950s and is described on page 137. A big step forward was the use of 10 ft. × 5 ft. (3 m. × 1·5 m.) sections to construct the pen. This made the system very flexible and permitted the easy extension or moving of the pens in any direction. The Fordingbridge system is still giving excellent results on many shoots.

Because of the saving in labour, the difficulty of obtaining reliable broody hens, and the occasional flare-up of Newcastle disease (fowl pest), brooder rearing is the normal system. If such birds are correctly reared and properly acclimatised, they are every bit as hardy as those reared on free range. This has been convincingly demonstrated by many years' wing-tagging and subsequent observation of released birds.

There are many types of brooder techniques, from the fully intensive – with the birds kept indoors under very artificial conditions in semi-darkness – to the more natural methods in which the birds have access to grass runs almost from the very first day. The latter methods are at present preferred by the Game Conservancy. In all systems the key to success lies in three factors. The first is hygiene and the more intensive the unit the more meticulous must be the routine in this respect. The second is the hardening-off period when the birds are first taken away from the heat, and the third is the method of release.

Brooder units may vary in size from 80–500 chicks. The 'Rupert' (paraffin-heated) brooder is designed for 80–100 chicks; the Fordingbridge brooder system 100–120, and other units for 200 chicks. For large-scale rearing, a fixed brooder *house* with adjoining grass pens (as opposed to a *movable* brooder *hut*) can be used, which is capable of producing about 800–1,000 pheasants at a time.

Brooder systems can be used twice per season. This is economic as regards use of equipment, but from the labour point of view it may not always be convenient because to some extent it can tie a single-handed keeper to his rearing field for three months or more.

130

Type of heater

Before discussing brooder systems, it may be helpful to consider different types of heaters and compare their running costs.

Electrical equipment is relatively cheap to buy but running costs are continually increasing; it is clean and convenient, but it may be subject to power cuts. Propane (or Calor) gas also gives excellent results and seems to produce slightly better feathering. It can be used in isolated places such as inside coverts, where there is no power supply. The equipment and fuel costs are fairly high, however, and more maintenance is necessary.

With regard to oil-burning brooders, the 'Rupert' brooder has worked extremely well, and is by far the most economic in fuel costs. Its only disadvantage is its small capacity – approximately 100 pheasant chicks.

In uninsulated brooder houses sited in cold or exposed places it is sometimes difficult with a gas heating element to maintain the required minimum temperature. But this can usually be rectified by putting straw bales on the windward side of the house. Trials with aluminium foil as a lining to the lower part of the wall show that the heat is increased by several degrees.

42 Both pheasant and partridge chicks (these are young redlegs) grow well under an infra-red lamp

131

If it is decided to use electricity, the rearer will be wise to seek the advice of local authorities when siting the equipment. Apart from various safety precautions, such problems as voltage drops are best dealt with by an expert. Similarly, the local agent for Calor gas (or Maywick equipment) is usually willing to advise on the installation and maintenance of propane-burning heaters.

With regard to running costs, much depends on how the heat is applied. On a per bird basis larger units are usually cheaper to run than small units. Electricity is usually cheaper than gas, paraffin is cheaper still.

Electric heaters

The electric heater normally used at Fordingbridge is a 400-watt coil which screws into a bowl-shaped reflector. This type is preferred because it glows a very dull red – neither a bright lamp nor a 'black heat' type. Some form of light is essential, since the chicks are quickly able to 'home' back to the heat if scattered by some chance disturbance during the night.

Recent tests have shown that a ceramic dull emitter made by Hassett International is very satisfactory. The element is more robust than the coil type but produces less light. It can be supplied with an auxiliary attraction light and is then very effective.

The heater should be suspended from a chain or cord *slightly off centre* towards a back corner (see Figures 48 and 49). This ensures that there is a useful temperature gradient in the hut – a hot area for brooding and a cooler area for exercising, feeding, etc. The lamp should be adjusted so that it is 15 in. (38 cm.) above the ground. This applies mainly to the Wrenn heater; other makes with different reflectors and elements may work better at different heights. The temperature at ground level should be about 90–95°F. (32–35°C.) but the chicks themselves are the best indicators of the correct amount of heat. Thermometers do not give an accurate guide to the effective heat on the birds. By observing the chicks' behaviour (spreading out if too hot, crowding together if too cold) the heat can be adjusted to their needs by raising and lowering the lamp: this is best done by leading the supporting cord or chain through rings or pulleys to a fastening outside the house, so that there is no need to upset the chicks by opening the door to make adjustments. In all cases the makers' instructions should be studied carefully before risking a valuable batch of pheasant chicks. Up to 50 per cent of the heat may be lost if the reflector is allowed to become dirty.

One problem associated with electric heating in country districts can be that of power failures during the night. Luckily these cuts are often experienced during a thunderstorm, which means that it is not a very cold night. In any case, it is never wise to rush over to the brooder straight away, as the birds will be packed close and warm together, but if disturbed will scatter to the four

132

43 The ceramic dull emitter is very robust but an ancillary attraction light helps to keep the chicks near the heat

44 The Agrotherm heater has no legs and is suspended in the house

133

corners of the brooder house and not get together again. The keeper should wait therefore for about 2 hours.

If the heat does *not* go on, some sort of auxiliary heat, such as a couple of gallon tins filled with very hot water, can be placed inside the house, with an asbestos sheet over the top to contain the warmth. (Canopy heaters will automatically reflect the heat down.) Hurricane lamps, and portable paraffin-operated car sump heaters shielded by a cylinder of perforated zinc, can also be used.

Electric hen/warmback heaters

This type of brooder is very economic to run with only one-fifth of the electricity consumption of the radiant heat type of electric brooders. However, since there is no space heating, well-insulated draught-free brooder houses are essential. In adapted farm buildings excellent results have been obtained.

One considerable disadvantage of the usual type of electric hen is that one cannot see beneath them without tilting the whole apparatus. This causes considerable disturbance to the chicks. It is particularly important to avoid this in the first three days even if a few dead chicks are left beneath the heater as a result. It is helpful to remove the cover from these heaters, and fill the top with bedding, so that when birds get too large to go under for brooding, they can sit on top.

The similar Agrotherm heater has no legs, and is suspended in the house, height adjustment thus being quite easy. Waterproof models are being developed which are much easier to clean and sterilise.

With these types of heaters it is advantageous to fit a pilot light, so that if the chicks scatter, they can find their way back to the heat source.

Calor gas heaters

Maywick Calor gas appliances are used inside the standard Fordingbridge brooder hut with great success. Fitted with a thermostat, the heater will use a 104-lb. (47 kg.) cylinder of Calor gas for each batch of 100–125 chicks. Although some of the older models require frequent checking (pilot jet blowing out, burners becoming choked with dust, etc.) the newer type are completely trouble-free. However, the wisdom of studying the manufacturer's operating instructions regarding the daily cleaning of air filters, etc., cannot be over-emphasised. If the pilot light goes out always check that the rubber tube is securely connected to the brooder lamp before attempting to relight.

In certain cases it may be advantageous to supply a number of brooders from a service and reserve cylinder supply via a changeover valve, with a regulator and pipework distribution system, rather than locating an individual cylinder at each brooder. Advice on this type of installation will readily be supplied by any Calor gas dealer, or from the Calor Gas (Distributing) Co. Ltd.

134

The Rupert Brooder

The 'Rupert' brooder – capable of taking 100 pheasant chicks – is supplied either with paraffin or gas heating. Nevertheless there are a great many paraffin Ruperts still in use and we are sure that notes on how to handle them will be useful for some years to come. This brooder can be placed inside a sectional run (made up of 10 ft. × 5 ft. [3 m. × 1½ m.] sections) which can be moved or enlarged as required. The galvanised brooder and lamp is a self-contained unit which is easy to handle. The brooder has two pop-holes, which are shielded by a plastic skirt. (Incidentally, 1½ in. [4 cm.] should be trimmed off the plastic skirt on the pop-hole entrance or vertical slits made to allow easy access by the chicks.) Both pop-holes are usually left open all day. For the first seven days the size of the pen can be reduced by forming a small 'nursery area' with 18-in. (45 cm.) partitions, leading from the pop-holes to the corners of the pen. Food is always placed under the porch and it might be wise in wet districts to place a nursery pen (as illustrated in Figures 50 and 51) over the brooder so that chicks can feed readily outside the heated area.

Early models suffered from overheating during long periods of sunshine and excessive heat loss at night. This has been cured by providing insulated mats which fit over the top of the brooder and it is well worth while fitting these. Nevertheless, the rearing field should be chosen with care. In windy, exposed sites the lamps can be blown out and, even if they are not, it can be difficult to maintain a sufficient temperature to avoid chilling.

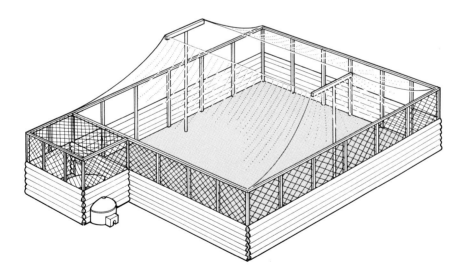

45 The Rupert Brooder has a reputation for producing tough, hardy poults

Difficulty is rarely experienced in 'driving-in' at night, since even at 4 weeks the poults seek the shelter of the brooder of their own accord. In the original models examination of the brooded area was difficult, but this has now been overcome by the provision of an inspection panel in the roof. Rather surprisingly, the noise of heavy rain on the tin roof does not seem to disturb the chicks, though another estate reported that their own young birds were frightened out of the brooder by a heavy hailstorm. This trouble will not arise if the insulated mats are fitted since they deaden the noise. One problem that has arisen is a tendency for chicks to jug out near the light shining from the observation window of a brooder in another pen when several units are sited close together. This can be avoided by masking the pilot light with one of the tin pop-hole doors.

If the brooder is not required for a second batch of chicks, it can be raised on a few bricks to form a 'night shelter' for the poults during the hardening-off stages (i.e. from 4 weeks of age onwards).

Paraffin models

It is essential that the wicks are trimmed with great care before placing the

46 The new Hardwick Brooder runs on gas and being larger than the Rupert can take more chicks

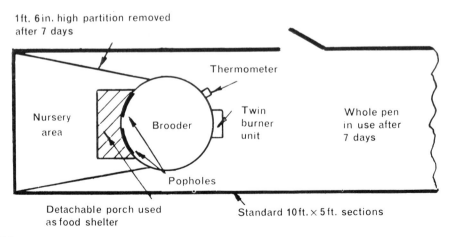

47 Diagram of brooder

lamps in the brooder. Smoke can soot up the air ducts and greatly reduce the amount of heat that is transferred to the canopy. Incidentally, new wicks can often be slightly damp when delivered and this can cause smoking. If placed in a low oven for an hour this can be avoided.

It is necessary to raise the wicks slightly in the evening to maintain a standard temperature, and to lower them again in the mornings, although they can be set to maintain a night temperature and the chicks will avoid the excess heat in the daytime. At 4 weeks of age one wick is turned out. The paraffin is topped up daily, but the wicks are not normally trimmed during the whole rearing season.

The Fordingbridge brooder system

This brooder house is a very simple unit (see photograph 48) 5 ft. (1·5 m.) square and 4 ft. 6 in. (1·4 m.) high at the front sloping to 4 ft. (1 m.) at the back. It is clad with resin-bonded plywood. Ventilation and light come from wire-netting covered apertures occupying the top third of the door and the wall next to it. These can be partially or completely closed by flaps according to the outside temperature. Additional ventilation is provided by a row of 2-in. (5 cm.) diameter holes or slots at roof level. There is a pop-hole in each side but most houses include a third pop-hole at the back. This allows great flexibility of penning without moving the house. The pop-holes can be closed by means of sliding shutters. Except when used on a commercial scale (and it becomes uneconomic to move a large number of brooders), a wooden floor is not recommended since it has been found that the birds feather better when brooded directly on gravel over grass.

Where the brooder area does have a floor, whether wood or concrete, it is essential to have an appropriate covering. We find that wood chips from a planing machine are most satisfactory. They can be packed down tight to provide a flat, absorbent pad beneath the heater.

It is essential to take great care in the purchase of wood chips. There have been several cases reported of heavy casualties by litter that has been derived from treated timber. Insist on 'poultry quality' from your supplier and obtain an assurance that no toxic substances are present.

Wood shavings are too 'springy' and will restrict the movement of the smallest chicks. However, if covered with corrugated cardboard or hessian for the first week this problem should be overcome.

Sawdust and peat should never be used – they cause excessive dust and the chicks sometimes eat them in such large quantities that they die of starvation usually caused by impacted gizzards.

The amount of light admitted to the house can be important. The chicks need enough light to feed easily, otherwise some may die from 'starve out', but if the brooder is too brightly lit troubles like toe-picking and early feather-picking can result. Once they are feeding well light can be reduced.

137

48 100 unit brooder hut with side removed to show first stage with corrugated cardboard screen in open position. Alternatively, a plywood baffle can be used to reduce the brooding area. Wrenn 400-watt electric heater. Paper egg tray used for early stage crumb feeder, jam jar fountain, metal chick food trough for later use

Setting up the brooder house

Choose a piece of level ground, and cut the grass down to an inch in height, brushing away the cuttings. A thin layer of gravel should be spread under the brooding area (about 4 ft. [1 m.] in diameter). Corners should be blanked off either by piling the floor material into them or by fitting triangular inserts of metal or plywood. Fine wire mesh is also effective.

In all cases a small ramp of earth should be made inside and outside the pop-hole to enable the tiny chicks to cross the lower framework of the house. Place a 16-in. (41 cm.) high screen of corrugated cardboard (see Figure 49) or similar flexible material in a 4-ft. (1 m.) diameter circle round the heated area under the lamp. This should stay in position for the first two or three nights to keep the chicks within the heated area.

Management

1. Take the dried-off chicks from the incubator during the morning, and put them into cardboard poultry chick boxes (the smaller size) with a little untreated wood wool or hay in the bottom, 25 chicks to a box.

2. Switch on the heater in the brooder house to warm up the ground: this should be done at least half a day before being used.

3. Leave them in the boxes in a room at an even temperature until the evening (say 6–8 hours). They can be left for 24 hours if necessary, and this period in the

138

boxes seems to strengthen the chicks and get them well on their feet before they are put in the brooder. They can quite safely make a long journey in these boxes at this stage, such as overnight by rail.

4. During the early evening put the chicks from the boxes under the brooder heater, with the card surround in position, making sure they are warm enough at dusk, and leave them undisturbed for the night. If they bunch into the centre spot under the heater it is too cold and after having checked there are no draughts the heater* should be lowered a few inches. If it is too hot the chicks will keep away from the central area. Although they must be discreetly watched during this early period *do not disturb them unduly*. Do not, for example, flash a torch into the brooder house during the night, which will only cause alarm among the chicks.

5. Food and water are supplied inside the brooder at this stage. Papiermâché egg trays make good food 'troughs' in the very early stages and have the virtue of being cheap and disposable, although care should be taken that chicks cannot squeeze underneath.

6. After a few days the card circle should be opened to extend to the pop-hole (see Figure 49.) If the weather is fine, the pop-hole to the nursery pens could be opened, but the run space outside should be restricted to a few square feet by boards or a piece of wire netting.

The chicks are shut back into the card circle for the following night. In bad weather it does no harm to keep them inside for the first day or two, but the earlier they are let out the quicker they learn to use the brooder and run. Once the pop-hole is open it is advisable to place a small plywood or metal screen inside the entrance and 1 ft. (30 cm.) from it to act as a draught baffle.

7. Chicks soon learn the habit of popping in and out of the brooder, and can be given the whole 20-ft. (6 m.) run with food and water both inside and outside. The card circle is removed after a week or so.

8. After the first week when the chicks should have learnt the way in and out of the brooder and be feeding actively, there is usually very little to worry about, beyond filling the feed troughs and making sure that ample supplies of water are always present. The pop-hole slides are normally shut every evening, in case the chicks are disturbed during the night and run outside, opening them again early in the morning. The heater should be raised about 3 in. ($7\frac{1}{2}$ cm.) at the end of the second week. In very warm weather, after a fortnight, the heater can be raised a further 3 or 4 in. ($7\frac{1}{2}$ or 10 cm.) and switched off in the day. As early as the third week the chicks often attempt to jug out in the run, so it is wise to make sure they are all in before shutting the pop-hole.

* There is a minimum height for some brooder lamps.

The sectional penning system

For use with the normal 5-ft. ($1\frac{1}{2}$ m.) square brooder unit, standard penning equipment has been developed which can be erected easily and quickly to make pens of any multiple of 10-ft. (3 m.) perimeter length. The basic sections are simply panels measuring 10 ft. × 5 ft. (3 m. × $1\frac{1}{2}$ m.) made with two 7 in. × $\frac{3}{8}$ in. (18 cm. × 1 cm.) baseboards, screwed to a frame of 2 in. × 1 in. (5 cm. × $2\frac{1}{2}$ cm.) or $1\frac{1}{2}$ in. × 1 in. (4 cm. × $2\frac{1}{2}$ cm.) batten, and covered with 1-in. ($2\frac{1}{2}$ cm.) mesh wire netting. A few sections are gated, and it is useful to have a few half-sections 5 ft. × 5 ft. ($1\frac{1}{2}$ m. × $1\frac{1}{2}$ m.). The sections are easily joined together with wire sack ties.

Some form of supporting stays, fixed either inside or outside the pens, are useful as otherwise they can blow down in a high wind.

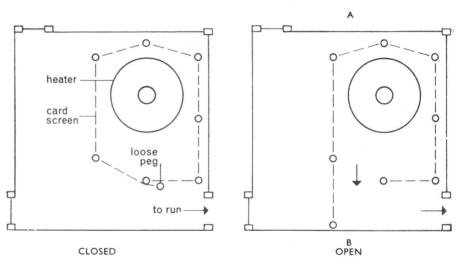

49 A convenient way of setting the card surround in the brooder hut for the first two or three nights to prevent draughts when the pop-hole is opened

heater

card screen

loose peg

to run ⟶

CLOSED

A

B
OPEN

For roof coverings 'Netlon' synthetic fibre materials are effective if erected properly and stretched tightly. A useful way of fastening the net is to knock in broad-headed, galvanised roofing-felt nails along the outside of the top rail of each pen section at 6-in. (15 cm.) intervals, leaving the heads projecting $\frac{1}{2}$ in. ($1\frac{1}{4}$ cm.) from the wood. The net can then be easily hooked over these. Alternatively the net can be stretched and held in position with size C plastic bits which are hooked into the rolled edge of the net and the wire netting at the top edges of the sections.

This penning system can, of course, be used at all times of the year for chicks, poults, adults and laying stock, for pheasants, partridges and ducks – also poultry. This type of equipment is now manufactured by several firms or the standard 10 ft. × 5 ft. (3 m. × $1\frac{1}{2}$ m.) panels can be made very easily and cheaply by any handyman.

Sections can be used to make 10-ft. (3 m.) wide runs, extending up to 40 ft. (12 m.) which are erected either side of the brooder house as fresh ground is required. Alternatively, a pen 20 ft. × 20 ft. (6 m. × 6 m.), roofed with 'Netlon', will house 100 birds, when used in conjunction with a 10 ft. × 5 ft. (3 m. × 1½ m.) shelter pen.

If the vegetation is short and lacking in cover, it will be necessary to move the 20-ft. (6 m.) square pen at least once during the 6-week rearing period. Many game rearers use a larger size of brooder hut, to house up to 200 or so birds. For these units a larger run of 30 ft. × 30 ft. (9 m. × 9 m.) will be found advantageous.

An alternative system of penning, which removes the need for a roof net, uses sections approximately 9 ft. (1·4 m.) high which are erected ∧-shaped to provide a long run approximately 12 ft. (1·8 m.) wide. A potential problem with this is of birds damaging themselves if they fly up against the wire, but in practice they usually hide under the sloping edges rather than flying up.

Nursery pen

The most efficient type of nursery pen is shown in Figure 50. The pheasants can use this from very early days, even if it is raining. The food utensils can be placed inside, enabling brooding to take place in near-darkness in the hut itself, rather than having it adequately lit for feeding purposes. This is important if feather-picking is to be minimised. A covered 10 ft. × 6 ft. (3 m. × 2 m.) pen can be used for this purpose, or a ∧-shaped erection made from two 10 ft. × 5 ft.

50 Brooder hut and nursery pen with run made up of 10 ft. × 8 ft. (3 m. × 1.5 m.) sections, roofed with soft netting

141

(3 m. × 1½ m.) pen sections – covered with waterproof sheets such as heavyweight polythene or fertiliser bags. If the brooder house is taken away at five weeks, the poults will still regard the shelter as home. This arrangement has the advantage of providing a dry, sunny area away from direct heat, which is used by the chicks as a 'sun parlour' and helps them to harden off more rapidly. Some ventilation of this nursery pen is very important, otherwise on bright, sunny days it can become very hot and lead to birds suffering from heat exhaustion.

When moving birds from one pen to another on this system the whole operation can be performed by running them from brooder to pen, or pen to pen as the sections are taken down and rearranged. There is no need – unless for debeaking – to catch up and disturb the chicks at any time before 6 weeks.

Frequent changes of pen, fresh leafy branches as cover in *different* places, every few days, all help to reduce the monotony of the flat grass pen. Feeders and drinkers are often placed close inside the gate to the pen and are left there throughout the rearing period. For a hard-pressed gamekeeper this obviously saves time but it invariably results in a large patch of bare earth often turned into a quagmire of mud, mouldy food and pheasant droppings. After the birds are 14 days old every effort should be made to move drinkers and feeders regularly to new positions. This is not only more hygienic but the change gives the birds a new interest and helps to prevent feather-picking. When running a large-scale rearing programme it is well worth while to cultivate strips of wheat about 5 ft. (1½ m.) wide on lines where the pens can be placed at the night shelter stage, so that each pen has a strip of cover – the weedier the better – running down the centre.

51 A similar hut to the one shown opposite but with ∧-shaped nursery pen and run made up of 9 ft. (1.4 m.) sections

Intensive rearing

On some estates where large numbers of pheasants are raised, varying degrees of intensive indoor rearing are carried out in different types of buildings. Disused pigsties, grain driers, poultry houses, Nissen huts, stables and even old cottages have all been successfully adapted for rearing pheasants up to the age of 3–4 weeks. The poults *may* be kept under cover until they go to the release pens at 6 weeks. This invariably results in soft feathering and they may also be at risk for the first few days of this open-air life should the weather be bad. To reduce this risk, birds should be 'hardened off' by allowing them into outdoor pens with no heated shelters for the last fortnight or so. It is normally wise to provide some sort of hut or night shelter area into which the poults may be driven on wet nights or in the early days out of buildings.

Units vary in size from 100 to 1,000 poults, but batches of 125–250 are usually easiest to manage. Where large buildings are concerned, separate units can be partitioned off with 1-in. (2·5 cm.) mesh wire-netting frames. Where batches of different ages are being reared, it is better to cover the frames with black polythene or use a hardboard partition so that light from one unit does not affect the next. A floor space of 10 ft. × 10 ft. (3 m. × 3 m.) should be used per 100 poults (i.e. 1 sq. ft. [0·09 sq. m.] per bird). Smaller areas sometimes 'get away with it', but are not to be recommended. Ventilation is often difficult to control in old or large buildings and deserves careful attention. While draughts must be avoided, it is important that there is some air flow. A duct in the roof and covered inlet in a side wall may be adequate, but because these units tend to become dusty an extra fan on the outlet may be useful.

Our pathologist has occasionally had to examine cases of death due to creosoted floors. Although the creosote has been applied the previous autumn, fumes given off under the heat of the brooder lamp apparently caused pneumonia or kidney damage.

Warmth can be supplied by brooder lamps of many types – the electric hen (400 watts) being particularly satisfactory under these conditions *provided* the building is well insulated. They are less satisfactory, for example, in plywood brooder houses. The heat should gradually be reduced until, at 3–4 weeks (the exact date depending on weather conditions), the poults are either transferred to unheated brooder houses of conventional type with access to grass, or moved to open sheds for hardening-off.

Solid floors, concrete, brick or wood should be covered with a layer of suitable bedding such as untreated hardwood shavings, Shredabed or Diceabed litter. Some keepers prefer to cover such bedding with hessian for the first few days in case the young chicks peck at the strands which can 'ball up' in the gizzard or crop. The litter can be kicked up into heaps in the corners instead of blanking them off with triangles. Initially the chicks should be limited to the central-heated area with a tin or hardboard surround.

143

Under intensive rearing systems feather-picking can occur at any time, and debeaking may have to be carried out before the birds are 3 weeks old. Where this is done as a routine at 10 days, only one debeaking (removing $\frac{1}{4}$ in. [6 mm.] of the upper mandible) should be necessary. (An alternative to debeaking is to fit the bird with bits – see page 129.) It is often considered that the incidence of feather-picking is partly controlled by the intensity of light in the brooded area – and daylight is frequently excluded. The feeding utensils must however be lit. A low-wattage electric lamp normally using a red bulb on a dimmer switch gives the opportunity to control the level of lighting to something similar to that of a poultry house. By increasing the light slightly, the birds will become more active at feed times. It is important to have some access to sunlight otherwise some chicks may go blind. The access point to daylight in a darkened unit must be protected by a conical or triangular shaped grid to avoid pile-ups and suffocation.

Without access to grass or sunlight, good-quality food is essential and for the first 3 weeks a pheasant *super starter* crumb should be used. At about 3 weeks of age a change from starter to rearing crumbs or mini-pellets can be made. At first, food may be scattered on egg-trays *in the lighted area* but troughs – allowing $\frac{3}{4}$-in. (19 mm.) feeding space per bird – should be substituted within a few days. If the feeding utensils are placed on multi-layer paper sacks the top layers can be peeled off as they become soiled.

As already stated, most intensive systems compromise with more orthodox methods by allowing the poults access to grass and sunlight when they are between 3 and 4 weeks old. In some cases the poults run directly into pens with a night shelter immediately outside the brooder house, or they may be caught up and moved to unheated brooder houses (mainly used as night shelters) with grass runs, for a further 3 weeks before being placed in a release pen.

During this period feathering should be improved by dampening the poults once or twice a week with a fine spray of water from a hose, garden sprayer or a hand pump. It is important to place some poles in the run where birds can perch and preen and dry out quickly.

Where a more intensive system is practised and poults are kept indoors for 5 or 6 weeks, transferring them to barns or outbuildings for a week of acclimatisation softens the shock of exposing them directly to the elements. Here, although protected from the rain, they can become accustomed to daylight and may be sprayed with water periodically before going to the release pens at 7–8 weeks.

The advantages of adopting intensive systems, where suitable buildings exist, are principally in the large number of poults that one man can look after, the reduction in initial capital expenditure, and the chicks' high growth rate. However, unless healthy, well-feathered poults are produced, *which are then carefully acclimatised to life in the wild*, these early advantages can be offset by heavy post-release losses, particularly in wet weather.

144

52 A large shed, 18 ft. × 16 ft. (5·5 m. × 5 m.) which is used to rear two separate batches of 500 birds. The nursery pens and outside runs are much larger than those used with smaller huts

53 Inside a large shed the birds are retained in the heated area with a hardboard circle. A dull red light bulb suspended between the heating panels also attracts the chicks. The use of automatic chick drinkers saves labour but some form of guards (in this case, rings of plastic netting) are necessary to prevent chicks drowning

145

Feeding

The time involved

Studies of the amount of time involved in feeding birds and generally maintaining a 500 pheasant rearing unit at Fordingbridge showed the average period occupied each day was 41 minutes. But it should be emphasised that this is very much related to the type of unit and whether it is entirely indoors or not.

For our trial a compartment 130 sq ft. (12 m²) was used, with one large canopy gas brooder supplying the heat. Egg trays were replaced by chick feeders after four days. At three weeks – until release at seven weeks – five hoppers were placed in the run and night shelter.

The time taken to prepare the unit was two hours – including disinfecting, erecting the surround, hanging up the brooder and spreading litter on the floor. If additional units are prepared in the same operation (and later if they are also fed together) then obviously there is a further overall saving in time.

During the first four days the chicks were fed four times daily, each operation taking about 10–15 minutes. Once a day the brooder was lifted to see if any birds had died.

Cleaning and enlarging the brooder area took 30 minutes; but when covering the whole floor with wood shavings was added the job took an hour.

Preparation for bitting took 30 minutes. Catching up and the operation itself occupied two men for two hours.

A further two hours was needed to clean and disinfect the hut after release. As only wood shavings had been used they could be moved and burnt quite quickly.

A summary of all the operations involved appears below:

	Hrs.	Mins.
Preparing unit for chicks	2	00
Cleaning brooder area:		
1st time	0	30
2nd time – putting down wood shavings	1	00
Final cleaning and disinfection	2	00
Bitting (at 3 weeks)	4	30

Routine operations:

				Hrs.	Mins.
Feeding (0–4 days) – morning	(20 mins)	4 by 50 =		3	20
midday	(10 mins)				
afternoon	(10 mins)				
evening	(10 mins)				
Feeding (5–21 days) – morning	(20 mins)	17 by 40 =		11	20
midday	(10 mins)				
afternoon	(10 mins)				
Feeding (22–42 days) – morning	(10 mins every day)	21 by 10 =		3	30
Changing the water (0–42 days)	(4 mins daily)	42 by 4 =		2	48
Average time per day (all operations) = 41 mins.				28	58

General

Penned birds lack the opportunities of the free-ranging pheasant for supplementing their diet with natural food, and properly balanced food containing adequate protein, minerals and vitamins is therefore of paramount importance. Pelleted or crumbed foods are stable, store well, handle easily and are less wasteful than mashes. They also result in slightly higher growth rates, since every pellet is a complete cross-section of the balanced diet. All feed should be stored in cool dry conditions away from vermin.

It is commonly asked whether it is wise to feed only in troughs or hoppers, or whether it is better to hand-feed the birds at regular intervals. Experience has shown that it may be beneficial to hand-feed for the first few days, but that once the birds are eating well, hoppers are perfectly satisfactory *up to a month old*.

At this age it is essential to start teaching the birds about the feeding system to be used after release. Where hand feeding is to be adopted the keeper will probably call or whistle to signify the arrival of the food. The part-time keeper may wish to condition his birds to the Parsons Automatic feeder or gravity hoppers. Once a routine is established it should continue in the release pen, and in covert. When the ground is dry, pellets and grain can be scattered on the grass near the hoppers, so that the birds have to hunt for their food. Otherwise the food containers should be placed under a rain shelter.

Will proprietary poultry and turkey foods do?

The short answer is 'yes', provided the right one is selected. For free-range rearing, poultry chick crumbs will be adequate, but special pheasant crumbs or turkey starter crumbs are recommended for the first 3 weeks when pheasants are reared in brooders. Standard poultry chick crumbs can then be substituted.

Pheasant chicks will take the standard pheasant starter crumbs quite happily from the start. A typical sample contains 23 per cent protein. Some keepers prefer to start day-old chicks on super chick crumb which might be as high as 28 per cent protein. Tapping on the food tray or dropping the crumbs from a height may stimulate reluctant feeders during the early stages.

It is suggested that during the third week the gradual change-over to mini pellets (pheasant chick pellets) should be made by mixing the two sizes (protein level approximately 23 per cent). From $4\frac{1}{2}$ weeks onwards it is possible to feed the larger pheasant rearing pellet (20 per cent protein) or equivalent poultry ration. If wheat is to be fed in the release pen and coverts then either soaked or kibbled wheat can be introduced from 5 weeks in a mixture with the pellets. The pellets are a complete food so too much grain in the early stages is apt to upset the balance of the various ingredients.

This food will carry the birds on to 8 weeks if necessary, but it is cheaper after 6 weeks to change to 'poultry grower's' size pellets (approximately 16 per cent protein) and include some whole grain. Between 6 and 8 weeks the grain content can be increased. But at this stage the poults are growing fast, and if good natural food is scarce it is a wise plan to continue some pellet feeding as long as possible.

Fresh greenstuff will be appreciated by growing pheasants in movable pens and brooders if there is insufficient natural plant food available. Unripe ears of wheat and shredded lettuce are two favourites; also chickweed, watercress, fresh green turves, agricultural chicory and chopped onion tops. Cabbages, kale, artichokes, swedes and potatoes will be greatly appreciated by older pheasants.

Food additives

Birds have been satisfactorily reared on balanced crumbs, with and without antibiotics – with no noticeable difference.

With regard to coccidiostats, most pheasant rearing foods will contain a low-level concentration of a drug which is intended to control outbreaks. If, however, the ground is heavily infected, and particularly when the food is diluted with kibbled wheat at the 4-week-old stage, the coccidiostat may be at too low a concentration to give full protection. When this occurs losses can be heavy unless the birds are supplied with a curative dose of 'Saquadil' or 'Whitsyn S' in the drinking water. When they are being used for treatment, *no coccidiostat* should be included in the food, or poisoning may result. The recognition of an outbreak of coccidiosis in the early stages is not easy, but reduced food intake and a 'drooping' appearance (particularly at the 4–6-week-old stage) should be taken as a warning, and weakly birds sent for post-mortem examination.*

If gapes is diagnosed Mebenvet or Gapex will provide good control. These are curative treatments and do not necessarily prevent further outbreaks.

Propcorn

One way of keeping down the cost of feeding may be by using Propcorn. Corn which has been harvested with a moisture content as high as 30 per cent, and is intended for feeding purposes, can be treated with Propcorn, the trade name of BP's preparation of proprionic acid which, by preventing germination and mould forming on the grain, allows for its safe storage and use in hoppers. A considerable saving can be achieved where corn would otherwise have to be transported to and from a commercial dryer. Most leading agricultural feed merchants can give advice about the product or enquiries should be made to: BP Chemicals, Agricultural Division, Greenfield House, 69–73 Manor Road, Wallington, Surrey.

Trials in which treated and untreated wheat was fed to pheasants have shown that Propcorn in no way affects palatability. Comparisons between eggs

* All specimens should be sent by first-class post, sealed in a polythene bag, and securely fastened in a tough, outer container marked 'Perishable' to the Game Conservancy, Fordingbridge, Hants SP6 1EF.

from pheasants which have been overwintered on Propcorn-treated grain and untreated grain, showed that Propcorn treatment had in no way affected fertility or hatchability.

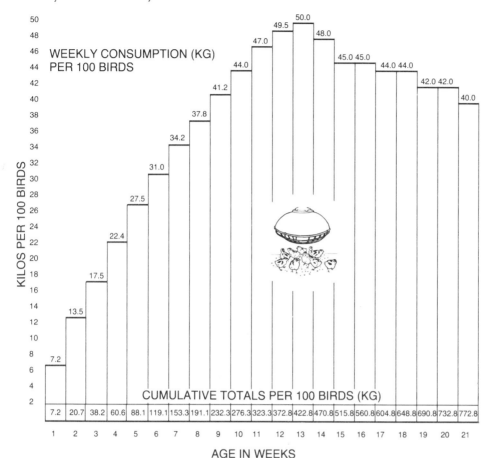

WEEKLY CONSUMPTION (KG) PER 100 BIRDS

KILOS PER 100 BIRDS

7.2	13.5	17.5	22.4	27.5	31.0	34.2	37.8	41.2	44.0	47.0	49.5	50.0	48.0	45.0	45.0	44.0	44.0	42.0	42.0	40.0

CUMULATIVE TOTALS PER 100 BIRDS (KG)

7.2	20.7	38.2	60.6	88.1	119.1	153.3	191.1	232.3	276.3	323.3	372.8	422.8	470.8	515.8	560.8	604.8	648.8	690.8	732.8	772.8

| 1 | 2 | 3 | 4 | 5 | 6 | 7 | 8 | 9 | 10 | 11 | 12 | 13 | 14 | 15 | 16 | 17 | 18 | 19 | 20 | 21 |

AGE IN WEEKS

WHAT TO FEED AND WHEN
Lines and dashes indicate recommended periods

——— Super Chick Crumbs: First 2-3 weeks especially with intensively reared stock

— — — ——— Pheasant Chick Crumbs: Up to 5-6 weeks

— — ——— Pheasant Chick Pellets: From 3-5 weeks depending on bitting and familiarisation needs.

——— Pheasant Rearing Pellets: A good acclimatising ration: A little grain if desired.

——— Pheasant Growing Pellet: with increasing use of grain.

1 2 3 4 5 6 7 8 9 10 11 12

54 Guide to food consumption per 100 pheasants reared in pens on crumbs, pellets and grain. The amount eaten per week reaches a maximum at about 13 weeks (about 50 kg. per 100 birds) then falls off

Watering
Fresh water should be available at all times. This can either be supplied in founts or by automatic waterers (such as the B.E.C. Water-master system, obtainable from the Broiler Equipment Co. Ltd, Winnal, Winchester, Hants).

149

At the chick stage it is important to prevent the birds from soaking or drowning, by placing either pebbles or a piece of hose-pipe into the water troughs. Once the birds are a week or so old, these can be safely removed. As the birds grow, more and larger drinkers should be supplied. Automatic watering has a great advantage in saving time and labour, and also ensuring a continuous water supply. Care should be taken that the automatic drinkers cannot tip over where they are placed on the ground rather than suspended from the roof. To prevent this, chick drinkers can be screwed to wooden boards to improve stability.

One disadvantage of automatic watering occurs if the need to give medication in the water arises, as it is usually more difficult to calculate dosage rates and concentrations. When the system is connected to a header tank of known volume and the water main is switched off, this problem is alleviated.

55 Fresh water should be available at all times

Quantities of food required
It is frequently asked how much food would be required to rear a certain number of pheasants. This is not easy to answer accurately, as so much depends on the method of feeding, rearing field conditions, the nature of the food, the weather, experience of the keeper, etc.

150

The total amount needed to rear 1,000 pheasants up to 6 weeks will be about 24 cwt. (1,200 kg.), made up of:

Chick crumbs and pellets   20 cwt. (1,000 kg.)
Kibbled wheat   4 cwt. (200 kg.)

If they are kept in pens to 8 weeks (for example in pens in the wood before release) a further quantity will be needed of about:

Growers' pellets   9 cwt. (450 kg.)
Whole wheat   5 cwt. (250 kg.)

Making a total of 38 cwt. (1,900 kg.) of food for 1,000 birds up to 8 weeks.

Obviously birds reared under broodies which are released in covert at 6 weeks will soon be picking up a lot of natural food themselves, and will not need as much as is suggested above.

Chapter 12
Releasing Pheasants and Holding in Covert

Among the factors which must be considered are: the best age for release, the date for carrying out the operation, the method of liberation, the choice of environment in which the birds are to be naturalised and their subsequent management in covert. If any one of these is badly planned, fewer reared birds will be harvested.

The quality of the birds is also of the utmost importance. Unfortunately, this is extremely difficult to judge objectively and most groups of poults will show considerable variation. Weight, although easily measured, is by itself an unsatisfactory criterion, since a well-grown but badly feathered (or feather-picked) bird is probably less likely to survive than a small but well-feathered poult. The often-heard phrases '*It'll make a bird*' or '*Perhaps they'll pick up once they're released*' are wishful thinking when applied to sub-standard poults, and bag returns from such birds are almost invariably low.

On average, approximately 40 per cent of the pheasants released are shot during the first year, and subsequent seasons increase the total to about 45 per cent. But the range in recovery rates is very large. On many shoots of 1,000 acres (400 h.) or less, or where the number of pheasants reared is less than 500, recovery rates may be well below 20 per cent. On some large estates where more than 2,000 pheasants are released, between 50 and 60 per cent are shot. While the size of the shoot may be significant, the extra manpower often available on the larger estates means that greater attention can be paid to the details of releasing.

Shooting intensity and the accuracy of the Guns will also affect the recovery rates. And on estates where wild pheasants provide the larger part of the bag and a good breeding stock must be left, the number of reared pheasants shot will be proportionally lower.

Wing-tagging has shown that the sex-ratio of the released poults is important, since, excluding 'cocks only' days, cocks in the bag outnumber hens in the ratio 3 : 2. Contrary to popular belief it is the reared hens rather than the cocks that are most likely to wander. It now seems fairly clear that mortality – possibly within a few weeks of release – is mainly responsible for the proportion

152

56 Releasing
pheasants. Note that
the birds are walking
out of the boxes

57 Wing-clipping a
7-week-old poult. Only
the juvenile primaries
outside the most
recent blood quills
should be cut

153

of tagged birds that are never seen again. Detailed studies on individually marked poults – and daily ride counts carried out for us by keepers on a large sample of shoots – show that the rate of loss is greatest in the first month after the birds start to leave the release pen. Thus, the largest mortality occurs in poults up to 12 weeks of age. Predation, accidents, starvation, feather- or vent-picking, adverse weather and disease are the main factors responsible for these losses. Thoroughly good management can affect a reduction in poult mortality – correct feeding and predator control are especially important. It has been estimated that between the time of release and the start of the shooting season between 25 and 30 per cent may be missing from the released stock.

The best age at which to move pheasant poults to the release pen is about 6–7 weeks, although the actual date is not infrequently determined by an outbreak of feather-picking. Younger birds may be more vulnerable to natural hazards, while older birds may be less adaptable to environmental changes. One has to compromise. In most release systems a further period of up to 2 to 3 weeks will elapse before the birds are ranging freely in and out of the pens. In the north, especially on high ground, it can pay to release at 8 weeks of age. The poults should be hardier and better able to withstand the harsh conditions which can occur even in the summer.

Since the optimum age for liberation is 6–7 weeks, the time of release is obviously largely determined by the hatching date. There is some evidence from several well-documented shoots that recovery rates are highest from the *later* release groups. These birds have less time to wander – and incidentally their food requirements will be less. On shoots where releasing is on a 'put and take' basis, birds hatched in early July may be an advantage. If increasing the breeding stock is the main objective, however, then mid-season hatched birds should be chosen.

A release pen must provide naturally attractive habitat where pheasants will want to stay. It should contain adequate cover in which to hide and shelter from rainstorms, plenty of open sunny areas, and sufficient shrubs and trees to encourage roosting. An ideal site would be part of a young plantation (7–12 years old) of mixed conifers and hardwoods, where the pen could enclose a wide ride as a sunning area. If the ground cover it too dense, 'rides' should be cut through nettles and brambles to ensure that the poults have adequate drying-out places and can find their way back to the feed hoppers.

It is often said, with some truth, that release pens that catch the very early morning sun hold birds better than those which do not.

The crops in the fields adjoining release sites must also be considered, and, if possible, release dates adjusted so that the cornfields are cut before the poults are moving freely in and out of the pens. *Harvesting machines and stubble burning can be very disturbing factors.*

Weather conditions immediately after the poults have been moved to the release pen can seriously affect survival rates. Heavy rainstorms at night

154

combined with low temperatures can cause losses among the poults during the first night or two without their familiar night-shelter, particularly in pens short of good rainproof cover. It is often advisable to delay a release for a day or two, until a bad spell of weather is over.

The important decision as to whether to use a single large central release site or a number of smaller, more peripheral sites must be determined by consideration of local factors. Generally speaking, one single large release site is more cost-effective and less time-absorbing than a number of smaller pens.

Methods of release

The essential feature of any release system is that the transition from a sheltered life in captivity to a much more rigorous life in the wild, should be a gradual one. To lavish care and attention on the relatively inexpensive egg, and then throw out the seven or eight times more valuable poult to fend for itself in an unfriendly world, is the height of folly.

Two main methods of acclimatising the pheasant poults are in common use. For smaller numbers a conditioning pen made up from brooder pen sections and roofed over with netting can be constructed on the release site. After a week or ten days, the door should be opened and some of the poults allowed to *walk* out. The remainder are similarly 'leaked' out at intervals, while the earlier released birds are held by having their familiar feeding and drinking utensils placed outside the pen nearby. If using this system ground predators must be under control.

58 Release pens should contain plenty of cover and shelter as well as some sunny areas

155

For larger numbers of poults a more permanent release pen should be used. As a rough guide, approximately 1 yd. (1 m.) of perimeter netting per bird is required, although this ratio may be nearly halved for numbers between 500 and 1,000 poults. The actual height of the wire netting may vary from 6 ft. to 9 ft. (2 m. to 3 m.) and is usually made of two rolls in two mesh sizes – $1\frac{1}{4}$ in. (3·125 cm.) for the lower half and 2 in. (5 cm.) for the upper half. The bottom 9 in. (23 cm.) is turned out, securely pegged down or buried, while the top 18 in. (46 cm.) is allowed to flop outwards to provide an efficient anti-fox fringing.

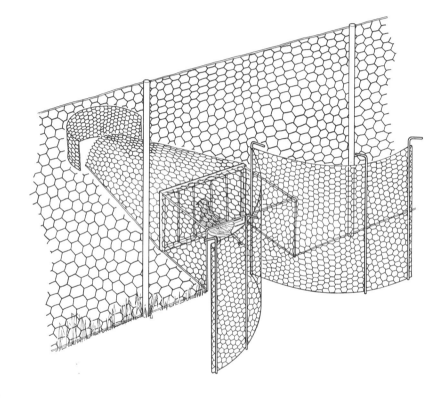

59 The fox grid should be recessed into the release pen perimeter with two high wings to guide the birds into the opening, and a small circle of netting at the inward end of the funnel to deter any poults from walking out again

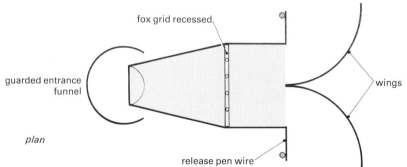

156

The two rolls of netting may be 4 ft. or 5 ft. (1 m. or 1½ m.) wide, securely joined by fasteners or tightly laced with wire. A bad join will allow poaching cats, foxes or hunting dogs an easy entry. Added insurance in the form of an electric fence wire, 9 in. (23 cm.) above ground level and 9 in. (23 cm.) from the base of the wire netting, can be used – two strands, the second one 9 in. (23 cm.) above the lower one, are even better – but precautions must be taken (e.g. spraying the ground with 'Gramoxone') so that rapidly growing vegetation does not short-circuit the system. Electric fence wire can also be used as a substitute for the top anti-fox fringe. Outward facing wooden battens must be nailed to the top of the fence posts and fitted with two insulators to support the wire. The insulators should be 3 in. (8 cm.) and 12 in. (30 cm.) from the top of the wire netting.

There are now transistorised electric fences on the market, powered by one or two small batteries which operate for 4–5 months. An added attraction is that the battery life is unaffected by a dead short on the line, although of course the shock is reduced.

The large release pens are not roofed and poults are prevented from flying out by clipping the primary feathers of *one* wing. At 6–7 weeks of age only the outermost seven feathers should be cut. The remaining stubs are moulted at weekly intervals and the poults will begin to fly out of the pen in about a fortnight.

From pens sited on steeply sloping ground poults may be able to escape prematurely. This can be prevented by *pulling* out the three primaries nearest the body, which are *adult* feathers – the juveniles having been moulted. If these were cut, they would not be replaced until the following year.

Trees and shrubs close to the wire netting should be removed, or the poults may flutter half-way up and then eventually get out – before they can fly sufficiently strongly to escape from their enemies. All branches hanging into the pen should be removed to two or three yards from the pen.

Protection from predators

The Game Conservancy carried out a study into predation of pheasant poults in new release pens by tawny owls, jointly with BFSS, RSPB and BASC (then WAGBI).

Birds of prey are protected by law at all times under the Wildlife and Countryside Act though a defence may exist other than in the case of Schedule 1 species if it can be shown that they have caused serious damage in release pens. The following recommendations should provide ways of minimising losses where attack by birds of prey are expected.

1. Release older poults, at least 7 or preferably 8 weeks old.

2. If only one release is planned it is better to release older birds in August than younger ones in July.

3. Release groups should be less than 500 birds. If larger groups must be released the number should not exceed one bird per half yard of pen perimeter.

4. Release pens should have at least 60 per cent herb cover and 20 per cent shrub cover. Existing pens should be modified to conform to this pattern by planting where possible or by using piles of brashings.

5. Release pens should be placed in small woods of less than 50 acres when possible and should not extend outside the wood to include open ground.

6. If owl predation starts, deterrents such as flashing lights, hanging bags or sacks, or strips of tin foil should be put up around the pen and moved about regularly. To frighten sparrowhawks, aluminium foil bird scarers (Glitter bangs) should be hung around the pen and across lines of access.

7. Make release pens proof against mammals by including an overhanging fringe, digging in and pegging down the wire and putting anti-fox grids in all the pop-holes. An electric fence will give further protection. This will help to prevent mass kills by mammals that are often mistakenly blamed on owls.

The advantages gained by taking measures to reduce losses from predators must be weighed against certain disadvantages; for example, the increased risk of feather-picking in delayed releases and the cost of constructing additional pens if more than 500 poults are to be released at a time.

Having given the birds their liberty, it is important to allow them to work in and out of the release pen whenever they want to. They tend to regard the pen as their base – returning home at night – and these habits should be encouraged. We have seen release pens with a track worn as smooth as a rat-run all round the perimeter, made by pheasants unable to find their way in. If there is only one gate left propped open at an angle and acting as a 'catcher', only birds approaching from one direction will be able to get inside. If two gates are fitted they should be hung on opposite sides, so that pheasants coming from either direction will be guided into the pen. Unfortunately open gates mean that foxes will also be able to get in. A funnel entrance is therefore a better proposition, with an anti-fox grid with $3\frac{1}{2}$ in. (9 cm.) gaps between the bars (see Figure 59). This will allow the pheasants to pass through up to about 12 weeks of age but will deter the average fox. If there is no danger from foxes the 'gate' can be removed.

Wire-netting 'wings' or baffles leading out from the grid entrance will be necessary to direct the pheasants in. Game Conservancy advisers recommend one fox grid per 50 metres of perimeter.

Well-grown 16-week-old poults have been squeezing through the standard Game Conservancy fox grid, but on a shoot in Belgium some of the larger Mongolian pheasants had difficulty in passing through a duplicate model after 10 weeks!

158

To encourage poults that may at first be reluctant to pass through the grids the area between the wings and the grid can be lightly furnished with a few branches. The birds will then push through the twigs and pass the grid without noticing. To make them even easier to use, the grids may be recessed into the funnel. Feed can also be scattered in the funnel entrance.

When the funnels are heavily used a distinct track appears which allows the pheasants to identify the exit from inside the pen. They will then use the funnels to *walk* out whereas one wants to force them to fly out. A small half circle of netting should be fitted around the funnel exit leaving just sufficient room for the bird to jump over it into the pen. This eliminates the tell-tale track and also effectively blocks the exit to a bird attempting to walk out. This screen should be about twice as high as the funnel exit. For the first week or so after the pheasants have started to fly out of the pen, it is a good idea to walk quickly round the perimeter of the pen at dusk. In this way, poults still dithering outside the netting may be 'nudged' gently towards the re-entry grids and be guided inside.

Very occasionally fox cubs have been known to enter the grid, but it will deter the average adult. To prevent young foxes entering the pen before the clipped flight feathers of the pheasants have regrown, the grid can be temporarily blocked with a piece of wire netting or closed with a proper wooden sliding hatch. This should be opened as soon as the first birds have been seen outside the pen – normally two or three weeks after wing-clipping.

A big kill in the pen by a cub at this stage is unlikely as the poults should have learnt to fly up to roost inside the enclosure. If there is no danger from foxes the 'gate' can be removed.

Management after release

With the poults moving freely in and out of the release pens comes the problem of preventing them from straying beyond the shoot boundaries. If the release site has been well chosen, by providing an adequate supply of suitable food and keeping the coverts free from disturbance, the birds will be retained. Regular feeding is essential – the same time every day – and heralded by whistling, rattling bucket handles or some other familiar noise, will also help to hold the birds. Well-distributed water points must be provided. Two feeds each day – early morning and late afternoon – is the minimum required, and three is better. Some skill is needed to judge the right amount at each feed – just enough to satisfy the birds until the next time when they will return hungry for more. The food should be scattered so that the pheasants spend much of their time searching for it and have less opportunity to wander. Initially the birds must obviously have the same food as they have been accustomed to in the rearing pens. By release time some kibbled wheat should have been introduced into the diet and it is important now to start changing them over to a whole grain and gradually to increase the quantity. This changeover in diet must be carefully

159

done and those who purchase poults for immediate release should take great care to find out what their diet has been before delivery. Frequently it is pellets and no grain. Where a daily hand-feeding routine is impractical an automatic feeder or hoppers must be used.

Feeding can represent a significant item of overall shoot costs. The success of a restocking programme is dependent on establishing an effective feeding routine to acclimatise and hold the birds. The timing, quantity and system employed is influenced by the programme on shooting days. Details of hand- and hopper-feeding may be found in Game Conservancy Booklet No. 14 *The Feeding and Management of Game in Winter.*

Arranging a visit from your local Game Conservancy adviser is probably the best way to decide on the most suitable feeding policy for your particular shoot and the labour available.

Where time permits driving- or dogging-in can be of considerable importance to holding birds on the shoot. If the birds are seen wandering along hedgerows and belts leading away from the coverts they should be carefully shepherded, preferably with a well-trained dog, back to the centre of the shoot. In certain places driving-in may be necessary as a regular daily routine.

60 Drinkers should also be provided in the feeding area

Because local conditions, the number of wild birds and the amount of natural food vary so enormously, precise figures cannot be given for the quantities of food that should be provided in covert. It is known, however, that a pheasant will eat about 2 oz. (57 g.) of food a day and assuming that the pheasants will supplement their diet with natural food – and that finches and pigeons will also take some of the grain provided – then 1,000 birds in covert would require about 1 cwt. (50 kg.) of food each day.

Wing-tagging and leg-ringing

Pheasant rearers can learn a great deal by marking their poults before they are released. Information will be forthcoming concerning the proportion of released birds that are shot, the ratio of wild birds to reared, the 'holding' capacity of different release points, the direction in which the birds tend to stray and so on.

The system is particularly valuable when building up a new shoot since it provides accurate information on the fate of released birds as opposed to mere guess work. But it can also be useful on an established shoot. As an example, one of our members had two release pens, one in the centre of the shoot and one close to his boundary. He was contemplating removing the boundary pen and enlarging the central one to accommodate all the birds. Before doing so, however, he wisely tagged the birds for one season to check whether he was taking the right decision.

To his surprise (and ours!) the boundary release pen showed a 10 per cent better return than the central one and he therefore decided to leave well alone.

If the maximum use of marking is to be obtained some extra work is necessarily involved – not only in the application of rings or wing-tags *but also in recording the subsequent recoveries*. This extra work is well worthwhile. Marking release groups of less than a hundred birds is under most circumstances unlikely to produce any reliable information.

Two methods of marking are available:

1. *Wing-tags.* These may be applied when the poults are put to covert and we consider them to be far the most efficient method of marking the birds. It is just possible for a few tags to come off, particularly where the person putting them on is carrying out the operation at high speed. To check the losses we marked a large number of birds on both wings and carefully noted those subsequently recovered with only one tag. The loss only amounted to 2 per cent.

The tags are affixed with special pliers to the 'leading edge' of the wing (on *no* account should the operation be attempted with ordinary pliers). We have noticed two common faults when people first use tags and both are caused by understandable timidity. In the first place the tag is not fastened far enough into the wing. It is only necessary to have $\frac{1}{4}$ in. protruding in front of the leading edge of the 6-week-old bird's wing to allow for growth. The second fault is not

161

61 A misty morning on the Downs. In this release pen adequate escape cover has been provided, also sunning areas and roosting sites. An anti-fox fringe on the netting would give added security

62 Wing-tagging provides accurate information on the fate of reared birds

162

closing the tags sufficiently firmly to make them lock properly. The special pliers are very strong and should be squeezed hard until they come onto the raised stop which prevents them from being closed too far. The tags are unlikely to be *seen* until the bird is plucked, so neighbouring shoots should be asked to *feel* for the tags when examining the bag. This is easily and quickly done.

The way to remove the tags on a shooting day is to cut with a sharp knife through the leading edge of the shot bird's wing on one side of the tag. It will then come free with a sharp pull. Removing the tags without cutting the wing requires considerable strength and invariably results in sore fingers!

The Game Conservancy can supply wing-tags (trade name Quadtag). They are available in six different colours at no extra cost. Special tags printed to the purchaser's requirements are available. It is important to use the special Quadtag applicators (pliers).

2. *Rings*. Rings should not be applied to pheasants until they are at least 8 weeks old, the rings being put on above the spur. A few people prefer rings to wing-tags because they are visible from a distance providing the birds' legs are not hidden in vegetation. However we think this slight advantage is heavily outweighed by their insecurity (many come off) and the fact that the birds are normally released before they are old enough to be ringed.

Unlike wing-tags, rings can be re-used but, although this may appear to be an economy, we have only found it an almost certain way of throwing the records into utter confusion. In days gone by one of our rings was sold to a shoot in Kent who subsequently informed us that it had been fitted to a handreared partridge released on the estate. It turned up on a bantam in Reading Market eight years later!

Rings are no longer supplied by the Game Conservancy.

Chapter 13
Wild Pheasant Habitat and Management

Habitat requirements

In the next two chapters we shall be dealing with the layouts of pheasant coverts, game belts, instant spinneys and other forms of cover which will produce good shooting in the autumn and winter months. Most – though not all – of the requirements of a good *shooting* wood are the same as those needed to provide good habitat in the nesting and chick-production season, i.e. warmth at ground level, as wide rides as possible, an external hedge enclosing a grassy headland and so on. The arable crops near the wood have a bearing on both.

In this chapter we shall consider briefly the main territorial and nesting requirements for wild pheasants. Many of the points can be incorporated into the design of the shooting coverts.

In an average season over two thirds of the bag on the *ordinary* shoot will consist of wild pheasants. All too often these days their welfare tends to be neglected in favour of the reared bird.

Pheasants need four principal types of habitat: woodland, open scrub, grassland and arable. Ideally they should be well dispersed in roughly equal proportions.

Although some good pheasant shoots have no natural water supply, the best places for breeding success appear to be in permanent cover – especially in deciduous copses situated in valleys, with rivers, streams, etc. Here the fertile valley soil produces a lush vegetation and nutritious food supplies necessary to ensure good production rates.

For escape cover and nesting, pheasants also use hedges and thickets. Although there is usually sufficient cover of this type, in winter and early spring – when most of the herbaceous cover has died down – there is often a need for the extra protection of woodlands and spinneys.

For sleeping, pheasants also prefer permanent cover, especially woodland in areas where there is a high risk from foxes. In other places they frequently jug on the ground, particularly in blocks of dead bracken and bramble. Marshland and reed beds are also favoured localities. Early in the breeding season nesting pheasants again require the permanent cover provided by woodland, scrub or hedgerow. Later nests may be sited in foot-high grass or cereal crops. For rearing their young, pheasants prefer the edges of cereal fields where, in a favourable year, sufficient insects may be found. For at least two weeks these form the main diet of the pheasant chick. Beetles are most important, followed by sawfly larvae, aphids, land-bugs (*Heteroptera*) and spring-tails (*Collembola*). The pheasant chick's diet is similar – but more varied than – that of the grey partridge chick, but as pheasants hatch about two weeks earlier, competition for food between the species is reduced.

At this time pheasant chicks are vulnerable to both weather and predators – especially stoats, weasels and crows. Pheasant broods – chaperoned by their mothers – frequent clearings and tracks, using the adjoining cover to escape from danger. In dense cover they may feel less secure from unseen attack.

Pheasants, both chicks and adults, need adequate supplies of grit. This can fulfil two functions: to help digest the food in the gizzard, and also – if the soil is of the right kind – to supply a considerable part of the essential calcium requirements. Both in North America and Britain the best pheasant country either overlies calcareous substrata or occurs where glacial deposits were formed during the Ice Age. Conversely on some acid soils wild pheasant densities are relatively low and although such conditions may be difficult to alter, they should be considered when acquiring a new shoot.

The main habitat factor to remember is that pheasants are essentially birds of the 'edge', i.e. where several different types of cover meet. Analysis of territories occupied by cock pheasants in spring in southern England showed that the average size of the territory was 4·5 acres (2 h.) – the smallest being approximately 3 acres (1 h.) and the larger ones nearly 6 acres (2½ h.). In these territories the average cover distribution was*

Woodland canopy and understorey	(*a*) without scrub layer	2%–3%
	(*b*) with scrub layer	26%
Open scrub layer (no trees)	(*a*) shrubs	17%
	(*b*) tall herbs	2%
Open fields	(*a*) grassland	40%
	(*b*) arable	12%

The scrub layer is important! On our study areas both in the open and under woodland canopy it occupied about 45 per cent of the total, and since only 26 per cent of the land surveyed was under scrub, this showed that cock pheasants preferred to include this type of cover in their territories.

Probably the most constant feature of the cock territories was the length of field edge – an average of 400 yds. (365 m.) per territory.

Trees, although occurring in most territories, were not an essential component. Among the scrub species hazel and bramble predominated. Hazel

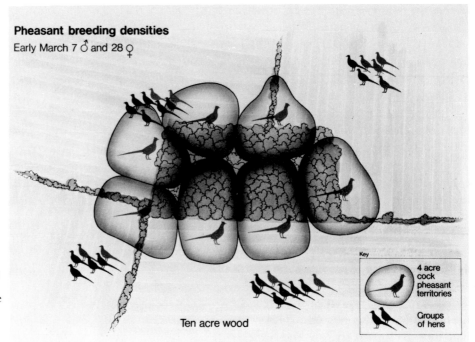

Pheasant breeding densities
Early March 7 ♂ and 28 ♀

Key

4 acre cock pheasant territories

Groups of hens

Ten acre wood

63a In March the cocks establish territories of approximately 4 acres; half woodland or scrub, half arable. The hens wander about in groups – their behaviour being promiscuous

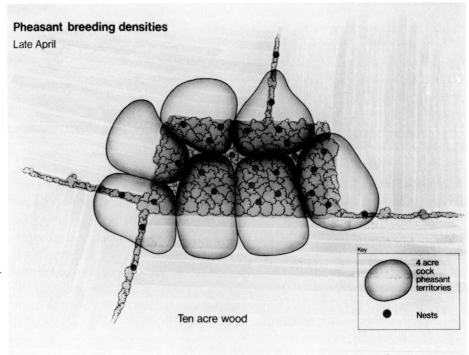

Pheasant breeding densities
Late April

Key

4 acre cock pheasant territories

Nests

Ten acre wood

b Later the hens move in to their nesting territories. Under suitable cover conditions these can achieve a density of 3 or 4 to the acre. This semi-promiscuous mating system allows a more even spacing of nests than true polygamy, which would cause several hens to crowd into the territory of the preferred cock

166

was rarely used for roosting but pheasants frequently jugged under it among brambles or tall herbs which also provided a variety of autumn fruit.

In the spring the open fields are used mainly for feeding, territorial displays and courtship. During the peak crowing period at dawn, most cocks move from cover into fields, woodland rides or clearings. Fields of grass, winter wheat, newly sown barley and even ploughed ground are all searched for food. Although the ranges of cock pheasants vary in extent at different times of the year – in the winter they may be half as large again as the spring/summer range – those of the hens remained approximately the same size throughout the year.

In contrast to cocks, hen pheasants do not select well-defined territories but in the spring they have home ranges that may cover the territories of four or more different cocks. Nor do they form any strong bond with individual cocks except for relatively short periods.

Although pheasants nest in a wide variety of different sites, they show a distinct preference for moderate shrub cover. There are fewer nests where the cover is either dense or sparse, and nest-site selection appears to be little affected by the density of the herb layer. In medium-sized (10–15 acre [4–6 h.]) blocks of woodland without shelter hedges around the perimeter the highest nesting density is found about 30–40 yds. (27–36 m.) in from the edge and particularly within 10 yds. of the edge of the rides.

Nesting success is usually highest in woodland and lowest in silage fields and hedgerows (where losses from predation can be high).

Management

Management for wild pheasants implies a knowledge of the holding capacity of the land as well as the number of pheasants present at different times of the year. Keepers have an approximate idea of the pheasant breeding density, but the numbers of cock pheasants in the spring can be ascertained by a combination of direct observation and pin-pointing crow-calls in the early morning. Sample counts of 'harems' will provide a cock/hen ratio from which the numbers of hens are calculated. In late July and August – before the reared pheasants have escaped from the release pens – sample counts of pheasant broods can be made. From the young/old hen ratio obtained and the spring breeding density the total pheasant population is calculated and the number that can be shot without impairing the next year's breeding stock assessed.

Keepering for wild pheasants is little different from looking after partridges. We have already quoted the Norfolk saying: 'If you look after the partridges the pheasants will look after themselves.' Like all axioms, this one is a slight oversimplification, but certainly if predators in hedgerows and woodland are carefully controlled, nests protected, deserted clutches salvaged, forestry work avoided during nesting time and an eye kept on all possible harm that may be caused by farming operations, then the chicks will have the best possible chance of survival. Wire netting round plantations can mean chicks trapped inside – unable to get out to feed in the fields. It can also make it easy for a fox to catch growing poults.

Our monitoring of newly hatched broods of chicks by telemetry is telling us where the hen prefers to take a brood and why. Although pheasant chicks are somewhat less dependent on insect life than young partridges, it does form an important part of their diet. Many types of woodlands, e.g. softwoods set in parkland or dairying country, can be hungry places. Diversity of cover and crops – not always easy to achieve – is the answer.

Chapter 14
Forestry and Pheasants: Part 1

It is not so long ago that forestry and pheasants were looked upon as alternatives. An estate could have well-managed woodlands or it could have a good shoot – but not both. Fortunately attitudes have altered. The concept of 'multiple use' of forest areas has now been accepted in this country, as it has been for many years overseas, and foresters here have realised the value of shooting rights. Great strides have also been made in management techniques which allow game to breed and be shown in woodland without detriment to the forester's interests.

In the early 1950s our forests – both private and State – were still lying ruined by wartime fellings and years of neglect. Estate owners tackling the backlog of maintenance and repair had little enough to spare for forestry, despite the offer of government grants. Since then there has been a great upsurge of afforestation.

The word 'game' was formerly only mentioned in a hushed whisper when in the presence of a dedicated forester, who probably declared that game and forestry were incompatible. But the time had come to call a halt to a process which was turning the view from the estate owner's study into a hedgeless desert, relieved here and there by a rectangular box of sombre conifers.

This may be a slight exaggeration, but the process of whittling away our handsome deciduous hardwoods with their magnificent spring and autumn foliage in favour of the static dullness of most conifers has been a depressing sight in recent years. However, game shooting in forest areas is governed not by aesthetics or the owner's passing whim – but by *sound economics*. Together with farming and forestry, the sporting interests have a valuable part to play which can be integrated into the estate pattern without friction.

Anyone interested in shooting or forestry knows of large conifer woods which have been let at rents of a few pounds a year. As a result, foresters have scoffed at the suggestion that sporting rights are valuable. It must be borne in mind, however, that re-planting or rehabilitation plans should include the sporting side at an early stage. When an estate is taken over, the owner's first concern is usually with the farming problems. Once these have been tackled, he turns to

169

the forestry. Several years later he may consider game – but it is often too late. Lack of early planning makes it expensive to provide game habitat.

There have been many cases of irreparable damage caused by the planting of unshootable woodlands or the destruction of hedgerows. To a certain extent this has been aggravated by a lack of knowledge on the part of both forester and farmer about the requirements of game.

These are very small, but they must be planned from the start.

About 5 per cent of the woodland acreage is all that need be unproductive of timber to produce a good crop of fast, high pheasants and conditions which will later encourage them to stay and breed in the woods.

If this small percentage is devoted to game habitat the woodland – even if it is composed entirely of conifers – will be capable of development into a valuable shoot. If not, its potential is almost certainly NIL.

A 2,000-acre (810 h.) estate with 200 acres (81 h.) of woodland, for example, could be ruined as a pheasant shoot by unsympathetic forestry. If 5 per cent of the 200 acres (81 h.) was deducted for game interests, at an annual rental value of even £20 per acre, the total 'sacrifice' would be £200 each year.

To recover this amount, the shooting rent for the estate as a whole would have to be increased by only 10p per acre. This is a very small sum when it is realised that the differences between the rent of a good shoot and a bad one could be 50p an acre or more. Whether the 'sacrifice' of the 5 per cent required by the gamebirds had to be made by farm or forest, on balance the owner would be better off – the shooting value, rental or capital, would be significantly improved.

To look at this problem in another way: if the forestry department is going to reduce the rentable value of the shoot by 50p per acre over 2,000 acres (810 h.), it should carry a fixed charge of £1,000 per annum in the estate account. A charge of £1,000 or £100 for game? Whether the estate or farm owner is interested in shooting or not, there can be no doubt as to the correct answer.

In the following pages an attempt has been made to break down the requirements of woodland pheasants into separate features, which will be described in detail. This will help shoot owners, keepers, foresters and land agents to plan new woodlands with game in mind and also to improve existing woods.

Planning a new wood

There are four main features which must be present if a woodland area is to be of high sporting quality:

(*a*) Protection from wind
(*b*) Breeding cover for the production of wild pheasants
(*c*) Holding cover to retain both wild and reared birds
(*d*) Provision for showing high pheasants on a shooting day

170

We repeat that these features need not clash with economic forestry layouts or managements. We will deal with the first three, starting at the outside of the wood and working inwards, before discussing (d), the question of shooting.

Protection from the wind

Pheasants require protection from the wind at two levels. Provision must be made for shelter at ground level and also for 'draught-proofing' the roosting trees. A pheasant spends all the daylight hours on the ground (and occasionally the night hours as well) and it is here that covert planning so often fails. Any new plantation will give good ground-level shelter for about 10 years and then, quite suddenly, the trees are brashed up and the wind comes whistling in. This is tantamount to pulling down the walls of the pheasant's house, leaving him with only a roof.

Leaving trees unbrashed is rarely effective. The only satisfactory answer is to surround the wood with a good hedge. If it is to be efficient, some thought must be given to its planting.

The perimeter hedge

A shelter hedge need be no more than 4–5 ft. (1–1½ m.) high and 2 ft. (0·6 m.) wide, but it must be thick at the bottom. It is essential that it is planted in the right position and *properly managed afterwards*. The usual cause of deterioration in perimeter hedges is that they are planted too close to the trees. They can be trimmed only by hand – and with labour kept to the bare minimum, neglect is the inevitable result.

Even if there is labour to spare, a hedge planted under the trees will eventually become starved of light and moisture and gradually die out. It is, therefore, vital to position the hedge correctly so that it is unshaded and can be maintained from the seat of a tractor.

A simple solution is to form a 'perimeter zone' inside the wood by leaving a space of at least 15 ft. (5 m.) between the hedge and the first row of trees. This perimeter zone has many advantages and it is one of the basic features of a successful covert plan.

1. It allows access on both sides of the hedge for a mechanical cutter.
2. The hedge can be trimmed from inside the wood by the type of cutter that reaches over, even when the adjoining field has a growing crop.
3. If there is a boundary ditch, it will be free of tree roots and leaves.
4. The trees cannot shade adjacent crops or rob them of moisture.
5. The unplanted space will provide excellent nesting cover for both pheasants and partridges. Patchy grass gives spaces in which to dust, bask in the sun or dry out. This area can easily be trimmed over with a mechanical cutter to prevent the growth of a jungle of thorns and briars.

It can be seen that the perimeter zone is as much a practical proposition for the farmer and forester as it is for the gamekeeper.

Hedge species

The best stock-proof hedge plant (and one of the most handsome) is the quickthorn (*Crataegus monogyna*). It should be planted in a double row, 9 in. (23 cm.) between the plants and 6 in. (15 cm.) between the rows (which should be staggered). For the hedge to be stock-proof and wind-proof it is best that it should be cut and laid – usually around the sixth to ninth year after planting. This is a 'once-only' operation provided the hedge is regularly trimmed afterwards. Simply cutting the tops off will cause deterioration and eventually dying out. *Lonicera nitida* will make a fine wind baffle but it would probably be at least 10 to 15 years before it is stock-proof – nevertheless it has the great advantage of requiring far less management than thorn.

Wind-proof hedges can also be established with tree species such as Lawson's cypress (*Cupressus lawsonia*), beech (*Fagus* sp.), Norway spruce (*Picea Norvegicus*), Scots pine (*Pinus sylvestris*) or thuya planted about 2 ft. (61 cm.) apart. Their disadvantage is that they are inclined to become bare at the bottom, particularly in exposed positions, although this is not so much of a problem where the trees are topped at 7–8 ft. ($2-2\frac{1}{2}$ m.) and so closely spaced that any dead branches at the bottom remain interlocked. Tree hedges can certainly be valuable in the more exposed areas of Scotland and Wales, where quickthorn is not always practicable. The Scottish stone wall or dyke is, of course, the best of all as a draught-excluder but since it provides little nesting cover, it is important to combine it with a perimeter zone.

High shelter

Pheasants must be comfortable when roosting at night. Shelter can be provided by a belt of softwoods, such as Norway spruce, Douglas fir or tsuga, at least three rows wide, right around the wood inside the perimeter zone. The cypresses (Lawson's, Leyland, etc.) are not so satisfactory for roosting because of the dense and upward growing habit of their branches (in the younger trees) but are very effective as high shelter for other roosting trees. Larch (*Larix* sp.) is a favourite roost, despite its bare winter branches, and can be screened effectively against wind and prying poachers by an outer row or two of cypress or spruce.

Breeding and holding cover

Breeding cover consists of evenly distributed low ground vegetation – not too dense and protected from the wind. Holding cover can be similarly defined, with the addition of warm and sheltered night roosting.

It is important to let sunlight enter the wood – in moderation. The correct amount will allow the growth of sufficient natural ground cover. Too little will

172

shaded
crop   hedge   wood

ditch

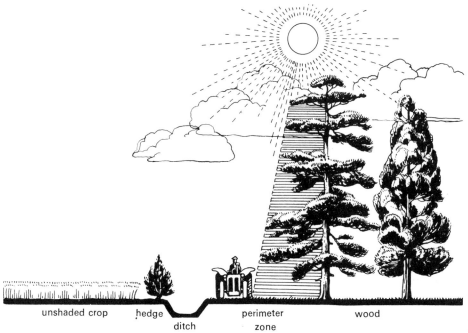

unshaded crop   hedge   perimeter   wood

ditch   zone

64 A perimeter zone
will provide an area
for dusting, drying-out
and nesting. The
boundary hedge can
also be correctly
maintained

173

leave the ground bare as in a mature beech or conifer wood, and too much will produce a jungle of the type found in new plantations.

The cover problem in a plantation is usually summed up by the keeper as 'too thick at the start and too thin at the end'. This can be overcome by planning. When replanting clear felled woodland the very thick initial growth of weed, particularly brambles and coppice, is partly overcome in the first five years or so by the forester's normal weeding programme. The next five years in softwood (and up to ten in hardwoods) can be very difficult. Some of the excessive growth can be suppressed if the initial planting is carried out under dapple shade thrown by a thin stock of trees left from the previous crop or by spraying with a brushwood killer before replanting. This problem is not so great, of course, when planting is carried out on virgin ground.

Thick undergrowth is not undesirable for either breeding or holding cover, but birds will tend to use only the fringe for nesting and it may become too dense for beaters on a shooting day. A number of tracks cut through the undergrowth will give a much greater choice of nesting sites. The keeper will also be able to feed along the tracks and control predators, beaters will be able to work properly, and the forester can see what is happening to the young trees.

When the tree canopy closes, the problem is to get enough ground cover *evenly distributed* through the wood. This is where the pure conifer plantation is so difficult. Even the best of planning tends to leave all the cover concentrated in the perimeter zone and ride sides. In such a situation, nesting birds are far more vulnerable to their enemies because only a *limited* area of cover has to be hunted out. Cover should therefore be encouraged on every inch of ground where the sun can get in.

Drainage is also very important. Although the pheasant is quite at home in the marshes of Central Asia, damp woodland does not produce the right type of cover and is fatal to young chicks. Impeded drainage also predisposes the area to wind blow.

Adequate ground cover will always grow naturally, given sufficient sunlight and drainage. The correct amount can be expected, however, for only a proportion of the life of a wood. Some provision must be made for the lean years. A good pattern of rides (including the perimeter zone) and judicious planting of shrubs can go a long way towards solving this problem.

Rides

Before deciding on the correct pattern of rides, their function should be understood.

The forester requires wide, well-drained rides for timber extraction and stacking, or occasionally as firebreaks. He also requires narrow intermediate rides for inspecting young trees and extracting thinnings. We have seen many plans of operations for woodlands, but these have never included anything other than a purely perfunctory *extraction plan*. One wood of 36 acres (15 h.) had

174

been planted with only a single track, the width of a tractor, running through the middle. After 15 years this had completely disappeared and the owner was obliged to spend £500 on bulldozing new rides before he could even see whether the trees were still growing!

The keeper needs several narrow rides for feeding his birds, trapping predators and handling beaters (particularly in a young plantation). He needs wide, well-drained sunny rides for turning down reared stock. These also provide marginal nesting cover and sunny places for the wild birds to bring their chicks. These rides will also give space for Guns to stand and birds to flush.

In a small covert the best system is to base the plan on one big central ride with radiating subsidiary rides. This central ride should be 20 yds. (18 m.) wide. Although this may sound excessive, there are a number of reasons for this width.

65 Narrow rides quickly become overgrown – even by trees as young as these beeches – making the area unsuitable for pheasant management

175

It is rarely satisfactory to begin with a narrow ride and gradually open it up as the trees grow. No forester is going to agree amicably to widening until the trees are marketable as thinnings. If the rides are opened at that stage, they will be extremely difficult to manage subsequently: they will be a mass of stumps which cannot be grassed down or trimmed with a mechanical cutter. (Stumps cut to 'ground level' are usually about 6 in. [15 cm.] *above* the ground.) The original narrow ride will also be churned up by transport constantly running in the same tracks. This is expensive to repair.

There is a quick-return cash market which could be exploited on wide rides. This is for so-called 'instant trees' used in landscaping development schemes, motorways, and so on. To get the best returns, it is necessary to be selective in choosing the specimens to be planted and to *maintain them carefully* over the years before marketing. Since the numbers involved are small and the sale price substantial this is well worth doing.

Species in demand include maple (*Acer* spp.), cherry (*Prunus* spp.), horse chestnut (*Aesculus hippocastanum* L.), lime (*Tilia* spp.), silver birch (*Betula verrucosa*), whitebeam and mountain ash (*Sorbus* spp.). Good prices can be obtained for well-grown specimens, particularly if they are *easily accessible*. The time for growth to marketable size varies with the species but is usually 5–10 years.

The management of rides is just as important as their planning. They are often left for years in young plantations with little attention except for an occasional run over with a small motor scythe. This can result in a gradual invasion of unwanted species such as coppice from old tree stumps or self-seeded ash, sycamore and birch. Eventually an expensive clearing operation is required. Even on virgin ground it is important to see that the rides do not become a jungle of brambles and thistles. They should be levelled, cultivated and sown with grass which will ensure rapid and cheap maintenance with ordinary tractor-drawn farm equipment.

When making new rides during a replanting operation, growth from old coppice stools and young shoots from tree stumps can be killed off with a chemical brushwood killer. Subsequent management can be difficult if there are large numbers of tree stumps and uneven ground and bulldozing is really the only answer.

Other points to watch when planning rides are the problems of *drainage* and *wind*.

Drainage is important, particularly on heavy soils and peat. Without it, the rides are quickly cut up by the passage of vehicles and tend to foster a rank growth of vegetation which can become a fire risk in later winter and spring. Deep side ditches should be avoided because they are potential death traps for young pheasants. They can also be ineffective on heavy soil, leaving the centre of the ride undrained. By far the best answer is to use a bulldozer to construct the ride with a good steep camber – 4 ft. (1 m.) should not be too much on a

176

20-yd. (18 m.) width – allowing a *wide, shallow*, drainage ditch on each side. With no steep banks to cave in, this ditch will be easily kept clean and will not trap pheasant chicks.

Wind should never be allowed to blow directly into a ride. Access to a wood should always be made at an angle to avoid this. Where an existing ride opens straight into a wood, a new access should be cut through at an angle. The old entrance should be blocked off by planting a small group of quick-growing conifers behind a wall of straw bales to give temporary shelter. Rides which are 20 yds. (18 m.) in width can also be draughty if over 100 yds. (90 m.) long, even where the ends are blocked. Effective wind baffles can be made by planting a row of conifers across the ride at 50-yd. (46 m.) intervals leaving a central gap for access.

There is another traditional reason for avoiding long, straight rides which open on to roads or public paths – any passing poacher can sum up the pheasant situation at a glance without entering the wood!

Tree species

The subject of tree species is undoubtedly at the centre of most arguments between forester and game preserver.

The old-fashioned hardwood plantations with coppice underwood and a few conifers for roosting were ideal for game. This type of woodland was very long-lived and produced a continuous succession of all types and densities of undergrowth as the coppice was regularly cropped. The demand for timber in the UK is now predominantly softwood – over 80 per cent of the total. Since a large proportion of this is for pulpwood on a fairly short rotation, this appears more attractive than the long-term process of producing mature hardwood.

The high rainfall 'tree factory' areas of the North and West are the least productive for game, and forestry has an economic place, whether as a State or a private enterprise. In the South and East – the best game production areas – the proportion of forestry acreage tends to be small and this makes marketing *much more flexible*. Small parcels of timber and even individual specimen trees can be extracted as they reach maturity, avoiding the necessity of clear felling – the only economical system in the big pulpwood areas. It is here that the private woodland owner has a big advantage where hardwood species are concerned. There has been a tendency in private forestry to ignore this advantage and try to create 'mini-forests' in imitation of the larger producer. It should be remembered, however, that Britain still requires more than 250 million cu. ft. (7·1 million cu. m.) of hardwood each year, of which 200 *millions* (5·7 million cu. m.) *has to be imported*.

It is certainly true that there is always a good market for *well-grown* hardwood timber. Much of the difficulty of selling hardwoods today is due to a preponderance of bad timber resulting from neglect many years ago. Matters are very different now – knowledgeable and efficient forestry management

177

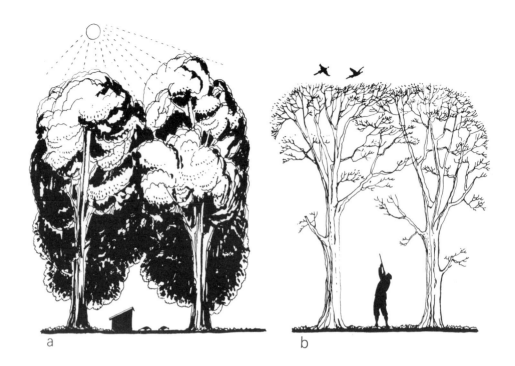

66a The sun cannot reach the ride, and this will make it too shady for pheasant poults

b In the shooting season there will not be enough room for the Guns.
A narrow ride with fairly tall trees on either side

c By felling, say, two rows of trees on either side and replanting with coppice or Christmas trees (in rotation), the sun will be able to reach the ride and the Guns will have room to shoot

178

being the rule rather than the exception. Softwoods may always be the 'bread and butter' of the forester but there seems to be no reason why the traditional hardwood areas of the United Kingdom should not continue to grow a fair proportion of our most handsome deciduous trees. Certainly from the aesthetic point of view, no one wants to see our woodlands turned into a 'poor man's Scandinavia'.

A good mixture of species is the aim of the game preserver, and if asked for a precise definition the answer would be 60 per cent softwood and 40 per cent hardwood at the start, with the hardwood to form the final crop. A 'chessboard' pattern of hardwood groups in a softwood forest is to be preferred to ordinary line planting. The choice of the softwood species is important. Wherever possible, pines and larches should be planted since they allow a fair amount of undergrowth, while the spruces, firs and cypresses produce a completely bare floor. Unfortunately, the spruces produce the greatest volume of timber for the pulpwood industry and greater areas of these conifers will be planted in the future.

There are some areas where the soil and climate rule out any species other than conifers. However, if the general principles set out in this chapter – hedge, perimeter zone, wide rides and well-designed flushing points – are incorporated in the woodland plan, pure conifer woods can be made reasonably productive for pheasants. The game food bill will always be heavier and the stock of breeding birds lower in these conifer woods, but food requirements will be reduced in direct proportion to the amount of sunlight that is admitted. More sun means more growth of food and cover plants. A dense canopy of conifers (particularly spruce) can reduce the ground temperature by as much as 10°F. (5·5°C.) compared to hardwoods. Warmth thus becomes a vital factor. For this reason, a draught-excluding barrier, hedge or stone wall is of great importance in a pure conifer wood.

The hardwood species that can cause most problems are beech and sycamore when grown as a pure stand. Even in this case, some forethought will ensure good ground cover for the future. Common laurel (*Prunus laurocerasus*) will prosper under a fairly dense beech canopy. To be effective the laurel should be planted at the same time as the beech in groups spaced about 50 ft. (15 m.) apart, with three or four plants in each group. Box (*Buxus*) will also prosper under beech but it is very slow growing.

Generally speaking, the choice of tree species to be grown must be decided by soil, climate and economics, but big blocks of one species should be avoided except where they can be used deliberately to exclude pheasants from certain areas as described Chapter 15.

Flushing points

To show high, fast pheasants, there must be openings in the wood from which they can rise easily and fly strongly over the Guns. They must not be forced to fight their way up through a thick canopy or allowed to run to the *edge* of the wood before flushing.

It is easiest to get birds on the wing by planting areas of suitable cover from which they are encouraged to fly when the beaters tap them out. It is also possible to put obstacles in their way, such as 'sewelling' or brushwood. Sewelling consists of stout cord with 2-in. (5 cm.) wide strips of coloured plastic (old fertiliser bags are the best sources of material) hanging down at intervals of about 9 in. (23 cm.). It is hung across the wood supported on forked sticks and must be placed in position *immediately* before a pheasant drive starts. It should be jerked occasionally by a hidden operator at the pheasants' approach. But any form of impenetrable barrier such as wire netting or hazel hurdles is inclined to collect groups of birds which flush in a cloud, spoiling the drive. This disadvantage is usually the result of having bare ground in front of the netting. If there is a good growth of lowland shrubs, the birds will usually take cover in it, rather than crowd against the barrier, and they can be flushed in twos and threes by the beaters. Pheasants that run up and down the wire netting trying to push their way through can become exhausted which means they will fly poorly when they rise.

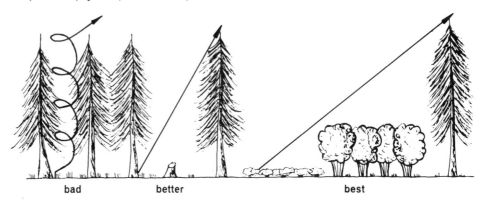

67 Rising areas

bad   better   best

The ideal pheasant wood should have patches of flushing cover – such as low shrubs or young naturally-regenerated trees. These should be distributed at intervals from the point where the beaters enter. They can be about 15 ft. (4½ m.) square, or in the form of strips. They will ensure an intermittent rise of birds – from the very start of the drive – as the beaters work their way through the covert. The fewer the strips of cover, the bigger the rise of birds at each flush – the extreme example being where all the birds run forward and rise together at the edge of the wood.

Careful beating helps to avoid the problem, even where there is a single flushing point at the edge of the covert. But it is better to be certain of even flushes by having numerous flushing points.

When planting this type of cover, the undergrowth must be kept open enough for the beaters to put the birds out of it. If an old shrubbery or a tangle

180

of brambles is converted into a flushing strip, it should be divided into sections small enough for the beaters to tap out properly.

Neglected hazel coppice under large trees poses a common problem. There is usually a completely bare floor with little room above for the birds to fly up. The answer is to cut out small areas of the coppice – two or three stools is usually enough – and these openings should be spaced about 30 yds. (27 m.) apart. If this is done beneath openings in the main canopy, ground cover will soon grow and create a series of small flushing points.

No matter how efficient the flushing cover, some of the birds will inevitably run on to the end. The final flushing point – which must deal with these pedestrians – should be most carefully planned. It must not be too small. As a general rule if the ground is level it should be 40–50 yds. (36–46 m.) back from the edge of the wood.

It must be capable of holding a large number of birds which can be tapped out gently without panicking them and causing one big flush. The area between the flushing point and the edge of the wood should give the birds an easy climb towards the trees in front. This 'rising area' will help even the most reluctant fliers to travel high and fast by the time they clear the wood and find themselves in the open.

In a thick tangle of undergrowth, pheasants often penetrate so far that they become trapped and cannot fly.

To achieve the first of these requirements, therefore, a shrub should be planted which allows the birds to move freely about underneath. One excellent species for this purpose is *Lonicera nitida*.

The shape of a flushing point should be triangular with the point towards the Guns so that the moving beaters close up until they are shoulder to shoulder as they approach the point. *Lonicera* should be planted in single rows with the plants 4 ft. (1 m.) apart and the rows should run parallel to the line of beaters. There should be a 15-ft. ($4\frac{1}{2}$ m.) space between each double row. This space and its width are very important. Observation of pheasants that are being driven out of a wood shows that they reach a critical stage when they either fly or decide that the beaters are too close, bury themselves in cover if it is available, and sit tight. They can be made to rise close to the beaters if they believe they *cannot be seen*. The 15-ft. ($4\frac{1}{2}$ m.) gap between the rows gives them this facility; an essential feature where a large number of birds may have collected at the end of a covert. The importance of beaters moving *very slowly* as they approach the end of a drive should be remembered. The faster they move the more birds will sit tight and be walked over. (A practical leaflet about the art of beating is available from the Game Conservancy.)

The importance of giving the birds a gentle gradient in the rising area is illustrated in Figure 67. It takes a great deal of the 'steam' out of pheasants if they are forced to corkscrew up through tall trees. When this happens they often plane down as soon as they reach the open, passing low over the Guns.

Making provision for this rising gradient (ideally 30°) is not always easy, because it needs space. Chestnut coppice is the best plant: it is not only of medium height but produces durable and valuable fencing stakes. There are, however, only a limited number of areas where it can be grown profitably – basically in S.E. England. Christmas trees would be a good substitute. Any form of coppice can be planted as an alternative if the soil is unsuitable for chestnut. However, such species as hazel and birch are unlikely to have a market and the area is liable to become neglected.

A suggestion is to plant a 'half-crop' of trees in rows running away from the flushing point. These should have a very wide gap – say 10–15 ft. (3–4½ m.) – between the rows, larch being the best species. With suitable soil, poplars would also be successful if planted 20 ft. × 20 ft. (6 m. × 6 m.). If none of these solutions is practical, then common laurel or *Cotoneaster frigida* would serve the purpose.

In a long, narrow wood (say 50 yards [46 m.] wide) it may be difficult to find enough width for a 'set piece' flushing point at the end. A useful compromise might be a double row of *Lonicera* on either side of a central ride, forming a long continuous flush, or an interspersion of laurel plants throughout the woods.

Siting a new covert

Finding the correct position for a new covert needs careful thought. If time permits, several sites can be tried out by using temporary cover such as kale, mustard or game food mixtures. A lot can be learned from this type of experiment about the distances birds will fly, the direction they favour, the effect of wind and so on. Generally speaking, anything between 200 and 400 yds. (180 and 360 m.) is a good distance over which to drive pheasants between coverts.

Where the choice exists, it is obviously best to plant on a slightly elevated site. This will enable a line of Guns to be placed well below, in the line of flight to other cover. For example, two coverts on opposite sides of a valley produce high pheasants whichever way they are driven.

Sometimes an existing wood is situated in a hollow, which makes it impossible to show high-flying birds from the wood itself. A solution is to plant a small covert on neighbouring high ground and link it to the main wood by means of a belt. The beaters can then gently blank out the larger wood and continue half-way up the belt before the Guns are in position. When blanking, it is important to see that the birds are free to run and are not forced to fly because of thick undergrowth. The belt should, if possible, be pure conifer. This will eventually be open underneath but if there is a good hedge on either side, the birds will be able to run through without being seen.

Where possible, a site should be chosen which enables the wood to be driven in more than one direction. Advantage can then be taken of a neighbouring crop, or allowance made for a change of wind, although coverts on the boundary will usually have to be driven in towards the centre of the shoot.

The ideal pattern is a compact group of small coverts (5–10 acres [2–4 h.] each) in a circle around a central, rather larger wood (20–30 acres [8–12 h.]). This large wood acts like the hub of a wheel. Releasing pheasants in the centre will have the same effect as dropping a stone into the middle of a pool – the birds will ripple out to the smaller coverts from which they can be driven 'home'.

Basic layout for a game covert

As an illustration of how the principal features of a good game covert can knit together, they have all been incorporated into the basic layout on page 184 (Figure 68). A number of coverts (12 on one estate) have been planted using the layout exactly as shown. Many other estates have incorporated the main features in existing woodlands.

The outer hedge screens the perimeter zone, which in this case is shown planted with weed-suppressing and berry-bearing shrubs. Shrubs should be of low growth so that the hedge-cutting tractor can run over them without causing too much damage. Inside the perimeter zone, a high sheltering conifer belt is shown on the diagram.

The use of a 20-yd. (18 m.) ride as a central spine is clearly illustrated. Leading off it are 3-yd. (3 m.) wide paths (they hardly warrant the term 'ride') at 50-yd. (46 m.) intervals. These are very important to the keeper. In the early life of a wood – and particularly at the thicket stage – they will provide spaces for the birds to rise and for the keeper to realign the beaters. Later, they will be used as feed tracks. One or two of these 50-yd. (46 m.) compartments could be wired in to form a useful release pen for pheasants. The paths will also be useful to the forester when examining his trees and for extracting thinnings.

The central ride should be held in reserve for major forestry operations and not used constantly by both keeper's and forester's transport hauling game foods and small loads of timber. An additional ride, only 5 yds. (4½ m.) wide, which runs down each side and across the top of the covert, is provided for these minor operations. The access ride to the wood should be set at an angle to prevent the wind blowing in. The layout of the secondary ride is shown more clearly on page 187 (Figure 70).

The flushing points are 50 yds. (46 m.) across the base and 25 yds. (23 m.) from base to apex. Each flushing point should be surrounded by a 5-yd. (4½ m.) wide ride which will have several uses. It will be used by wild chicks that have hatched in the shrubs during the nesting season and later for winter feeding the

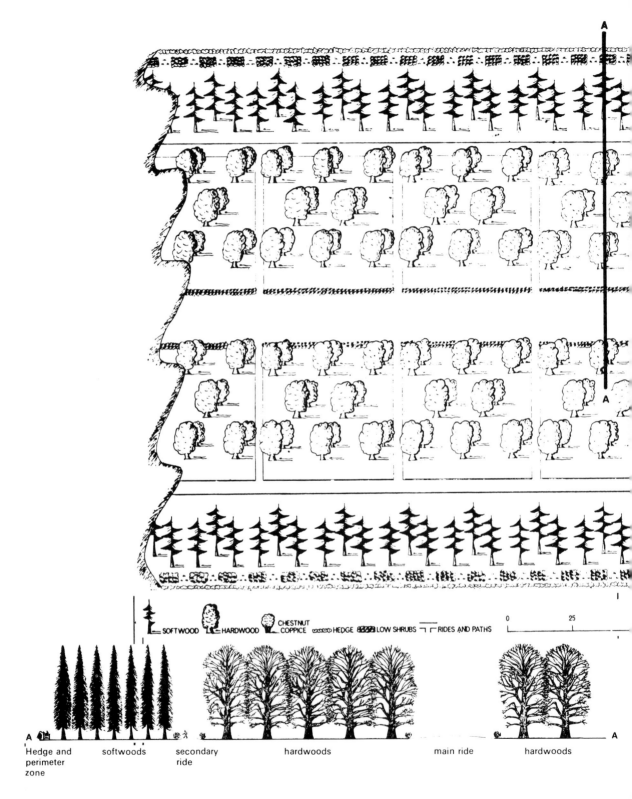

SOFTWOOD — HARDWOOD — CHESTNUT COPPICE — HEDGE — LOW SHRUBS — ⌐ ⌐ RIDES AND PATHS

0   25

Hedge and   softwoods   secondary   hardwoods   main ride   hardwoods
perimeter   ride
zone

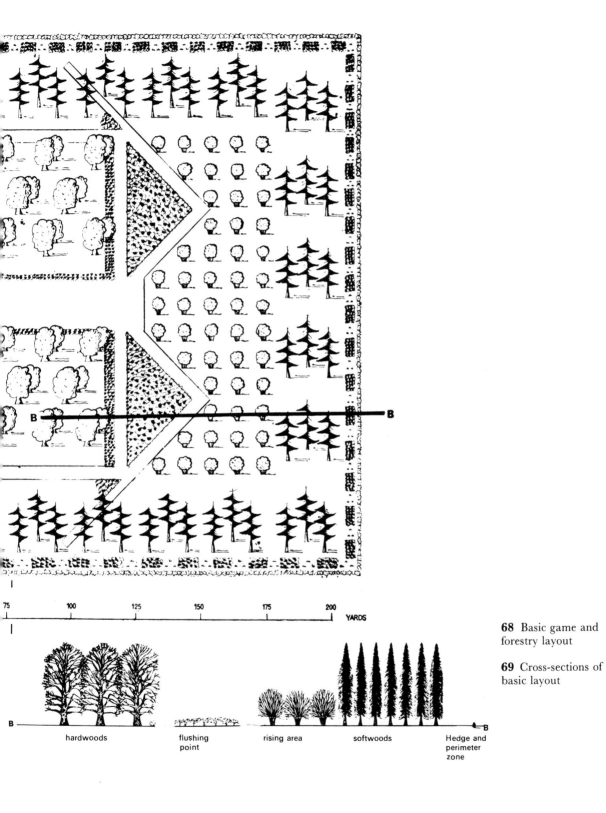

75   100   125   150   175   200

YARDS

68 Basic game and forestry layout

69 Cross-sections of basic layout

B ——— hardwoods   flushing point   rising area   softwoods   Hedge and perimeter zone ——— B

adult stock. On shooting days, 'sewelling' or wire netting should follow the edge of the ride *farthest* from the flushing points and run right out to the edge of the wood along the path leading to the perimeter zone. Pheasants approaching will see the sewelling clearly, take cover in the flushing point shrubs and have plenty of room to rise in the ride when flushed.

Beyond the flushing points is the rising area. In this case it is shown planted with chestnut coppice. The amount of ground needed is 0·54 of an acre (0·21 h.) for the flushing points and ride and 1·06 acres (0·42 h.) for the rising area.

Fitting the basic layout to the site

The diagram (Figure 68) shows two flushing triangles on a 200-yd. (183 m.) width, but the basic layout is designed for multiples of 100 yds. (91 m.) in width and is extremely flexible. In this way it is possible to get one triangle for 100 yds. (91 m.), two for 200 yds. (183 m.), three for 300 yds. (274 m.), four for 400 yds. (360 m.) (which has a 30-yd. [27 m.] central ride to enable the wood to be driven in two halves) and so on.

If the site has an irregular shape, the basic layout is set out in the centre and the irregularities are filled with softwoods (see diagram). When the trees in these fringe areas are mature or have been brashed up, it will be easy on a shooting day to run the birds out of them into the centre. The hedge and perimeter zone should still be on the outside of the wood. The actual sites and size of flushing points can be adjusted to take advantage of any natural rise in the ground by shifting the position away from the Guns or towards them – but a minimum of four rows of softwoods must always be kept as an outer belt at the flushing end. A long narrow wood can have two opposing flushes so that it can be driven in alternate directions. (See page 187, Figure 70b.)

Basic layout for a shelter belt

Many shelter belts established in the early part of the century have deteriorated to such an extent that they are now practically useless – or at best only partly effective. This appears to be particularly true on arable land where marginal hedges have been grubbed up and the plough taken right up to the trees. In some instances on stock farms, animals have been allowed to graze into belts making them bare and open at ground level. Where this occurs in a narrow belt, the stems of the trees can actually *increase* the wind speed for a short distance both before and behind them.

For a belt to be efficient as a windbreak it must have shelter at all levels along its length. A couple of rows of naked trees like too many telegraph poles (see photograph 72 on page 190) are completely ineffective. Animals and birds lose a great deal of body heat when exposed to cold winds without shelter – and American game management technicians who planted shelter belts for game found that heat losses in some mid-West farmsteads were so reduced by the windbreaks that fuel bills fell by as much as 29 per cent.

A thin belt of two rows of trees and a straggling hedge will reduce the wind speed by a constant amount of about 20 per cent for a distance of 15 times the tree height. A dense belt, on the other hand, will reduce it by 80 per cent in the first instance, dropping steadily to 20 per cent at the same distance.

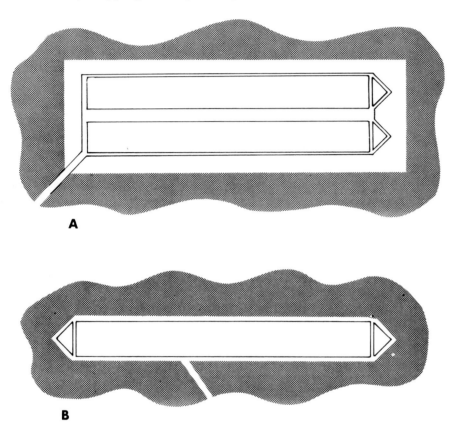

A

B

70a To fit layout into an irregular shape fill shaded areas with conifers and plant hedge around outside boundary

b Double-ended layout for driving in alternate directions

Most shelter belts planted today are similar to those of 40 or 50 years ago. In those days large farm staffs were available in the winter months for the traditional work of 'hedging and ditching'. The gradual reduction of this labour force has contributed to the neglect of the old belts. As in woodlands, it is essential to plan today for efficient and rapid mechanical management and these requirements have been incorporated into the shelter belt shown in cross-section on pages 188–9. It can be conveniently divided into four sections:

(a) Hedge
(b) Perimeter zone
(c) Coppice
(d) Central compartment

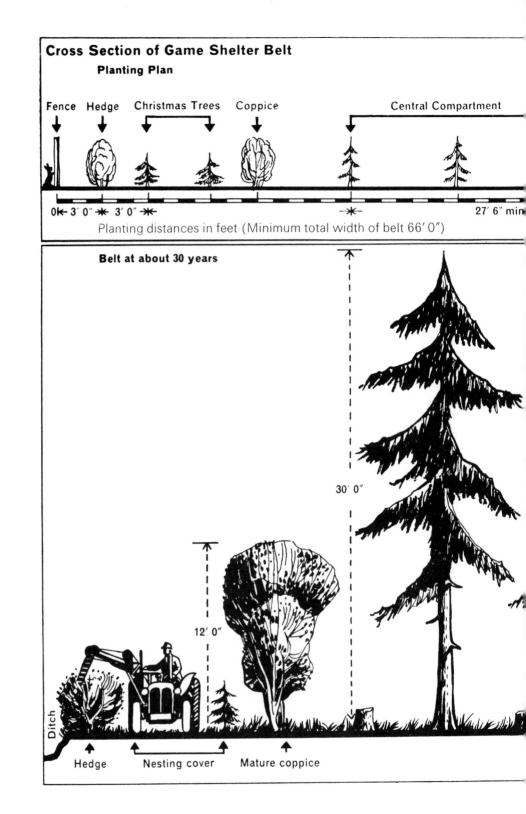

Cross Section of Game Shelter Belt

Planting Plan

Fence Hedge Christmas Trees Coppice Central Compartment

0 ← 3′ 0″ → 3′ 0″ → 27′ 6″ min

Planting distances in feet (Minimum total width of belt 66′ 0″)

Belt at about 30 years

30′ 0″

12′ 0″

Ditch

Hedge Nesting cover Mature coppice

Christmas Trees   Hedge Fence

*Note replant this row with coppice at 7 years

6' 0"

Central compartment (thinned)   Young coppice   Nesting Cover   Hedge

71 Cross-section of game shelter belt

The hedge and perimeter zone are repeated from the woodland layout and serve the same function. The perimeter zone is even more important in a shelter belt since it provides the principal source of nesting cover, particularly for partridges. This space can be used to grow Christmas trees in the early stages.

If the central compartment is to be properly managed for timber, the hedge alone will not provide enough shelter when the lower branches of the tree die off. This gap can be filled by a row of coppice or shrubs. In choosing a species for the coppice we are faced with a similar problem to the rising areas of a game covert and chestnut would be the best answer, where it can be grown.

If the chestnut were to be cut every 14 years, it would be planted *on one side* only when establishing the belt. An extra row of Christmas trees can be grown on the opposite side and replanted with chestnut at 7 years. Subsequent coppicing of alternate sides every 7 years will ensure continuity of shelter and a regular supply of fencing stakes. Bearing in mind that it is medium-height shelter that is specifically wanted the only satisfactory alternatives to chestnut would be common laurel, *Cotoneaster frigida* or similar shrubs. Laurel has the advantage of being evergreen, but *Cotoneaster frigida* does produce berries regularly every year which are eaten by pheasants. Of course, neither of these shrubs need be coppiced, but in view of their expense it would probably be necessary to space them at least 8–10 ft. (2½–3 m.) apart when planting. Laurel

72 Neglected shelter belts such as this are of little value to game and can be positively damaging to the farming. The bare stems of the trees have a venturi effect and actually increase the wind speed at ground level

190

on the windward side of the belt and cotoneaster on the other would be a good combination.

With the two marginal strips of hedge, perimeter zone and coppice or shrubs established, the central compartment can be any width convenient to the site, although an overall width of 22 yds. (20 m.) for the whole belt must be considered the minimum. The choice of tree species for this compartment is not very important for game because the perimeter zone provides most of their requirements. Naturally, seed-bearing hardwoods such as oak, chestnut or beech would be advantageous and provide a pleasing diversion from the regimentation of pure conifers, but softwoods make rather better shelter than hardwoods and are the most likely choice, particularly on exposed sites.

This layout is also valuable when the time comes for the trees to be felled as through eventual deterioration with age. Replanting will then be much easier, with the old hedge and coppice still providing good shelter for the young trees. Throughout its whole existence it can be easily managed and will provide good nesting sites and winter cover for both partridges and pheasants.

Basic layout for a game spinney

Many arable farmers who have been planting plots of kale for pheasant cover over the last few years are now deciding to make some of these areas into permanent cover. Kale is helpful for shooting, but it cannot compare with warm woodland when it comes to nesting time, releasing reared stock or holding birds in bitter weather. Figure 73 on pages 192–3 shows a standard spinney layout which will meet the requirements of most farms or small estates considering long-term plans for improvement.

Although only just over half an acre (33 yds. × 83 yds. [30 m. × 76 m]) it can be increased in length or breadth to suit individual sites. The spinney has four purposes:

(a) *Nesting cover*. The layout provides good nesting cover suitable for both pheasants and partridges – something that can be sadly lacking on a modern arable farm.

(b) *Release point*. The whole centre portion inside the Lawson's cypress shelter belt could be wired in to make a release pen for 200–300 reared pheasant poults. This would be much more satisfactory than releasing into a cover crop, from which poults usually stray rather quickly – probably in search of sunshine and warmth.

Since the spinney is also to be used for nesting and for gathering birds on a shooting day, provision must be made for rolling up the bottom 18 in. (46 cm.) of wire netting of the pen. Gates must also be provided to give access for beaters at *both* ends to allow for drives in different directions.

191

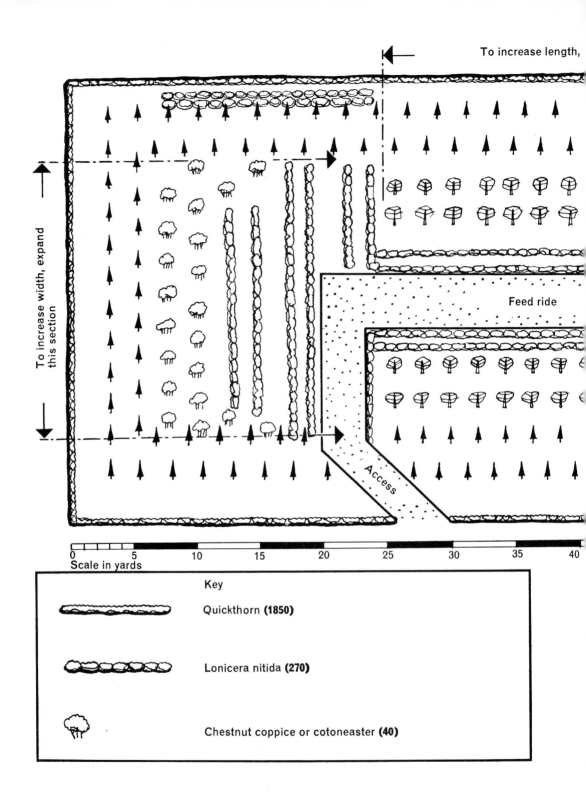

To increase length,

To increase width, expand this section

Feed ride

Access

Scale in yards
0   5   10   15   20   25   30   35   40

Key

Quickthorn **(1850)**

Lonicera nitida **(270)**

Chestnut coppice or cotoneaster **(40)**

ection →

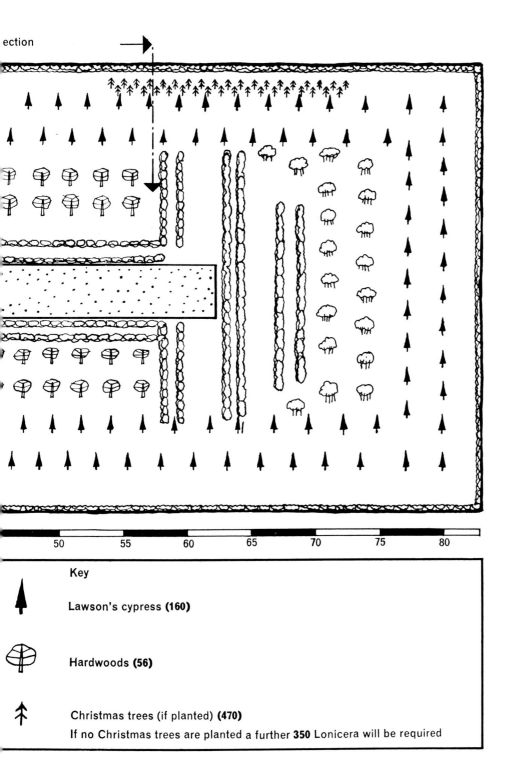

| 50 | 55 | 60 | 65 | 70 | 75 | 80 |

Key

Lawson's cypress (160)

Hardwoods (56)

Christmas trees (if planted) (470)
If no Christmas trees are planted a further **350** Lonicera will be required

73 Game spinney

(*c*) *Flushing area for an adjoining crop.* The spinney can be expanded by sowing an adjoining cover crop such as kale or mustard. Birds can be run into the spinney, from which they can be tapped out in a steady stream rather than the big flushes sometimes seen from a cover crop. Although this type of crop is invaluable, it is generally easier to show birds well from woodlands.

The 'expansion' crop can be planted in eight different positions on the ideal site – where four fields meet – without using the same ground. The spinney is driven 6–2 in favour of one direction so that the actual siting in relation to the hedgerow corners must be decided according to the prevailing wind or proximity of other woodlands. The spinney is planned so that it can be driven in either direction.

(*d*) *Late winter holding cover.* Towards the end of the shooting season it will not be necessary to have so much cover, since the stock of birds will be very much lower than in the previous July. The expansion crop could be ploughed in during January, if necessary for farming operations, since the spinney will continue to provide good holding cover. Even if the crop is left, the birds will still prefer the warmth of the wood.

74 Game spinney view

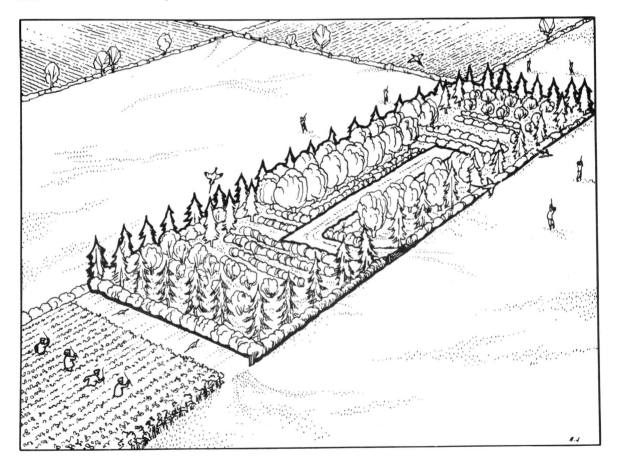

Planting

Suitable tree or shrub species should be chosen for the soil, always providing that another conifer is used as a substitute for the Lawson's cypress and a hardwood for the oak. If chestnut coppice cannot be grown, cotoneaster or laurel are suitable replacements.

Instead of being sown with the traditional grass, the central ride could be drilled with wheat or barley and left for the pheasants to harvest, occasionally giving it a 'rest' with kale or mustard.

The access ride can be anywhere on the perimeter but should meet the main ride at an angle to keep out the wind.

On a 500-acre (200 h.) arable farm where land cannot be spared for sizable coverts or shelter belts, half a dozen of these little game spinneys could greatly increase the ability to hold a really good stock of pheasants providing the adjoining strips of kale or mustard were put in as 'over-spill' areas during the peak stock periods between July and December.

The 'instant' spinney

The disadvantages of the game spinney as described on page 191 are that it takes quite a long time before it begins to hold an appreciable number of pheasants (anything from five to eight years) and fencing against rabbits can account for as much as 70 per cent of the total cost.

To eliminate these two disadvantages the instant spinney system can be used.

The rabbit netting (and all fencing where there is no farm stock) is eliminated by using half-standard hardwoods (4–5 ft. [1–1½ m.] high) protected by plastic sleeves, and hedges of *Lonicera nitida* which is rarely eaten by either rabbits or hares. Widely spaced trees (20 ft. × 20 ft. [6 m. × 6 m.]) are interplanted with triple rows of Jerusalem artichokes to provide suitable pheasant cover *in the first year of planting* and, incidentally, to suppress weed growth and shelter the growing trees.

A detailed cross-section is shown on page 196 (Figure 75b) and it is important to understand the principal features which go to make up the design.

The instant spinney is expected to produce a pheasant drive on its own and not in conjunction with an adjoining game crop. The size must therefore be greater than the ordinary game spinney.

200 yds. × 50 yds. (180 m × 45 m.) has been decided upon as basic dimensions because, apart from the fact that few people will wish to spare more land, there is the important question of beaters who get more expensive every year. This means that the width of the spinney (and, therefore, the number of beaters) must be kept to a minimum consistent with being able to produce sufficient sheltered cover to hold a good stock of birds. Naturally, it is not essential to adhere to these exact dimensions. The same principles of the spinney layout can be applied to an area of any shape or size. Then there is the

75a The 'instant spinney' one year after planting. The photograph shows one of the lines of half-standard trees protected from rabbits by spiral tree guards. The Jerusalem artichokes provide shelter for the growing trees as well as gamebirds

Key: Row A. *Lonicera nitida*. The plants in the outside row should be spaced 2 ft. (0·6 m.) apart and the inside row 4 ft. (1·20 m.) apart.

Row B. Trees 20 ft. (6·0 m.) apart. Recommended species: *Crataegus prunifolia, Crataegus carrierei, Malus floribunda, Sorbus aucuparia* (mountain ash), *Sorbus aria* (whitebeam).

Row C. Trees 20 ft. (6·0 m.) apart. Recommended species: *Alnus* (alder), *Betula* (birch), *Castanea sativa* (sweet chestnut), *Fagus* (beech), *Quercus* (oak).

Jerusalem Artichokes (*Helianthus tuberosus*): the three rows between the lines of trees should be spaced 5 ft. (1·50 m.) apart and the artichokes 20 in. (0·5 m) apart in the rows. The space between the hedges can be planted with two more rows of artichokes if desired but most people prefer to leave it to grass over or sow annual crops of barley or wheat.

Note: Rows A and B should be continued round the ends of the spinney. The recommended overall length is 200 yds. (183 m.)

b Cross-section of instant game spinney

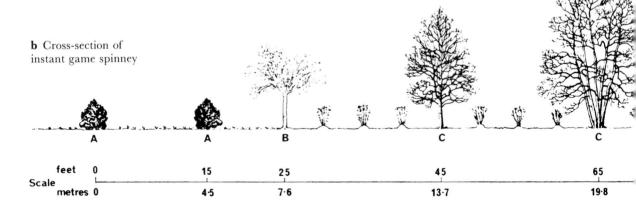

	A	A	B			C		C

	feet	0		15	25		45		65
Scale									
	metres	0		4·5	7·6		13·7		19·8

question of hedges. In small spinneys, often planted on exposed hilltop sites to show good birds, good shelter from wind at ground level is *absolutely essential*. Nothing provides this better than *Lonicera nitida* which is dense, evergreen, does not spread by suckers and requires virtually no management. Hedges of thorn (*Crataegus monogyna*) give comparatively poor shelter during the winter and even then require annual cutting for the best results. With the increased size one can afford to have a double hedge which will ensure that, whatever the wind direction, there is always a sheltered area. The outside row should be planted at 2-ft. (61 cm.) spacing to make quite sure that the wind is kept out and the inside row at 4-ft. (1 m.) spacing.

Tree species

Hardwoods must be used because it is impractical to transplant conifers of sufficient height to allow the fitting of protective sleeves. However, since small conifers are so cheap it would be worth planting two between each pair of hardwoods to increase the tree density and let them take their chance with the rabbits and hares. The outside row of trees should all be species of medium height and fairly slow growing. Our present choice is *Crataegus prunifolia*, *Crataegus carrierei*, *Sorbus aria* (whitebeam), *Sorbus aucuparia* (mountain ash) and *Malus floribunda*. The berries from all these trees are eaten by pheasants. The reason for restricting the outside tree to medium-height species is to reduce the shading and root competition on the farm headland to a minimum. The layout shows no tall forest tree less than 45 ft. ($13\frac{1}{2}$ m.) from the boundary of the spinney.

The hardwood species in the centre are chosen for their value as a source of food for game: oak (*Quercus*) and beech (*Fagus*) for long term; sweet chestnut (*Castanea sativa*), alder (*Alnus*) and birch (*Betula*) for more rapid growth.

Three rows of artichokes are planted between the tree lines with at least 5 ft. ($1\frac{1}{2}$ m.) between the rows. The best machine to use is a potato planter (such as a rotoplanter). If this is not available the lines should be made with a plough

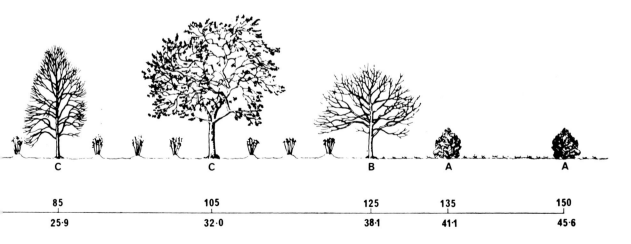

C		C		B	A		A
85		105		125	135		150
25·9		32·0		38·1	41·1		45·6

(preferable single furrow), the seed tubers put in at 20-in. (50 cm.) intervals and the furrow covered. Management of artichokes is important: if left untended the tubers eventually become too dense and the tops too low. Grass, weeds and thistles can also be a problem. Artichokes can normally be left for two or three seasons without attention after which they need to be cleaned. This is best done with a rotavator between the rows. After some years the artichokes may become too dense in the rows when it is best to spin them out and replant.

The spaces between the hedges are normally left to grass over as marginal nesting cover for both pheasants and partridges. It can be cut with a mower each year to keep the weeds down.

A great advantage of the instant spinney is that it is quite possible to create a whole new day's shooting on a large estate or to make shooting on a bare arable farm where none existed before. On a 500-acre (200 h.) farm, for instance, ten pheasant drives will require a maximum of 20 acres (8 h.) of land or 4 per cent of the total area.

Small areas for game

On many farms it may not be possible to spare the half acre needed for a straightforward game spinney layout. Even on the most efficient farm, however, there are a surprising number of odd corners beyond the reach of the plough. These areas have usually been dismissed as too small to bother about, but they must now be developed if game is to thrive in the modern agricultural 'desert'.

The principal reason why people are put off planting very small areas is the high cost of rabbit fencing, planting and maintenance, if standard forestry practices are used. The planting pattern described in this chapter should cut these costs by about 40 per cent.

As with the instant spinney the rabbit fencing is eliminated by using a combination of *Lonicera nitida*, and small half-standard trees protected by spiral plastic sleeves.

In recent years some criticism has arisen for recommending *Lonicera* in woodland plantings because it 'has no value for wildlife'. This is not so. While it rarely has berries and produces little insect life *Lonicera*, if intelligently used, does have a beneficial overall effect. It provides the best low wind-proof cover available; it is cheap to buy, easy to establish, and requires practically no management. It is also used by a number of songbird species for nesting.

No doubt quickthorn would be more valuable in itself as wildlife habitat but it provides poor shelter to a small wood in wintertime, even when trimmed hard and frequently like a garden hedge. The cost of this type of maintenance usually leads to neglect causing the hedge to grow out and become valueless as shelter. A *Lonicera* hedge, occupying an insignificant percentage of the total woodland

198

area can make the difference between a warm, sheltered wildlife sanctuary and a windswept area supporting little animal or plant life.

Lonicera nitida growing in groups inside the wood provides protective cover for game and gives valuable flushing points for shooting days. These groups are widely dispersed leaving plenty of room for eventual colonisation by natural shrub species.

In choosing trees suitable for this type of planting, mention has been made mainly of those which will provide some food for game and will only grow to medium height. In very small areas, shade on the farm headland can only be avoided by planting medium height species.

Our provisional list is *Crataegus prunifolia, Crataegus carrierei, Cotoneaster frigida, Malus floribunda, Sorbus aucuparia* (the rowan or mountain ash), *Sorbus aria* (the whitebeam) and *Castanea sativa* (sweet chestnut). None of these trees is likely to grow more than 20 or 30 ft. (6 or 9 m.) except sweet chestnut, which should be coppiced seven years after planting to control its height. Subsequent cutting would be every twelve to sixteen years, providing useful fencing stakes.

Oak is probably the most valuable wildlife tree species and it is

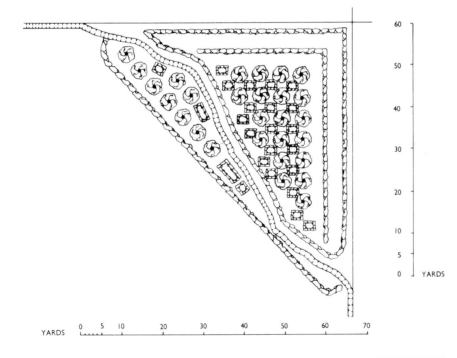

KEY

—————— DITCH

—————— LONICERA NITIDA HEDGE

LONICERA NITIDA CLUMP

————— FIELD BOUNDARY

SMALL STANDARD TREE

76 The planning pattern can be varied according to the site

199

recommended that a few are included in larger areas where there is sufficient room to plant them 40 ft. (12 m.) or more from the farm headland.

The diagram above shows how the planting pattern can be varied according to the site. The hypothetical case has been taken of a ditch cutting across the corner of a field, leaving an awkward piece of ground to cultivate. As in the instant spinney the plants in the perimeter hedge of *Lonicera* should be spaced 2 ft. (61 cm.) apart to ensure a really wind-proof barrier. The inside hedge can be planted at 4-ft. (1 m.) spacing. Most of the groups are square, with 4 plants at 6-ft. (2 m.) spacing, and where there is room for bigger groups the 6-ft. (2 m.) spacing should remain. The trees are 15 ft. ($4\frac{1}{2}$ m.) apart. The ditch sides are left clear to avoid root damage and leaf fall. If a machine runs over the *Lonicera*, when cleaning the ditch, most of the plants will recover, and if a few gaps occur, this is of no importance.

Small spaces, planted in this fashion, could be invaluable as breeding areas on farms where most, if not all, of the hedges have been removed. They can also be 'expanded' for the shooting season with an adjacent game cover crop, as described in the previous section on game spinneys.

The system can be used on areas as little as 5 yds. ($4\frac{1}{2}$ m.) square, planting a *Lonicera* hedge around the outside and one tree in the middle! This would be sufficient for one or two nesting pheasants or perhaps a partridge, in the summer, and a feeding point in the winter.

Although this type of planting will be cheapest on arable land, it will also be valuable on a stock farm. In this case fencing will be necessary, but rabbit netting will not be required.

200

Chapter 15

Forestry and Pheasants: Part 2

Large woodlands

It is not very difficult to incorporate the necessary features into a big area of woodland to provide good breeding and holding conditions for game. It is quite a challenging task, however, to plan the shooting in order to show tall birds. There are three problems:

(a) If the area is flat, the birds may fly at tree-top height, making indifferent shooting.
(b) It can be difficult to get pheasants to fly out of a big wood and over Guns standing in the open.
(c) Unless the rides and flushing points are carefully sited, all day can be spent in moving the birds without getting them over the Guns.

Solving the problem of showing high, fast birds is, to some extent, a matter of luck and depends on the lie of the land. The height at which the birds fly is largely governed by the height of the trees. To give better shooting in a large wood it is easier to put the Guns *down*, rather than try to make the birds fly higher. When planning flushing points therefore, advantage should be taken of every hill or valley to increase the distance between the birds and the Guns. For instance, where there is a small valley within the wood at one end, it is often possible to blank the whole wood up into an area beyond the valley and then bring the birds back over it.

A nearby covert or crop may make it possible to drive out of a big wood. Any projections (such as drive No. 5a in Figure 78 on page 205) should be planned to take advantage of this. If a cover crop, such as sugarbeet, runs right up to a wood, a successful drive can sometimes be made by lining the Guns along the edge and *beating away* from it so that the birds curl back over the beaters to the Guns. When doing this, it is best for the Guns to follow the beaters out until they are about 30 yds. (27 m.) from the wood and then stand in full view of the birds as they fly back.

The beating of large compartments divided by narrow winding rides frequently allows pheasants to 'leak out' at the sides during the drive. Dividing rides should, therefore, be as straight as possible to enable beaters and Guns to contain the birds within the drive more easily. These rides should, if possible, also converge so that the birds are concentrated into a good flushing point where the beaters are much closer together.

New rides can be created in two ways:

(a) If the trees are young, they can be felled to provide the space required as soon as they are marketable.

(b) With mature or semi-mature trees it is necessary only to clean up the side branches to a reasonable height and then *keep the ground clean* underneath. This can be done by cutting all undergrowth and coppice to ground level and trimming annually with an implement such as a tractor-mounted scrub cutter. Where practicable, spraying with a brushwood killer to eradicate coppice and brambles will make the job much more effective.

When planning the replanting of a large woodland area, the siting of the compartments and the choice of species can have a critical effect on the shooting. Small manageable compartments for shooting can be planted with a good mixture of hard and softwood species and bounded by large compartments of pure softwood. In this way a 50-acre (20 h.) wood could be split into five 5-acre (2 h.) pheasant drives separated by three softwood blocks of approximately 8 acres (3 h.), from which any birds could easily be blanked before a drive.

77 Laurel gives excellent pheasant cover, as in this wood in Moray, where it is growing under 60-year-old Scots pine

There is no doubt that the big woodland provides the most difficult problems when considered from the game management angle. We often wish there was a law against planting any wood of more than 15 acres (6 h.) and less than 200 yds. (180 m.) from its neighbour! Nevertheless many of the difficulties can be overcome after careful study and by co-operation between the game and forestry departments.

Woodland rehabilitation

As an example of how the problem of woodland rehabilitation may be planned, the map on page 205 shows the game and forestry plan for a woodland area on an estate in Surrey. The practice of game management in forestry areas always requires slight amendments on the basic theory and the map shows the alterations to our layouts which have been made to suit conditions on this estate.

The game aspects of the forestry plan were studied when the owner took over the 1,200-acre (485 h.) property, which included 400 acres (160 h.) of derelict woods. Nearly all the woodland was in three large blocks. In conjunction with the forestry contractors, the Game Conservancy was able to prepare a comprehensive plan of rides and flushing points before any re-afforestation was started.

The 110-acre (45 h.) wood shown on the map is typical of the large blocks, which are awkwardly shaped and were completely neglected. The boundary of the estate runs along the northern edge of the wood shown and there are no neighbouring woods to which the birds can be driven. The working plan is based on creating a series of coverts within the area. Only two outward drives will take occasional advantage of nearby cover crops such as kale, mustard or fodder radish.

The area is fairly flat except for two high spots at A and B. The adjoining land falls away fairly sharply beyond the southern tip. Apart from a clearing for a gun stand at point C, there were no open spaces in the wood. All the 'rides' were narrow tracks – just passable for a tractor – rutted, wet and enclosed by a canopy of overgrown hazel.

The first problem was to decide how many drives should be made and how to divide these up into separate coverts within the framework of the wood without using too much ground for rides. The working plan shows a pattern of new rides, 1,070 yds. (980 m.) in length and 22 yds. (20 m.) wide. The southernmost of these rides running across the wood was in any case necessary as a new farm access road. After deducting this ride (170 yds. [155 m.]), 970 yds. (885 m.) or 4·4 acres (1·8 h.) were left. If commercial forestry insisted that 11 yds. (10 m.) was sufficient width for rides, the contribution to shooting amounted to only 2·2 acres (0·9 h.).

A further area (D on the plan) is to be reclaimed for the farm, having the effect of converting the small area on the northern boundary into a completely separate wood and taking advantage of the high ground at B as a good flushing point. This reclamation, of course, entails no loss of production from the land. The new rides divide the wood into six separate coverts giving a similar number of main drives with four alternative drives in case of adverse winds or the availability of nearby cover crops. The main drives are shown as 1, 2, 3, etc., and the alternatives as 2a, 4a, 5a and 6a.

There are 17 triangular flushing points planted with *Lonicera nitida*. These are the same size as in the standard layout – covering an area of approximately 0·27 of an acre (0·1 h.) each, including their surrounding rides. The total area of the 17 triangles is thus 4·59 acres (1·85 h.). Sweet chestnut, which grows well in the district, has been planted in the rising areas to be coppiced and provide a useful pole crop for the farm.

The total area of unproductive ground in the 110-acre (45 h.) wood is 6·79 acres (3 h.). This is offset by planting up all the new rides with 20,000 Christmas trees, leaving access tracks down the centre. However, if the soil had been unsuitable for sweet chestnut in the rising areas and no other useful substitute could have been found, a further 6·63 acres (3 h.) would have been unproductive, making a total of 13·42 acres (5 h.). The best solution in that case would have been to grow a 'half crop' of larch as described on page 182, thus making the area reasonably productive.

Flushing points and rising areas can be altered in shape and size to suit the site. In drives 3 and 4, for instance, the flushing points have been set at an angle to suit the direction of the drive. In No. 1 drive there was no room for a large rising area and the flushing point had to be made to fit the pointed shape of the wood.

The work of cutting out the new rides and planting Christmas trees, flushing points and rising areas has been completed. The gradual process of rehabilitating the forestry is now being undertaken.

The first compartment to be planted will be drive No. 4 and 4a. The reason for this is that the area was burnt out by a fire some years ago and is only thinly stocked with scrub. It is important to plant before it is re-colonised with scrub and coppice. The next compartment will be the area marked E. At first sight it might appear that the flushing points for drive 2a ought to have been sited in compartment E but this would have made the drive rather too long and the birds on flushing would have faced the fairly steep rise at point A. In all probability many would have broken back. E will, therefore, be planted with pure conifer so that when the trees are brashed it will be a simple matter to blank the area into drive No. 5 or 2a.

The subsequent order of planting will be drives 1, 6, 3, 5 and 2. This will involve seven compartments in all (including E), with at least a three-year interval between each operation. All planting will start with a chain-wide

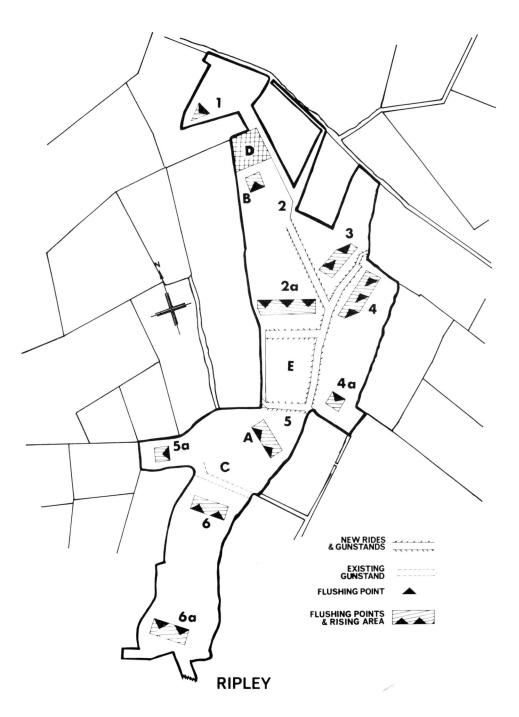

Legend:

NEW RIDES & GUNSTANDS

EXISTING GUNSTAND

FLUSHING POINT

FLUSHING POINTS & RISING AREA

RIPLEY

78 Ripley (see text)

softwood belt around each compartment and a mixture of hard and softwood in the centre. *The object of spreading the planting rather than working through in consecutive compartments is to break up the age structure. It is important to avoid large areas reaching the thicket stage at the same time and becoming virtually unshootable.* If the planting plan is studied it can be seen, for instance, that by the time drive No. 3 is replanted, No. 4 is already 9 years old and getting over the worst stage. Similarly, when No. 5 is replanted, No. 6 will be six years old. It would be better to have four-year intervals between plantings, but this would probably be unacceptable to the forestry plan.

Other woods on the estate will be treated in the same way. Planting will take place on one or other every year to ensure continuity of rehabilitation. The operation will be complete in 18 years. This would be an absolute minimum for the game requirements and it would have been better spread over 24 years. If the estate employed its own forestry staff it would probably *need* 24 years, but all the work is being done by outside contractors.

The temptation is to rush things and reduce the timetable to four or five years. This would cause chaos to the shooting by a constant succession of large-scale operations of weeding, brashing, thinning, felling and replanting. The result would be a series of ups and downs in the game crop. A gradual rehabilitation, on the other hand, ensures that most of the woodland is shootable *at all times*.

In considering this plan, a professional forester would no doubt seize on two points: the loss of productive acreage and the additional cost of fencing involved in the spread-out system of planting, but seen in relation to the costs and production of the *whole woodland operation*, these are not significant. On the other hand, these points are of vital importance to the game.

This shoot is only 25 miles (40 km.) from the centre of London and the value of the sporting rights is very important to the estate economy as a whole. When the present owner took over, the woods were very nearly unshootable. The improvements being carried out should double the rentable value at least.

Sloping and exposed sites

Over much of Scotland, Wales and the North of England, woodlands are frequently located on exposed hillsides. These steep woods pose different game management problems from those encountered on relatively level sites.

The aerodynamics of sloping sites will vary enormously according to the direction of the wind and the contours of the land but the shelter value of perimeter hedges and belts is often nullified.

In a perfectly straightforward example of a sloping wood facing south, the perimeter hedge and shelter belt will vary in effectiveness as the direction of the wind alters from due east to due west. South of this line the shelter effect will decrease to a minimum at due south, and north of the line it will increase to a maximum at due north. The solution would be to plant the perimeter shelter in the normal way but *in addition* plant a series of shelter belts across the wood parallel to the contours. These belts should be Lawson's cypress or spruce and the intervening species hardwoods or (if essential) pines or larches.

Hedges and rides

Another difficulty on steeply sloping sites can be the maintenance of hedges and rides. Frequently, this will be impossible to mechanise since, even if the slope is not too great for a tractor to work, this type of site is usually broken by cliffs, gullies and boulders.

The 'formal' hedge must be abandoned in favour of a sheltering strip of *Lonicera nitida* or some similar shrub in two rows 10 ft. (3 m.) apart to facilitate rabbit control. These can be interspersed with fruit-bearing species, such as *Cotoneaster frigida*, *Cotoneaster Simonsii*, gean or rowan.

Ride maintenance is a difficult problem except on poor soil where the growth of coarse grasses and heather is unlikely to be excessive. Wide firebreaks, on the other hand, are often of sufficient area to warrant fencing and grazing but the fence should be well away from the trees to allow a good growth of marginal nesting cover.

79 Big woods pose their own problems, but wide firebreaks may help to make the gamekeeper's task easier

207

The rides should run as near north/south as possible to admit the maximum sunshine, but firebreaks, being much wider, can sometimes be set at an angle to facilitate shooting while still admitting plenty of sunshine. There are many instances of large isolated blocks of woodlands from which birds are reluctant to fly since there is no cover for them to make for. Diagonal firebreaks make it possible to drive the birds up to a narrow point where they can rise from a proper flushing point. The Guns are lined down the firebreaks and magnificent birds can be shown.

Flushing points

The siting of flushing points on sloping sites needs careful thought. Where the wood is fairly small magnificent birds can be shown by driving them *uphill* and out of the top, to break back over Guns along the floor of the valley. This works particularly well if the birds can fly across to another wood. In large blocks this is usually not practical and, if the diagonal firebreak layout cannot be applied, then the birds must be driven along or downhill to a conventional flushing point. The slope, if over 20°, eliminates the necessity for a rising area. If the wood does not run to the bottom of the slope, leaving plenty of room to place a line of Guns well below it, then there is no need to have the flushing point inside. In this instance, a strip 10 yds. (9 m.) wide should be planted up with flushing shrubs *outside* the bottom row of trees. If the shrubs are set out in small V's this will facilitate beating. The disadvantage of this system is that if the birds run to the edge and see the Guns *before* they flush, then a number may break back. To discourage this, a hedge of *Lonicera nitida* can be planted all along the edge at very close spacing (18 in. [46 cm.]) to prevent the birds from pushing through it.

Tree species

Since most steep sites tend to be exposed the choice of species is likely to be limited. It is very important, therefore, to decide on the amount of emphasis to be placed on the game content at the earliest stage of planning. The wish to avoid uneconomic early thinnings, particularly on sites which may be remote and expensive for extraction, makes wide plant spacing an attractive proposition. This will certainly help to admit more sunlight in the early life of the wood, but as the main canopy grows this advantage will eventually be lost. Using the system of contour shelter belts it would be advisable to plant some of the intervening spaces as 'game strips'. These need not be entirely uneconomic. Groups of pine and larch, for instance, could alternate with similar groups of hardwoods, such as sycamore, oak and ash, so that half the area of each strip could at least provide a pulp crop and each hardwood group would be sealed off from the wind. The number of 'game strips' included would have to depend on the economic balance between sport and forestry in each case. Even so, the tree growth on a north-facing wood, which can stand less evergreen content, would surely benefit from a general distribution of warmth in this way.

General

There is often a rather defeatist attitude towards exposed sites as far as game is concerned. This is largely due to familiarity with such areas growing mature or semi-mature timber where the game was never considered when planting. Co-operative thought and planning between owner, forester and keeper *before* planting can create good game coverts on sites which are sometimes dismissed as not worth bothering about.

Aesthetic considerations can also help the game. Some magnificent Scottish views, for instance, are fast disappearing as the roads become enclosed in gloomy evergreen tunnels. The loss of a few rows of trees would preserve the view and provide warm cover for game. Burn and loch sides could also be left more open with similar effect.

Even the most dedicated forester must feel slightly frustrated when driving along the south-west shore of Loch Maree, for example, where most of the view is blocked by trees – and there is nowhere to park where it isn't!

Forestry operations

All forestry operations, such as planting, weeding, thinning and felling can be a source of friction between forester and gamekeeper. This is quite unnecessary if the two departments understand each other's problems and work together. Keeper and forester should meet regularly to discuss and co-ordinate their respective plans – with the landowner or agent 'in the chair' whenever possible. If the two departments never meet except in head-on collision, neither will prosper and their employer is badly served.

Where an outside contractor is employed, the situation is likely to be aggravated by the fact that the two departments have different employers and loyalties. But it is the estate owner who pays the bills for both – and the man who pays the piper ought to call the tune!

The chief source of irritation seems to be based, not on lack of sympathy, but on lack of understanding. It is vital, therefore, that a gamekeeper should have some knowledge of forestry and the forester should know a little about game management. If the estate departments (including farming) remain in watertight compartments, there is always trouble.

In the following pages are discussed the relevant forestry operations together with ways in which the two departments can co-operate.

Planting

Planting distance varies greatly with the species, from 3 ft. × 3 ft. (0·9 m. × 0·9 m.) for some hardwoods to 40 ft. × 40 ft. (12 m. × 12 m.) for cricket bat willow. As a rule, however, most planting is done at around the 5 ft. × 5 ft. (1½ m. × 1½ m.) mark. These distances appear to have been established by tradition, but today's foresters are beginning to think in terms of wider spaces.

Some advantages of the wider spacing are the saving in the number of plants required, ease of mechanical weeding, less early and uneconomic thinning and less density at the thicket stage.

Certainly on good ground where a large percentage of the planting could be expected to be successful, the wider spacing has much to recommend it. Not all species can be treated in this way – Scots pine, for instance, grows very poorly when widely spaced. High pruning would be necessary after 10 years and larch will stand this better than spruce. However, there is room for experiment and wide spacing would certainly make it easier to control predators in the young plantation, make it more accessible to beaters and give plenty of room for pheasants to get on the wing.

Where possible, the rows of trees should run in the direction in which the birds are to be driven.

On an estate in Herefordshire, several sites for coverts were tried out by planting kale the previous season to see how the birds flew, as already recommended, and when the best places had been selected, the young trees were simply planted in standing crop. This had a similar effect to planting under dapple shade. The kale gives good protection from wind, suppresses a certain amount of weed growth and does not rob the trees of too much moisture. It makes good game cover for the first season and some will persist for the second. If the kale is seen to be giving too much shade, it is simple to cut rows for the trees with a small scythe before planting.

Weeding

This can cause considerable friction between keeper and forester, particularly when the operation is carried out at great speed by young men on piecework – each armed with a transistor radio and not knowing the difference between a pheasant's and a robin's egg!

The chief source of conflict, however, is the timing of the operation, because the weeding and nesting seasons coincide. The peak date for pheasants to start laying is about 16th April and for the start of incubation about 6th May. The main hatching period is usually 20th May to 20th June.

Hens disturbed during the laying period usually re-nest quite happily shortly afterwards. If the nest is destroyed during the incubation period, there is a reasonable chance of the hen nesting again, if she had been down for only a few days.

210

The most dangerous period for weeding is between 12th May and 20th June – just when the operation tends to be in full swing! This is where consultation between forester and keeper is so important. Where several plantations are concerned it is obviously best to weed those on the boundary, or with a lower density of hens, during the danger period. Areas where it is known that there will be a large number of nests could be left until later in the season.

This may not be possible, particularly where there are only one or two plantations on the whole shoot, but even here the losses can be limited by careful management. A system of rewards for nests found *and left to hatch undisturbed* can be very effective in opening the eyes of the weeders. Dummy eggs should always be available for placing in 'hot' nests found in the wood. The keeper should also try to make time for a visit once or twice a day for a friendly chat. A show of gratitude at the right time can be worth its weight in gold – or pheasant chicks!

Mechanical weeding is now more generally used, although it is mostly confined to plantations on new ground because old stumps and coppice stools can damage the machine and cause delays. This method can destroy a large number of nests, particularly with the type of machine that uses rotary blades or chain flails.

Whatever method is used, some damage is almost inevitable. But careful management and good labour relations can reduce it to reasonable proportions and a keeper must accept this.

Some of these problems can be solved or mitigated by using chemicals for forestry weed control. On arable or grassland sites, 'Gramoxone' (one of the Paraquat group of chemicals) is often used for spot weeding. This leaves 3-ft. (0·9 m.) circles of bare ground around each young tree – ideal places for a hen to brood her chicks in showery weather. The remaining growth between the circles provides good nesting cover. The first application of 'Gramoxone' would normally be made soon after planting time and subsequent treatment in July or August when the grasses are still green but approaching dormancy – the most effective time for control. The disturbance to nesting birds is, therefore, very slight.

Treating clear-felled woodland sites with selective chemical brushwood sprays is also becoming more general. This eliminates most of the brambles and coppice regrowth. Some spot weeding will still have to be done, but when this ceases the plantations are usually much more manageable than in the past when trees at the thicket stage were virtually impenetrable if liberally mixed with bramble and coppice.

Thinning and felling

These operations can have disastrous results for the keeper unless he is given plenty of warning beforehand – preferably 12 months. We recall one occasion when the forestry department arrived to thin a plantation 2 weeks after the keeper had turned 1,000 pheasant poults into it! Timber had been left after felling and then drawn through the neighbouring wood in the middle of the nesting season. This occurred because the rides were so narrow that all the vehicles quickly became bogged down and the contractor was forced to wait for dry weather. Such difficulties would never have occurred if keeper and forester had planned together, or rides were properly planned.

Many instances exist where no proper agreement has been reached with the purchaser of the timber to remove or burn the lop and top. If it is left lying as it falls, the area quickly becomes a jungle of old branches entwined with brambles from which it is impossible to flush pheasants or control predators. If a wood is left like this for a year, the cost of clearing for replanting can double or treble. Owners should make certain that the contractor is bound by his contract to burn all lop and top as he goes.

Brashing

The keeper can be helped considerably by brashing, because it opens up a young plantation and gives room for beaters and pheasants to get through. It also allows him to exercise proper control over the vermin.

If it involves letting in the wind because of the lack of a surrounding hedge, the forester can help by leaving the two outside rows unbrashed. This is not entirely effective but a great deal better than nothing. The brashings themselves can be a nuisance if left where they fall, hindering beaters and harbouring vermin. On the other hand, if drawn into neat rows running in the direction of a drive they can provide some cover for the birds and are easier for the beater to tap out. Another use for brashings is described later on.

Coppicing and brambles

It is unfortunate that there is so little demand for hazel these days because many areas of coppice are neglected. Such an area is a depressing sight for the shoot-owners, with nothing on the bare ground except a sprinkling of rotting branches fallen from the dying stools. Coppicing a few stools in places where there is a gap in the tree canopy will admit some light and encourage growth of ground cover. To avoid future work, the stools can be killed out with a chemical brushwood killer.

Where the coppice is still regularly worked, the forestry department can help the keeper by planning the cutting well ahead or perhaps arranging for a compartment to be cut a year or two early or late, to alter the pattern or size. Basically, the keeper wants many small areas cut each year whereas the hurdlemaker prefers the biggest area possible to avoid small dumps of hurdles, beansticks and thatching spars dotted about all over the estate. Some compromise can nearly always be worked out. As a rule, one can say that the

212

larger the wood, the bigger the area that can be cut at one time without opening up too much for the game. If too much is cut, the cleared wood will be very draughty for a year or two and this will be followed by a jungle of brambles if the tree canopy is thin.

Bramble control can be either by mechanical cutting or chemical spraying. Cutting is best done with a tractor-mounted implement because the type of small, hand-operated machine that cuts under the brambles is not always practicable. However, if the growth is not excessive, the hand-operated *rotary* mower may be very useful in small areas, although it can be a slow process. Where possible the cutting should be repeated annually, since a one-year growth can be speedily dealt with, but old bushes are hard, slow work.

Spraying with a brushwood killer is sometimes the answer. Care must be taken to avoid damaging young trees, particularly natural regeneration.

Where roe deer are to be considered as a crop, some brambles will be most useful as a buffer food – the roe will prefer them to other, more valuable trees and plants.

Rabbit fencing

Where the rabbit population is heavy, wire netting of $1\frac{1}{4}$-in. (3 cm.) mesh is essential all round a new plantation. The bottom 6 in. (15 cm.) of the 3 ft. 6in. (1 m.) roll should be turned *outwards* and held down on the ground by a heavy turf every 3–4 ft. (0·9 m.–1 m.). A single strand of barbed wire 6 in. (15 cm.) above the netting will provide an extra precaution against hares and stock.

If netting can be avoided with safety it certainly should not be used – apart from the heavy cost, it is most undesirable where game is concerned. Dogs and foxes can trap birds against the wire – especially reared poults – and kill them easily.

Pheasants will sometimes get half their broods through the wire and wander off, leaving the rest to their fate. The fault here is not in the netting itself but in the growth of vegetation which becomes interlaced with the wire mesh and forms a solid barrier. Experiments have shown that pheasant chicks can pass through $1\frac{1}{4}$-in. (3 cm.) mesh netting up to 10 days. Since these were hand-reared chicks fed on crumbs, they were likely to be heavier than less well-fed wild birds which might be able to pass through at a later age.

If possible, some of the grassy growth at the bottom of the netting should be prevented. It is not practical to eliminate it all because it is this growth which eventually holds the turned out portion of the netting firmly on the ground and in any case it would be a major operation on a long fence line. A better method would be to kill off the growth for short lengths of, say, 2 yds. (2 m.) at 15–20-yd. (14–18 m.) intervals and particularly at the corners of the enclosure. It is essential that this *should be done immediately the wire netting is in place*. It would be no use waiting until the growth has occurred since, alive or dead, it would effectively block the mesh.

213

Trials using chlorea, a persistent total weedkiller in granular form, have proved very satisfactory since it normally remains effective for 12 months. Application should be in the spring at the rate of 1 oz. per sq. yd. (33 g. per sq. m.). Chlorea is expensive but the cost of treating areas 2 yds. × 18 in. (2 m. × 46 cm.) along a fence line is only 1p. No detrimental effects have been noticed when chlorea granules were fed to pheasants.

Use of brashings to create nesting cover

Fir boughs have been successfully used to make nesting and holding cover under bare beech woods. If they are laid down in March it has been found that both pheasants and partridges will nest under them quite readily. Pine branches are the best, since they stand well up from the ground – Corsican pine is particularly good. Groups of three or four branches are better than single boughs. The groups should be spaced about 15 or 20 yds. (14 or 81 m.) apart. The heaps of branches usually last about three years and accumulate useful leafy nesting material which is still attractive to gamebirds long after the boughs themselves have become bare. Using this system, a few loads of brashings from a fir plantation and a couple of days' work can transform a bare wood or belt into an area which is at least of some value to game. This system will work well as holding cover under bare, semi-mature softwoods.

Shrubs

No technical literature contains more contradictions than the publications on shrubs for pheasant coverts. The writers, it seemed, often took the best nursery catalogues they could find and then proceeded to list *any* plants that produced berries – without discovering whether they were palatable to pheasants, fruited at the right time, were eaten by other birds and so on. The catalogues themselves were (and in many cases still are) in complete disagreement. One firm recommended a shrub for pheasants because it cropped heavily, while another nurseryman advocated planting it because birds never ate the berries and their beauty lasted a long time. Yet another recently recommended a shrub which carried poisonous berries.

The plain truth is that – apart from the Fordingbridge trials – very little research has been done on the suitability of various shrubs. Recommendations are often made as a result of hearsay or guesswork. Before discussing the Game Conservancy tests, it would be as well to summarise the principal advantages and disadvantages of shrubs as a whole.

Advantages

(*a*) Shrubs can give good warm ground cover and at the same time suppress less desirable plants.

(*b*) Some species produce fruits which are eaten by pheasants.

214

(*c*) Many varieties do not sucker and so remain open underneath, allowing pheasants to move about freely without becoming trapped.

(*d*) Thornless shrubs are available which are much easier than a jungle of brambles for keepers, foresters and beaters.

(*e*) Certain decorative foliage can sometimes produce a small but useful income for the estate.

Disadvantages

(*a*) Some species can get out of control and cause great trouble and expense to both forester and gamekeeper (i.e. broom on light sandy soil).

(*b*) Many produce berries which are *not* eaten by pheasants or which, if they grow too tall, are stripped by other birds first.

(*c*) Some are expensive to buy in the quantities needed on a forest scale.

For convenience, the shrubs have been divided into two groups which provide principally *cover* and *berries*, although a few provide both.

In existing woodlands, shrubs such as sloes, hawthorns or elder can be left to provide wild food, subject to forestry requirements. The same applies to brambles and wild raspberries in moderation. Naturally, we wish to avoid the mistake of recommending shrubs by guesswork and those listed in the following pages are the ones we know well – whether as friends or enemies.

Cover shrubs

Lonicera nitida (shrub honeysuckle). A rapid-growing, low (4–8 ft. [1 m.–2½ m.]), thornless evergreen shrub. It is extremely easy to propagate by cuttings put straight into open ground without heat or rooting substances. March is the best time to do this and the rooted cuttings can be planted out the following October. It does not sucker and, if planted about 6 ft. (2 m.) apart, produces cover in which birds can move about freely. It is remarkably tough and can be slashed with a hook or mechanical cutter and relied upon to shoot again. It is said that *Lonicera* is sometimes affected by frost in exposed positions, but appeared to be untouched by the very severe winter of 1963. It dislikes too much shade, but grows reasonably well under the broken canopy of mature hardwoods. It is rarely damaged by rabbits, hares or deer.

Symphoricarpus rivularis (snowberry). A rapid-growing (4–6 ft. [1–2 m.]) thornless, deciduous shrub producing variable crops of berries of doubtful value. Snowberry has probably been planted for game more than any other shrub, but on some soils it does tend to sucker badly and becomes impenetrable to pheasants and a harbour for rabbits. If cut over regularly, however, it is a useful flushing shrub and its deciduous habit partly offsets its tendency to thick growth since pheasants can rise fairly easily through the bare winter branches. It crackles well when beaters walk through. It is fairly tolerant of shade.

Ligustrum ovalifolium (Japanese hedging privet). Like *Lonicera nitida*, this is a rapid-growing thornless evergreen shrub, but it can get 'leggy' and grow up to

12–15 ft. ($3\frac{1}{2}$–$4\frac{1}{2}$ m.) high if not trimmed. It is reasonably easy to propagate from cuttings.

Buxus sempervirens (box). Very similar to privet but much slower growing and very tolerant of shade. Very old plants can frequently be seen in game coverts, proving the durability of box. Fairly easily propagated from cuttings and good on calcareous soils. In many areas the foliage finds a ready market among florists.

Prunus lusitanica (Portugal laurel). A tall (20 ft. [6 m.]) evergreen shrub useful for warming up a covert and as roosting for young pheasants. Excellent for calcareous soils.

Prunus laurocerasus (common laurel). This is also a good warming shrub but has a more spreading habit similar to *Rhododendron ponticum*, although not becoming such a problem to the forester. Old shrubs can be difficult to penetrate where they are planted close together, but if cut to the ground they will grow again. Both laurels are slow-growing and will prosper on almost every site which can grow commercial trees. It is an excellent shade bearer.

Cotoneaster horizontalis. An expensive shrub by forestry standards, but well known in gardens. It is used with great success on the Continent as a 'fringe' shrub to provide nesting cover. The berries are produced in fair quantity but they do not seem to be eaten as readily as those of other cotoneaster species.

Species to be avoided

Rhododendron ponticum. The tendency of this species to spread into an impenetrable jungle on acid soils in a mild climate has made it a pest to both gamekeeper and forester – and yet it is recommended in the catalogue of a famous garden nursery as 'invaluable for game coverts'! On less acid soils, or at high altitudes, it can be controlled, but it is better to be sure and plant laurel instead.

Ligustrum vulgare (common privet). This species can be a great nuisance on calcareous soils. It was almost certainly planted in bygone days because of its black berries. Pheasants eat them occasionally but this doubtful value is considered to be far outweighed by the plant's habit of spreading into a dense thicket. Under shade, it is tolerable, but when trees are felled it can become a serious nuisance.

Berried shrubs

Although trials with penned birds can make it possible to assess the *palatability* of berries, no such trials can determine the *availability*. Many berries occur on species that grow into quite tall trees – *Cotoneaster frigida* and *Crataegus prunifolia*, for instance – and are available to pheasants only on the lower branches or when they have dropped to the ground. To avoid this it is important to order *bushes* from the nurseryman and not standards. They must be cut over occasionally to ensure that they remain in bush form and do not grow out of

216

reach of the pheasants. With some species it is necessary only to cut the leading shoot to form a bush.

Pheasants will *sometimes* reach berries high up on hedges or bushes. For example, 30 pheasants have been observed in Ayrshire feeding in the branches of one large hawthorn early in October.

Some berries stay on the branch longer than others and it is probably the degree of ripeness which encourages birds to start eating them. Shrubs which regularly hold their fruit until late in the season are obviously the most valuable. It is pointless to produce berries at a time when there is an abundance of alternative wild food available. It is probable, too, that the less palatable varieties would be more readily taken if they were still on the bush in January when natural food becomes very scarce.

The following is a summary of the trials carried out at Fordingbridge during recent years.

80 Trials of berried shrubs for pheasants

Shrub		**Berry**
ALWAYS EATEN:		
Cotoneaster distichus	Cotoneaster sp.	Medium, red
Cotoneaster frigida	Cotoneaster sp.	Medium, red
Crataegus prunifolia	Hawthorn sp.	Large, red
Hippophae rhamnoides	Sea buckthorn	Medium, orange
Sorbus aucuparia	Mountain ash, rowan	Small, orange
Viburnum opulus	Guelder rose	Medium, red

217

Shrub		Berry
SOME EATEN:		
Cotoneaster conspicua	Cotoneaster sp.	Medium, red
Cotoneaster cornubia	Cotoneaster sp.	Medium, red
Cotoneaster pannosa	Cotoneaster sp.	Medium, red
Cotoneaster pendula	Cotoneaster sp.	Medium, red
Cotoneaster Rothschildiana	Cotoneaster sp.	Medium, yellow
Cotoneaster salicifolium	Cotoneaster sp.	Medium, red
Cotoneaster Simonsii	Cotoneaster sp.	Medium, orange
Cotoneaster Wardii	Cotoneaster sp.	Medium, orange
Crataegus Carrierei	Hawthorn sp.	Large, yellow
Crataegus monogyna	Common hawthorn	Medium, red
Malus floribunda	Flowering crab	Large, red
Pyracantha Rogersiana	Firethorn	Small, red
Pyracantha Rogersiana flavae	Firethorn	Small, yellow
Sorbus aria majestica	Whitebeam sp.	Large, yellow
Sorbus aria	Whitebeam sp.	Large, orange
Symphoricarpus rivularis	Snowberry	Large, white
FEW, IF ANY, EATEN:		
Cotoneaster horizontalis	Cotoneaster sp.	Small, red
Cotoneaster microphylla	Cotoneaster sp.	Medium, red
Cotoneaster moupinensis	Cotoneaster sp.	Medium, purple
Euonymus europaeus	Spindle tree	Small, orange
Ligustrum vulgare	Common privet	Medium, black
Malus Golden Hornet	Flowering crab	Large, yellow
Rhamnus catharticus	Purging buckthorn	Medium, black

Only the berries of the sea buckthorn were taken when alternative food was available. This shrub is grown extensively in Holland and Denmark. It grows mainly on sandy dune-land in the coastal areas where it is useful as a means of fixing the soil. Since it is often the only species growing on quite large tracts of land, pheasants eat so many of the berries that their flesh becomes tainted. It seems likely that this species may not be very tolerant of other soil and site conditions.

The cotoneasters can be particularly valuable since they tolerate considerable shade and drip from overhanging trees and are very hardy.

Shrubs have a very important role to play in establishing good pheasant habitat, but the correct *blend* of cover and fruiting species has not yet been established. For instance, most berry-bearing shrubs are deciduous and are therefore draughty. Conversely, most of the good evergreen species available produce little or no fruit. Careful planning and intelligent planting could probably combine the advantages of both, e.g. *Cotoneaster frigida* spaced 20 ft. (6 m.) apart in a flushing point of *Lonicera nitida*.

For *cover shrubs*, landowners are advised to plant only those listed as trouble-free and *known* to be beneficial.

With *berried shrubs* it is advisable to proceed carefully and plant a good sprinkling of those which are palatable.

Large-scale plantings of one species on the evidence of a few crop contents should be avoided. Otherwise an unlucky gardener might easily persuade you to fill your coverts with tulips!

Chapter 16
Rearing Partridges

For anyone interested in breeding birds, the grey partridge offers something of a challenge. *Perdix perdix* is strictly monogamous, quarrelsome in company, prone to disease, erratic in egg production, nervous, difficult to handle and was, until recent years, not very easy to rear! On the credit side, the species is readily sexed, easy to hatch and fairly accommodating about diet. The red-legged partridge (*Alectoris rufa*) adds the problem of being difficult to sex until fully mature, although it is easier to rear.

In an attempt to produce a simple, reliable method of rearing, many trials have been carried out at Fordingbridge, including intensive rearing with electric brooders, bantams and movable pens, and free-ranging systems. Owing to the time required for the unceasing 'anti-predator' guard the open-field system was given up, though it was otherwise a good one.

The importance of the personal element in partridge rearing cannot be over-emphasised. Some people seem to know instinctively how to look after partridges, while others – given the same equipment and food – will lose every chick in the first 10 days. It is an inherent sympathy with the birds, equivalent to – but even more complex than – the 'green fingers' of the successful gardener.

Apart from purchasing eggs from gamefarms, other ways of obtaining them are:

1. By penning breeding pairs. (Caught-up birds almost never lay well: only reared birds are worth penning as laying stock.)

2. By saving all the eggs from nests which are mowed-over in grass fields, disturbed by predators or sited in dangerous places.

3. By collecting surplus eggs from very large clutches. (Fifteen eggs will provide enough chicks for a pair of partridges to brood in an average summer, and too many in a bad one!)

4. By taking early clutches and *destroying the nests*, thereby forcing the birds to make second nests. (On the experimental estate 300 eggs were often collected in this way.) By inducing the hens to re-nest it also staggers the normal hatching peak (10th–20th June) and provides an insurance against bad weather when

the chicks are so vulnerable. It is, however, wise to *avoid taking clutches of eggs which are near mowing-grass fields, or the second nests may be made in the grass crop and lost at cutting time.*

Broodies for hatching

A good foster-mother is of great importance in partridge rearing – small, quiet bantams being much more successful than large fowls. A clumsy hen can soon destroy a whole brood of partridge chicks with her feet alone, particularly within the cramped confines of a coop. The Fordingbridge broody method of rearing partridges, in fact, involves a movable pen which has a large open shelter and *no coop*.

Bantam pullets are occasionally used as broodies and usually behave well, but obviously two- or three-year birds are better. Good breeds of bantams for hatching and rearing partridges include Orpingtons, Pekins, Sussex, Wyandottes, Silkies crossed with very small bantams, and 'mongrels' of all sorts. On shoots where it is proposed to rear partridges every year, it will be well worth while maintaining a flock of bantams for the purpose. According to the size of broody, up to 20 eggs may be put into the nest. When the chicks are taken to the field, the broods can be made up to 25 chicks.

Rearing field sites

The subject of choosing a site for the rearing field has been covered in detail in the chapter on Pheasant Rearing. With partridges the same basic principles apply, but even greater attention is necessary to ensure that the field is not too rough, since partridge chicks are very tiny and can escape through very small gaps under the edge of a pen. A field which has been lightly grazed, particularly

81 Bantam with brood of partridges on dusting tray of rearing pen

221

by sheep, will be more satisfactory than a freshly cut ley. However, if the sheep have left quantities of wool around the site, it would be wiser to choose another spot. Occasionally the young chicks can develop an impacted gizzard through swallowing the wool.

Movable pens with broodies

Movable pens (or brooders) provide almost complete protection from the weather and predators, and also give some measure of control against disease.

The use of a long, low pen (roofed with $\frac{3}{4}$-in. [19 mm.] mesh wire netting) enclosing a ground area of 10 ft. × 5 ft. (3 m. × 1$\frac{1}{2}$ m.) is recommended (see Figures 82, 83 and 84). Instead of a coop there is a roofed-in shelter at either end. At one end, transparent material such as 'Claritex' or 'Tenasco' is let into the roof to form a sun parlour. A dusting tray filled with very fine, dry sand or dusty soil is fitted in the sun parlour. Provided it can be made absolutely waterproof, the bantam and the partridge chicks will use it a great deal. In a wet season it will be found invaluable. The droppings should be removed from time to time and fresh sand and grit added. The pens are easily made by the average handyman.

Partridge chicks reared under such conditions are hardier than those shut up in a stuffy coop all night and then suddenly exposed to the cold, damp morning air when let out. And in a roomy pen there is little danger of a chick being crushed by the broody.

A few leafy branches should be placed on top of the pens for extra shade in very hot weather, as partridges can be susceptible to heat stroke.

An acre of good grassland will accommodate 20 partridge pens until the birds are six weeks of age, and allows for the necessary number of moves. The pens should be put out on the rearing field a few days before the partridges hatch so that the ground is reasonably dry, and the grass underneath the shelters at either end should be clipped fairly short. This will induce the bantam to brood the chicks there. The pens need not be moved until the end of the first week. Two moves are recommended in the second week, three moves in the third and daily after 21 days. We usually move the pens during the afternoon, when the dew has dried. In very wet weather, we do not move at all.

When moving, great care must be taken to avoid crushing any chicks that run to the edge of the pen. Most keepers find it easiest to pull the pen towards them so that it slides on the dusting tray, which acts as a skid, or to make two 'half-moves', lifting each end of the pen sideways in turn until it is entirely on clean ground. After each move, any small holes under the sides should be blocked up with turf.

CATCHING-UP: If partridges are reared in these low pens, when the time comes to move them they can be caught up with the minimum disturbance, by covering the whole pen with an old blanket or tarpaulin so that the interior is quite dark.

222

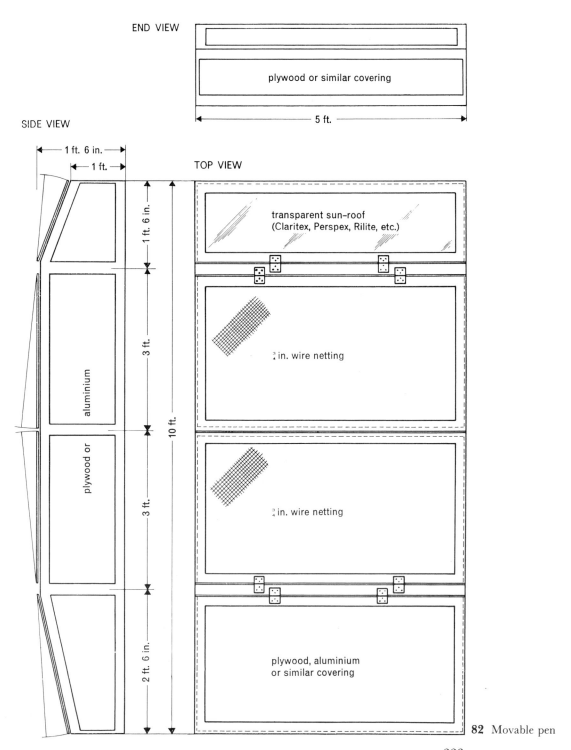

END VIEW

plywood or similar covering

5 ft.

SIDE VIEW

1 ft. 6 in.

1 ft.

TOP VIEW

1 ft. 6 in.

transparent sun–roof
(Claritex, Perspex, Rilite, etc.)

3 ft.

aluminium

$\frac{3}{4}$ in. wire netting

10 ft.

plywood or

3 ft.

$\frac{3}{4}$ in. wire netting

2 ft. 6 in.

plywood, aluminium
or similar covering

82 Movable pen

The hinged lid can then be opened just enough to get an arm in, and the birds be picked out one by one as they come up quietly to the crack of light. An alternative is to run the birds from the darkened pen into a little catcher placed outside a pop-hole cut in one end. The catcher should be made of $\frac{1}{2}$-in. (13 mm.) wire netting, 3 ft. (91 cm.) sq. and 1 ft. (30 cm.) high, with a hinged lid in the top.

FEEDING METHODS: In movable pens, the day-old chicks can be given partridge starter crumbs on a shallow platter or on the 'steps' of an inverted clay pigeon. The latter is very useful for this purpose, being dark in colour so that the crumbs show up well, and it is also cheap and disposable, which makes for good hygiene.

Proprietary partridge starter crumbs are used for 10–14 days, then the birds can go on to pheasant starter for another week. These crumb foods are given *ad lib* from the earliest stage, although the ration should be governed by the amount they will clear up before the next feed. Do not leave large quantities to become stale.

Questions are sometimes asked about hard-boiled egg and ants' eggs as partridge chick foods. Sieved, hard-boiled egg yolk, mixed with starter, often helps *slow* chicks to begin feeding, but it must be discontinued at 5–6 days, otherwise the chicks become very selective and may eat nothing else. Hard-boiled egg is useful – but rarely essential.

Ant eggs (in practice a mixture of soil, live ants and pupae) are not necessary with balanced foods, but partridges like them and they seem to stimulate enthusiastic activity among lethargic chicks. So if they are easily available there seems no harm in giving a few once a day. However, if chicks are given too many and too often, their interest in the dull crumbs will quickly fall off.

Fresh growing greenstuff is always beneficial, even with the most perfectly balanced artificial foods, so with chicks *not* penned on grass a little chopped lettuce in the early stages and whole lettuce leaves after about two weeks, helps to make up their diet and keep them interested. Do not feed too much at first, or the chicks will scour.

Partridge chicks prefer to peck bits of *growing* vegetation, and keepers have usually found it difficult to persuade them to eat *cut* green food other than lettuce. Bantam-reared partridges in movable pens will eat a great deal of wild white clover from the age of three weeks onwards if it is available, and benefit greatly from it.

From the third or fourth day, use 12-in. (30 cm.) 'Eltex' chick feeders for the crumbs. These prevent the broodies from scratching valuable food into the grass. The lids are left off until the partridges are about 14 days old. It is surprising how readily tiny chicks learn to jump in and out of the feed dishes, and the saving in food is well worth while.

224

83 Electric fencing allows livestock to share the rearing field

84 The special partridge pen contains a food-shelter at one end and a sun-parlour at the other

225

At 3 weeks of age, a further change of diet is made, to pheasant rearing (second-stage) crumbs or ordinary poultry chick crumbs. The partridge poults can go on to poultry grower's pellets by the time they are 6–8 weeks old. Wheat can be gradually added to the diet over the next few weeks, until it is used for alternate feeds. This applies mainly to birds being reared for release. The penned stock at Fordingbridge is maintained entirely on poultry grower's pellets, without grain, during the period August–March.

Water containers in the early stages should be very small and the tiny chicks should be prevented from getting wet – or even drowned – by placing some pebbles in the water. Care should be taken that water containers *never become empty*. If chicks get very thirsty and then fill themselves up suddenly they can quite easily die. When using brooder units, the water should be put in some time before the chicks are introduced, so that it is not too cold. A vitamin/antibiotic additive such as Whitmoyer Reed's AV25 (which can be obtained on veterinary prescription) may be valuable in the early stages.

85 Young partridges under a 400-watt infra-red lamp

226

Brooder rearing

Partridge chicks can be reared quite successfully in various types of brooder, heated by gas, electricity or paraffin.

The equipment and methods have been developed from those used for pheasants, already described in detail. In practice, partridges will equally well adapt themselves to an artificial heat source; in fact, they become conditioned to it more quickly and more permanently than pheasants, providing that considerable care is taken during the first few days and due allowance made for the small size of newly hatched partridge chicks. For example, they are capable of squeezing through the $\frac{1}{2}$-in. wire netting used to hold back chicks in some types of brooder.

All the partridges at Fordingbridge are reared with access to grass from very early stages, and this has been found more satisfactory from the point of view of hardening-off birds for release. Although the standard brooder will easily house 100 chicks, experience has shown that partridges do less well if reared in units of more than 70–75 birds.

In all brooders, partridges seem to spend a lot more time under the heater during the day than pheasants, using it regularly up to the age of about 5 weeks.

Although they rarely start to jug or roost outside at night before the sixth week, if the brooder is left attached to their run it is still wise to shut them back at night until they are at least 5 weeks old.

In one way partridges are easier to manage than pheasants in brooders as they rarely feather-pick – except under very intensive conditions – so allowing them to be reared in smaller runs with less frequent moves. About 60 or more partridges can be taken right through the brooding period up to 6 weeks in a 20 ft. × 10 ft. (6 m. × 3 m.) grass run attached to the 5-ft. (1½ m.) sq. brooder house, simply by changing the run around to fresh ground on the opposite side of the brooder during the fourth week. However, a 20-ft. (6 m.) sq. pen is even better, if the equipment can be made available.

The only major problem which is likely to arise is the puzzling disorder usually described as 'hysteria'. This occurs before the fourth week, and usually takes the form of the entire brood picking on one weakling, which is soon pecked to death, and then, after one or two further attacks of this kind, the entire group will 'run mad', fluttering around the pen and often injuring themselves in their frenzy. Groups which behave in this way should quickly be split up and this normally cures the difficulty. However, it is now believed that it is the shock of being caught up and moved which effects the cure, rather than the smaller unit in which they find themselves. Some breeders spray brooder groups with fine rain from a hose when hysteria is noted, and this treatment is continued until all the birds are thoroughly soaked. They then take some time to dry out and preen themselves: by the time they have achieved this, their mad behaviour is usually forgotten, and often completely cured. The treatment is effective in warm weather, but brings risks of chilling if the day turns cold.

227

86 Broods of about 25 partridges can be reared in suitable movable pens, using a low-wattage lamp

87 Pair of grey partridges in breeding pen

At Fordingbridge partridges are taken off heat at $4\frac{1}{2}$ to 5 weeks, leaving the shelter pen in position until they are at least 6 weeks old.

Many partridge rearers do not have enough chicks in one batch to fill a large brooder, and there is an obvious need for a small partridge brooder to deal with units of 10–50, as an alternative to the bantam. One efficient small unit is the Cotswold Game Farm brooder. This is designed for use indoors, or at least under a roofed shelter, and will take about 25 chicks up to 3 weeks. They are then transferred to an outside run with either a hay-box or a low-wattage electric lamp for the rest of the rearing period. After leading such a sheltered life in their early days, considerable care must be taken during the hardening-off period when the chicks are transferred to outside runs.

Another good outdoor brooder unit is the small 'Rupert' which is capable of taking 60–70 partridge chicks. It can be placed inside a sectional run (made with 10 ft. × 5 ft. [3 m. × $1\frac{1}{2}$ m.] sections), which can be moved or enlarged as required.

Releasing

The recovery rate of reared grey partridges, whether released for shooting or as future breeding stock, has up till now been disappointing. On the experimental estate a maximum of 30 per cent were shot from *selected* trial groups, but over a period of years the *average* was far less. Certainly some shoots make a success of it and hold their reared birds well, but it has been difficult to define the precise reasons why this should be so.

In the early days when partridges were mainly reared by bantams, they stayed on the ground quite well: certainly during the early part of the season. The partridges (15 per brood) were kept in their rearing pens for as long as possible – at least up till 8 weeks of age – when they were taken out on the estate. The pen sites were widely dispersed to prevent subsequent packing.

After a conditioning period of a few days, the young partridges were allowed to range out of the pen (by propping one end up on a brick or opening a small trapdoor). The broody bantam, being somewhat larger, was retained within the pen. Food and water were placed outside as well as inside. Sometimes after a further period the bantam was allowed to go free, though she rarely strayed far from the pen and continued to 'mother' and anchor the brood quite successfully.

Much the same release system was used for brooder-reared grey partridges. A unit of 60 or 70 birds would be split into artificial 'coveys' of 15–20 before being moved to the release pens on the shoot. After a settling-down period of a few days, *half* the reared birds would be released and food and water placed outside. At night they usually returned to jug near the pen. Three days later a further 3 or 4 young birds were released, and a day or two after that the last of the confined birds were liberated. The pen was retained as a home base and regularly serviced. In most cases the birds ranged back to it, until the activities of wild coveys or disturbance by farm cultivations and shooting drove them away.

There is still much to be learnt about release procedures, but some recent experimental work on the Continent may have made a contribution towards solving this problem. Some years ago an estate in Belgium left two 'callers' in each pen, after the rest of the partridges had been released. The penned birds called vociferously and the free-ranging brood seldom wandered far away – obviously attached to their companions. No less than 45 per cent of the 1,700 reared birds were recovered in the shooting season.

In the Somme region of France another estate successfully used much the same system, and the gamekeeper reported that the 'caller' groups reassembled very well after each day's shooting. On this particular shoot, 935 brooder-reared birds, bought in from three different gamefarms, formed the bulk of the bag. The recovery rate was about 30 per cent.

The callers are *released* after the shooting season, and the pens removed.

Obviously there is as yet insufficient data to draw any convincing conclusions, but the principle of 'callers' to anchor reared groups of birds certainly seems worthy of further study.

Experience in this country and abroad confirms that local conditions are most important in determining a good release site, but the ideal spot is usually the border between two suitable crops, providing food, shelter and drying-out places. Extremely dense cover must be avoided and *release should not be made until adjoining cornfields have been cut, because of the disturbance by machinery.*

The release of redlegs is discussed in Chapter 7.

RELEASING ADULTS: Reared partridges are sometimes retained in pens for release in the spring. Although on some shoots these birds have successfully established themselves in their release areas, subsequent breeding success has been difficult to ascertain.

Single hens may be released in February or March when there are invariably a number of single wild cocks searching for mates. One hen put out in a coop on the study area at 2 p.m. on 6th February had a suitor beside her at 2.10 p.m.! Elsewhere, an estate owner trapped 17 wild cocks to one caged hen on the lawn in front of his house.

Alternatively, *pairs* may be released on low-density areas. In either case, releasing should be as late in the spring as possible, when food and cover requirements are more adequately catered for. Partridges are pugnacious and need the privacy of growing crops. Unfortunately, unless pairs are individually penned, fighting among the confined birds sometimes enforces releasing at an earlier date than is desirable.

Wintering

Partridges which have been reared under bantams and kept for breeding stock can be put into their autumn quarters about the middle of August, when they are approximately 8 weeks old – cocks and hens mixed. (In most years, far more hens than cocks are found among reared partridges, although in the wild there is normally a surplus of cocks.) About 10 birds are placed in a 10 ft. × 6 ft. (3 m. × 2 m.) movable pen to form a mixed-sex group. Early in December the birds are sexed and form separate, male and female groups, again putting about 10 birds in each pen. The two groups of pens are sited some distance apart. This enforced separation enables the pairs to be arbitrarily mated the following spring. Coveys of mixed sexes will winter happily enough together, but some birds may refuse to pair off in the spring because of attachments formed within the covey. In other cases, birds will refuse to mate with a 'covey sister' or 'brother', perhaps following the wild bird's habit of seeking an unrelated partner, and fighting may start soon after Christmas if the weather turns milder.

As an alternative to the double handling involved in the foregoing method, the young partridges are often left in the rearing field pens until they are 11–12 weeks of age, when it is possible to sex normal birds. They are then transferred to their winter pens. It is essential not to leave them in overcrowded pens longer than necessary, or feather-picking and fighting will occur.

If it is necessary at any time to amalgamate broods of partridges into a larger group, the best procedure is to put all the birds together in a wicker hamper without food or water for 24 hours or more in a very dimly lit shed. They are released into their new quarters at dusk, and in their eagerness to reach the food hoppers and water trough, all thought of fighting is lost. By the following day, the covey has usually settled down. This method can also be used when separating mixed-sex coveys into separate cock and hen groups, without the deaths which often follow if the birds are merely moved into a pen together.

Brooder-reared birds, if there are no signs of trouble, can be kept in the large rearing pens until they are 12 weeks old. They are then split up into single-sex groups of 10 birds in the same way as those reared under bantams. These small groups seem to do better than large numbers in one pen, and it is certainly easier to move them to fresh ground, keep an eye on them for ailments and so on.

Ordinary 10 ft × 6 ft. (3 m. × 2 m.) movable pens, fitted with a shelter at one end, provide satisfactory accommodation and the shelter keeps the food dry.

Partridges can also be wintered in the low rearing pens with quite good results, but they never look as well as those kept in 5-ft. ($1\frac{1}{2}$ m.) high pens. A number of birds in the low pens may suffer from head injuries caused by persistent jumping up and scraping along the wire-netting roof. Soft netting, such as 'Netlon', will avoid this difficulty and it might be possible for one pen to be used for laying, rearing and wintering where the cost of equipment is critical.

Partridge can also be wintered successfully in wire-floored pens which stand on legs above the ground, and which are described later.

There seems to be no difficulty in wintering partridges in pens up to early January, and nearly nine out of ten of our reared birds survive until the New Year. However, fighting may break out just before the breeding season and occasionally in the late autumn. This is often sparked off by the presence of wild cocks which approach the penned birds and cause a great deal of restlessness and quarrelling. It is at this time that the most serious casualties may occur. If possible the wild cockbirds should be deterred from approaching the pens. The problem is most likely to arise where the surrounding countryside has a large surplus of spare males and these can be most persistent in their attempts to attract hens from among the penned stock.

It is important that any fighting should be nipped in the bud, because the sound of squabbling in one pen will excite the birds in others, leading to further trouble. It may be necessary to remove not only the weakest, but also the strongest bird from a covey, in order to prevent further trouble, and it is here that a few battery cages can come in very useful for housing quarrelsome individuals. Birds which are set upon by other members of the covey are not necessarily weaklings, but seem to be quite high in the pecking order until the moment when they are attacked: they are well worth saving. Mild weather may force the breeder to mate up his birds in January in order to stop losses due to fighting.

During the winter months use a poultry grower's pellet without any grain supplement. There is no need for a high-protein diet during the maintenance period August–March. In the wild state, of course, partridges live almost entirely on greenstuff during the winter months – though not necessarily from choice. The changeover to breeder's pellets is made during the first week of April.

Laying pairs

Reared grey partridges are ready to be paired up as soon as they start getting restless and excitable in late winter. The average mating date for *Perdix* on the experimental breeding field has been 10th February, with redlegs about a month later – but, as explained, the date may have to be advanced if quarrelling occurs.

When pairing up the birds it is necessary only to select a male and a female – that have been wintered apart – and put them together quietly in a pen. Providing that the determination of the sexes has been correct (which is straightforward with grey partridges) there will be little difficulty. If troubles do arise, it is often just prior to egg-laying, when one bird or the other may be in a more advanced condition and is likely to turn on its mate, usually with fatal results. With up to 80 experimental breeding pairs on the field during recent years, an average of just under 6 per cent of 'divorces' was recorded, which is probably an acceptable figure by any analysis.

The ordinary 10 ft. × 6 ft. (3 m. × 2 m.) pen (about 5 ft. [1½ m.] high) with a corrugated-iron shelter at one end makes a satisfactory breeding unit, and the sides of the pens should be 18–26 in. (46–66 cm.) high, with a *low* shelter inside, so that cocks cannot perch within sight of each other, causing constant disturbance. A straightforward and labour-saving system is to move the pens once each week: all feeding, watering and collecting of eggs being done at this time. The need for extensive attention only once a week makes the movable pen surprisingly efficient and economic.

The only disadvantage with pens on grass has been the tendency for laying hens to die of gapes (*Syngamus trachea* infestation) just as they were coming into peak production. This was the reason why trials with wire-floored pens were initiated, since in every other way the movable pen on grass has everything to recommend it. The birds are fed in open hoppers (under a rainproof shelter), and the diet is entirely poultry or turkey breeders' pellets during the period March–June.

With the present-day control of disease, movable pens on grass are still recommended to the average partridge egg producer, and only where lack of space or other considerations make it essential would the use of wire-floored compartments be advisable.

Wire-floored pens

Three different types of wire-floored pens are used at Fordingbridge – one for grey, one for redlegs and one which can be used for either species (Figure 91a).

In the latter the compartments are 6 ft. × 2 ft., and 1 ft. 4 in. high (2 m. × 0·6 m. × 41 cm.). The roof is covered with ¾-in. (19 mm.) mesh lightweight 'Netlon' netting, fastened down with thin wooden battens. A solid-floored nesting and dusting compartment, 1 ft. (30 cm.) high and 2 ft. (60 cm.) in length, is constructed at one end, while at the other a second covered area houses food and water containers, which are served daily from outside. Flooring is ½-in. (13 mm.) heavy-gauge wire netting. The pop-hole through the partition into the nesting area is 5 in. (13 cm.) sq., with a step at the base.

For some reason it was found that few grey partridges will lay in the nest boxes – most hens preferring to deposit their eggs on the wire. In France, however, in the same type of pen the birds seem to use them readily and there are fewer cracked eggs.

For redlegs only, compartments 4 ft. 5 in. × 1 ft. 5 in., and 1 ft. high (135 cm. × 43 cm. × 30 cm.) are used. Up to six can be built in one unit, which is still light enough to be moved when required. Redlegs will generally lay in the nesting area, which is lined with hay or wood-shavings.

The dusting boxes should be filled with 1–2 in. (2–5 mm.) of sifted earth or sand.

The eggs are collected daily, taking care to approach the pens in a direction which will allow the birds to move quietly under cover. If this is done a reduction in the number of broken eggs will certainly result. Where dogs or other stray animals are likely to wander under the pens it is a wise precaution to fence them around, since the birds can be easily alarmed.

Although partridges can be wintered in grass pens and then transferred to wire-floors, it is obviously something of a shock to the system. It is therefore better for birds that are destined for such laying units to be wintered in them. The larger grey partridge pens are particularly suitable for overwintering and groups of 6–8 birds can be kept in each 4-ft. (1 m.) wide compartment.

The pens are in batteries, clad with exterior quality $\frac{1}{4}$-in. (6 mm.) plywood. They should stand on legs to give a clearance of 2 ft. (60 cm.) from floor to ground level. These legs must be very strong (4 in. × 2 in. [10 cm. × 5 cm.] minimum) and firmly bolted on. An alternative method, which gives the pens better support in the middle, is to construct a platform from 3-in. × 2-in. (7$\frac{1}{2}$ cm. × 5 cm.) timber, with 6 legs. It is important to see that the pens, when resting on top, fit *exactly* to the inside edge of this framework. Any woodwork extending beneath the floor of the pen compartments will collect droppings which cannot be cleaned off without considerable disturbance to the birds.

88 Wire-floored partridge laying pens

234

89 Experimental breeding unit at St Benoit, France

90 Wire-floored and movable pens at Fordingbridge

235

The 'Weldmesh' floor of the red-legged partridge pens will be sufficiently rigid without extra support. The floor of the grey partridge pens should be supported by two lengths of $\frac{3}{8}$-in. ($9\frac{1}{2}$ mm.) steel rod running across the compartments and firmly fastened with staples to the dividing panels below the 'Weldmesh'. Do not use wooden battens for this purpose because they will collect droppings.

Dual-purpose partridge pens

KEY TO SKETCH PLAN (FIGURE 91A)

A. 3-in. ($7\frac{1}{2}$ cm.) high strip of batten.

B. Compartment, sub-divided for nesting and dusting, with a solid floor. Sifted earth or sand should be placed in the area where letter 'B' is shown. Hay in the other half of the compartment will encourage birds to lay there.

C. Pop-hole through the partition into the nesting area. It should be 5 in. (13 cm.) square with a 3-in. ($7\frac{1}{2}$ cm.) lip at the bottom.

D. The floor area here should be covered with $\frac{1}{2}$-in. (13 mm.) 'Weldmesh'. This must be fastened to the bottom edges of the partitions with strong staples at 3 in. ($7\frac{1}{2}$ cm.) intervals.

E. Drinker and feeder compartment. The 'Weldmesh' floor from the main pen continues through it. Notice that the lid for this compartment is in one piece for all five pens. Pellets are fed in an Eltex No. 71 trough (12 in. × 5 in. × 3 in. [30 cm. × 13 cm. × $7\frac{1}{2}$ cm.]), and water is available in an Eltex No. 117 plastic drinker ($4\frac{3}{4}$ in. × $3\frac{1}{2}$ in. $2\frac{1}{2}$ in. [12 cm. × 9 cm. × $6\frac{1}{4}$ cm.]).

F. Screen of 2-in. (5 cm.) mesh. 'Netlon' plastic netting which is obtainable at nearly all garden sundries shops. It should be fastened at the bottom to the narrow edge of a piece of 2-in. × 1-in. (5 cm. × $2\frac{1}{2}$ cm.) batten. In order to allow the birds to raise their heads when drinking, one of the 2-in. (5 cm.) cross-pieces of 'Netlon' should be cut out, leaving a 2-in. × 4-in. (5 cm. × 10 cm.) gap opposite the drinker.

G. The area between the lids should be covered with $\frac{3}{4}$-in. (19 mm.) mesh lightweight 'Netlon' netting fastened down with a thin wood batten.

GENERAL: The top lids should have an overhang of at least 2 in. (5 cm.) to carry rainwater well clear. The top edges of the partitions beneath the lids should be routed to provide a water escape channel. If this is not done moisture will get into the food dishes.

Special grey partridge pens

Although similar in construction to the dual-purpose pens, the compartments are larger (4 ft. × 8 ft. [1 m. × $2\frac{1}{2}$ m.]) and there is no solid floor to the shelter

236

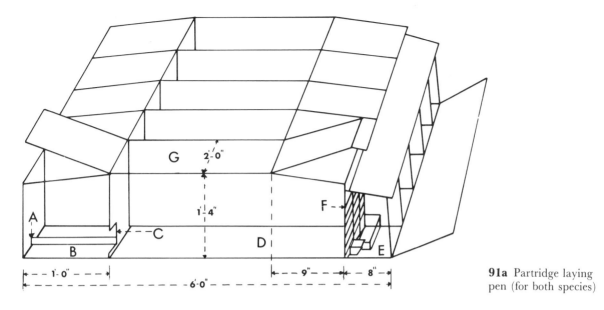

G 2'-0"

A

F

1'-4"

C

B

D

E

1'-0"

9"

8"

6'-0"

91a Partridge laying pen (for both species)

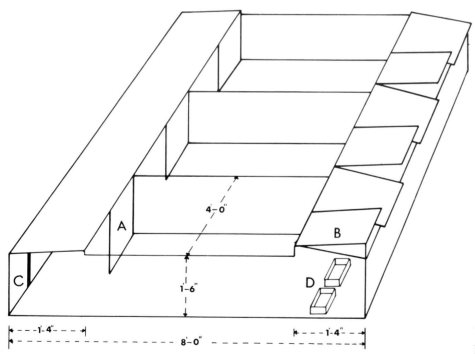

A

B

C

D

4'-0"

1'-6"

1'-4"

1'-4"

8'-0"

b Special grey partridge laying pen

237

compartment, $\frac{1}{2}$-in. (13 mm.) 'Weldmesh' being used throughout. Access to the drinkers and feeders is through top-opening lids. 'Netlon' netting should be used on the top of the compartments, as with the red-legged partridge pens.

KEY TO SKETCH PLAN (FIGURE 91B)
A. Baffle shutting off half the roofed area.
B. Lid extending to half the width of the compartment.
C. Sliding door extending to half the width of the compartment. This is essential for catching up birds.
D. Drinkers and feeders.

EGG YIELD: Normally the birds are expected to start laying in mid-April – about 10th–20th – though eggs by 20th March from domesticated stock have been known.

The average yield per pair (*Perdix*) in movable pens on grass has recently been 35·6 eggs. Peak production has been rather late and often the greatest number of eggs is picked up during the period 10th–20th June. Eggs laid after 1st July are not recorded, but just under 30 has been the average over the last 5 years.

In wire-floored pens it is possible to produce an annual average of 30–40 eggs from grey partridges. In France, redlegs produce a higher average number of eggs than grey partridges – often exceeding 40 eggs per pair. The fertility and hatchability of eggs has been extremely good – both from grass and wire-floored pens.

It is not profitable to keep grey partridges for a second season's laying, but as redlegs lay better in their second season they are certainly worth maintaining for two years.

Chapter 17
Some Diseases of Gamebirds

Most game rearers will at some time or another meet with outbreaks of disease. In the wild, large-scale die-offs are relatively rare. When they do occur, they are often associated with some degree of over-population, resulting in competition for food and cover, which may reduce the birds' natural resistance. Very little can be done to check such diseases once an outbreak has occurred, so discussion will be limited to diseases in *reared* birds.

Nearly all modern game rearing inevitably involves 'overcrowding' and it is under these artificial conditions that outbreaks of disease are most common. With units of 100 birds or more, in spite of adequate food and warmth, crowded conditions can create an ideal situation for the development and rapid spread of disease organisms. Fortunately, a number of the most common diseases of young gamebirds can be effectively treated by drugs which in many cases have been developed for treating similar diseases in domestic poultry.

The main problem lies in the early recognition of symptoms, so that the appropriate remedy can be applied as soon as possible. Unfortunately, with one or two notable exceptions, birds suffering from quite different diseases may show similar symptoms. Loose and ruffled feathers, and a general 'droopy' appearance coupled with loss of appetite, indicate a sick bird – but do little to help us diagnose the cause. A combination of factors – symptoms, species of game, age of poults and finally a post-mortem examination – will, however, help to produce the answer.

Among reared gamebirds a common disease (perhaps because it is the most easily recognised) is gapes, caused by the roundworm *Syngamus trachea* which spends its adult life attached to the internal lining of the trachea. Young pheasants (and adult hens) show very characteristic signs – a cough with a sideways flick of the head (commonly called 'snicking') in an attempt to dislodge the impediment to the passage of air down the windpipe. Partridges just gasp. Eggs laid by female gapeworms are coughed up, or swallowed and passed out in the droppings of the affected birds. Humus-eating invertebrates, such as earthworms, may swallow these eggs and the larvae which develop from them bore their way into the earthworm's muscles and encyst. If the earthworm is eaten by a gamebird chick, the encysted gapeworm larvae renew their activity, bore through the intestine wall and travel via the blood stream to the lungs and thence to their adult stations in the trachea. Individual female gapeworms can be up to 1 in. ($2\frac{1}{2}$ cm.) long and the large numbers sometimes present in poults may sometimes cause death as a result of asphyxiation. Outbreaks of the disease in birds of 3–5 weeks of age can result in heavy mortality, but in older poults losses are usually less severe.

Satisfactory methods of fully *preventing* this disease have not been discovered. The elimination of all potential invertebrate intermediate hosts from the rearing area is not a practical proposition. There is some suggestion from the U.S.A., however, that gapeworm eggs survive best where soil-water is neutral. Altering the acidity of the soil-water (by the addition of lime to slightly alkaline soils or ammonium sulphate to slightly acid soils) may reduce the incidence of the disease.

Outbreaks of gapes may be *cured* by the drugs Mebenvet and Thibenzole, which are most easily administered through the food, and many pheasant food manufacturers supply pellets incorporating the drugs at the correct level for a 14 day treatment. The demand for a water-soluble drug has led to the widespread development and use of the drug Gapex.

Coccidiosis, caused by a protozoan parasite, *Eimeria* spp., kills as many gamebird poults as any other disease, in spite of the low-level coccidiostats incorporated in many pheasant foods. However, recent developments may reduce the prevalence of this disease. Presence of coccidiostats in the food should not be taken as a guarantee that outbreaks of coccidiosis will not occur. There are several different species of *Eimeria* (the cause of coccidiosis), and different drugs vary in their degree of control over the different species. While young gamebirds may overcome a mild attack without the aid of drugs (or with drugs at a low level) a heavy challenge may be too much for the bird to fight off unless direct curative treatment is given. It may be complicated by a bacterial infection with *E. coli*, which itself needs treatment.

Recognition of the presence of the disease by external symptoms of the ailing birds is not easy. The typical signs of a sick bird – ruffled feathers, general 'droopiness', etc. – will certainly be present, but the oft-quoted symptom of 'blood in the droppings' is not seen under modern management systems. With pheasant poults of 2–5 weeks of age (the most susceptible period), perhaps the best indication of the onset of the disease may be a fall-off in the food intake. If a few birds are obviously ailing, one should be sacrificed for veterinary confirmation by examination of the blind guts (the caeca) which may show that the normally fluid contents have hardened to a cheesy consistency, while the caecal walls themselves are inflamed.

Curative treatment with one of the modern drugs Amprol Plus Solution, e.g. 'Whitsyn S.' or 'Saquadil' given in the drinking water, should start as soon as possible once the disease has been diagnosed. The method of treatment – with

92 Celluloid split rings are used to mark pedigree-bred partridge chicks

93 Wild red-legged partridge with newly hatched brood

241

graded doses or medicated water alternating with fresh water – helps to ensure that most of the poults will contract a mild dose of the disease and not only be cured but be immune to any future attack. If the poults are not exposed to coccidiosis on the rearing field, they could still fall victims to the disease in the release pen when their food may no longer include a coccidiostat. There is always the danger, too, that the more obvious, but usually less dangerous, gapes may mask the presence of the more lethal coccidiosis. Not infrequently, heavy losses in release pens have, on post-mortem examination, been shown to be due to coccidiosis although a mild infestation of gapes was also present.

Blackhead, another disease caused by a protozoan parasite (*Histomonas meleagridis*), has been badly named, since in no gamebird does the disease show itself in the way its name suggests. Partridge appear to be particularly susceptible to this disease and among young red-legged partridges losses from this cause can be considerable. Treatment with 'Emtryl' in the drinking water usually effects a rapid cure once the disease has been diagnosed. In adult birds loss of weight may be very considerable, with the keel of the breastbone becoming very prominent. Young birds, however, may die before any obvious emaciation occurs, and diagnosis depends on post-mortem examination. The walls of the blind guts (caeca) become thickened and inflamed, while in advanced stages areas of dead tissue appear as discolourations in the liver.

The growth in partridge rearing during the 1960s has focused attention on a disease, Moniliasis Candidiasis, caused by a fungus *Candida albicans*. Although diseases caused by this yeast-like fungus have been successfully treated in both turkeys and humans, infected young partridges have not reacted favourably to these treatments and in some years losses were heavy. *C. albicans* is probably widely distributed, perhaps living on the dead and decaying vegetation of grass tussocks. When this fungus is accidentally picked up and swallowed, it can proliferate rapidly in the partridge chick's crop, where it extracts the vitamin B in the chick food. The partridge chick's growth becomes stunted, the wing feathers twisted and distorted, and after a short period characterised by a staggering gait, death often occurs before the partridge is 3 or 4 weeks old. Prevention of the disease by spraying the chick food with diluted formic acid has given very satisfactory results, however, and at last promises to give a good measure of control.

With brooder rearing, and the concentration of a large number of poults in a warm humid atmosphere, respiratory diseases may be common. Similar diseases in poultry are treated with antibiotics for which a veterinary prescription is necessary.

One respiratory disease which can be a real killer results from a fungus infection in the lungs and air-sacs. Chicks and to some extent older poults can be affected, and since there is no known cure, prevention is of utmost importance. *Aspergillus fumigatus*, the causative agent which has given its name to the disease Aspergillosis, lives on dead and decaying vegetable matter. It

242

94 The late Dr Phyllis Clapham, a former Fordingbridge pathologist, examining a shot partridge for gapes

thrives on old, warm, wet hay or straw, and one of the worst outbreaks known to the Game Conservancy laboratories occurred when wet straw from old bales was used for blocking up cavities in the corners of brooder houses. In covert the common practice of strawing down feed-rides with straw from bales at the base of an old rick can be a very dangerous one. If the mould is present in quantity in the damp straw, myriad spores are breathed in by the pheasant poults while they peck among the straw, and small white nodules of the fungus and discs appear at various points in the lungs and air sacs of the young pheasants. By-products of the fungus are highly toxic, and poults can die without showing any loss in condition. The rule must be never to use mouldy straw for strawing down a feed-ride.

Obviously, there are many other diseases in addition to those mentioned above. While most disease stems from overcrowding, its incidence among reared birds will be reduced by meticulous attention to cleanliness, the judicious use of Ministry-approved disinfectants for all equipment and the selection of fresh ground wherever possible.

243

In all cases a quick diagnosis by a veterinarian laboratory will in the end save the fee many times over.

Fowl Pest or Newcastle Disease, once common in poultry in Britain, has also occurred in pheasants: many other species are believed to be susceptible. No cases have been reported since the mid-1970s. Typical symptoms are a rolling gait, general discoordination, green diarrhoea and a marked increase in water intake. Some of these symptoms are similar to, and were confused with, dieldrin poisoning. The causative agent is a virus which, like Foot and Mouth virus, may be spread by the wind. Cool, overcast and damp weather provides ideal conditions for the survival of virus particles.

Where this disease is suspected both breeding stock and poults should be vaccinated. However, this is no longer permitted in Britain. In those countries where vaccination may be carried out, stock birds can be injected during the late winter with the dead oil-based vaccine. This can be obtained from most suppliers of veterinary products and is administered underneath the skin of the neck. When the chicks hatch there is no need to vaccinate unless there is a local outbreak of the disease, in which case the live Hitchner B_1 vaccine should be administered by eye-dropping. Normally this would take place at three weeks, followed by an injection of the oil-based vaccine on release. These procedures should give an immunity until mid-winter when any birds for stock can be injected with dead vaccine. Vaccination presupposes that the birds are healthy.

New drugs

New drugs are always being developed and tested. Nowadays trials have to be even more extensive and nearly all drugs require a veterinary prescription. Examples of recent new products include Mebenvet and Gapex for the treatment of gapes and Coyden 25, a coccidiostat for the prevention of coccidiosis. The first two have already been mentioned, the former being dusted on the food or incorporated at manufacture. The latter is added to the drinking water. *Eimeria* often shows resistance to drugs and different coccidiostats have to be considered. At present Coyden is showing considerable value as a coccidiostat.

Chapter 18
Game and Shooting Crops

Some farmers may ask why we have included suggestions regarding the cultivation of most of the ordinary agricultural crops – as everyone will know how to grow cabbages or potatoes. However, these notes are not intended for farmers, but as guide lines for syndicate shooters who often do not know what is involved when they ask a farmer to put in some post-harvest mustard or some buckwheat. An understanding by the sportsman of the ubiquitous kale and its requirements can be helpful. And answers to questions such as: 'Would it be silly to try some maize in Yorkshire?'

The main suggestions regarding crop husbandry are printed in a different typesize.

General

Time devoted in early spring to the planning and distribution of the farm crops will be amply repaid during the shooting season. There is no question of the farmer making 'sacrifices'. Undoubtedly it will be beneficial if small areas of land can be given over to special sowings which will help game, but the main effort should be put into planning the layout so that, if there is a large acreage of one crop on the farm, it is not concentrated in a single block. It should be split up across the landscape to help provide a patchwork quilt of varied fields, so that each unit of game range will have its share of nesting places, escape cover, food and shelter.

A covey of grey partridges will range over approximately 100 acres (40 h.), and red-legged partridges over about 600 acres (200 h.).

There are basically three types of crops to be considered:

(i) Crops which are solely grown for agriculture, such as corn, potatoes, grass, etc.
(ii) Crops which are dual-purpose, like mustard or kale (and can also be useful to gamebirds or the game shooter, or both).
(iii) Special crops such as buckwheat or sunflowers which are grown purely for game.

245

It may seem odd to include grass as a game crop, but short-term leys undersown in cereals can build a high insect population which is vital for chick survival. In predominantly arable areas the occasional field of grass will provide some food and winter cover. Cereal crops can also be used to help provide winter cover and insect food in the spring.

It is difficult to give any firm ruling as to the ideal size of individual strips or blocks of game cover because this will largely be governed by local conditions. Small sowings of between one third of an acre and three acres are usually sufficient, but this will depend on the primary purpose of the crop – whether it be used for shooting cover, food, winter refuge or nesting cover.

The crops are discussed in alphabetical order and not in any 'order of merit'.

Artichokes *(Helianthus tuberosus)*

Jerusalem artichokes should be considered as a medium- to long-term crop, lasting up to ten years or more. They can give excellent results in terms of holding and showing pheasants, but can become very thick and weed-infested without correct management.

The best planting time is March to May: the tubers should be drilled in rows 60 in. (1½ m.) apart (preferably with a ridged potato planter) like kale, in the direction in which the birds are to be driven.

This system of planting has several advantages. The wide spacing of the rows enables subsequent cultivation to control weed growth or to manage another inter-row crop if desired. It provides easy access for beaters, and freedom for the pheasants to rise. It also allows the plants much more room to grow and saves a considerable quantity of seed. The sides of the ridges, built up by the planter, are gradually eroded by rainfall, exposing the growing tubers to the birds, which quickly take to them. The ridging is particularly important for those whose land is heavy, since without it at least some of the tubers have to be dug up for the birds. On very light land, of course, pheasants will scratch down to them.

Artichokes can be effectively used in other situations. For instance they provide good, quick cover if planted in the excavated earth around a new flight pond. Similarly a strip of 4 to 6 rows around small bare spinneys, pit-holes or areas of rough cover will improve pheasant holding capacity. They can be planted in small areas of no value to the farm, such as field corners, reservoir banks and underneath electricity pylons. Artichokes have also been used to fill gaps in the hedges!

To obtain better *initial* cover in the establishment year, some farmers plant the artichokes at ordinary single-row potato spacing (26 to 30 in. [66 to 76 cm.]) recognising the fact that thinning every alternate row will have to take place in the second or third year. It is also practicable to plant spring barley or spring wheat with the artichokes in the establishment year to provide some additional food for the birds the following winter.

246

95 Artichokes, when sown with a potato planter, provide excellent cover and food. The beaters hav plenty of room to drive the birds between the ridges

Using the normal spacing a seed rate of about 10 cwt. (500 kg.) per acre will be required if spaces of 24–30 in. (60–75 cm.) are left between the plants in the rows.

The crop will need fairly drastic treatment to keep the tubers under control and prevent a jungle forming. Some of the rows can be thinned with a potato-spinner, and the seed thus gained for another patch (or sold to a game-minded neighbour?). Natural regeneration will quickly fill in the gaps.

Once established, artichokes are difficult to eradicate should a particular patch have to revert to farm cropping. Spraying with 2, 4, 5-T can be effective – but probably a more efficient and profitable course is to wire off the artichokes and turn pigs in. They will soon root out every tuber most efficiently.

When planning a site for artichokes it should be remembered that the top growth (6 to 8 ft. [2 to $2\frac{1}{2}$ m.] in most years) will sometimes be blown flat in exposed sites. The crop can be cold in exposed areas – funnelling the wind down the rows – and shelter, preferably a hedge, is essential in such circumstances. A good alternative is a row of straw bales round the perimeter.

The storage of artichokes can be a problem, as they tend to dry up very quickly and are liable to Fusarium, which affects germination and subsequent growth. To avoid this they should be planted as quickly as possible after harvesting.

Fertiliser should generally be avoided as the crop usually grows strongly on most soils without additional nutrients, but on poorer soils up to 5 cwt. (250 kg.) per acre ICI No. 1 can be applied. There have been instances of extensive damage to fertilised artichokes from hares, deer and squirrels (both red and grey).

247

Couch and other grass weeds can smother the crop in a few years. Pre-emergence spraying with 'Gramoxone' or 'Round-Up' gives good control, and should be carried out in early April in the south and late April further north.

Beans *(Vicia vulgaris)*

Purely from the game point of view winter beans are preferable to the spring-sown varieties as they provide good overwintering cover in the bleak months of January to March. They give a higher yield than spring beans, but are more prone to chocolate spot. Varieties such as Maris Beaver and Throws M.S. should be sown before mid-October. Spring beans are generally sown too late and harvested too early to be of value to gamebirds, but if an unharvested strip is left alongside a hedgerow it will feed and hold pheasants.

The crop is very attractive to woodpigeons and rooks, so much so that this can be a cause of crop failure in some areas. Leaving strips of peas and beans as woodpigeon 'bait' can result in excellent shooting – and woodpigeon control! Both pheasants and partridges can be driven out of beans very well – often better than out of kale.

Insect counts carried out by our Partridge Survival Project show that some insects are present when insecticides are *not* used on the growing crop. Where 'Simazine' is used for weed control – as is normal – the insect population is naturally reduced.

Dwarf beans grown for *freezing* are frequently harvested at night, which can result in heavy losses among gamebirds jugging in the crop. Tick or risem beans can be a good food crop and are especially useful in a mixture with kale.

A seed rate of 2 cwt. (100 kg.) per acre is normal for pure stands, but if specially grown for game, kale and cereals should be drilled as well.

The crop does best on heavy soils, with variable results on sands and gravels. Soil for beans should not be acid as the crop may fail on any field with a soil pH under 6·0. The crop can be grown on peats after liming.

Adequate phosphate and potash, and a small quantity of nitrogen fertiliser, should be broadcast and harrowed into the seedbed before drilling.

Brussels sprouts *(Brassica oleracea* var. *gemmifera)*

Brussels sprouts are much liked by game. The value of the crop as holding cover largely depends on whether the plants have been picked. If run once (i.e. the bottom leaves stripped off and the first picking of brussels taken), partridge cover is good, because the birds can see each other at ground level but at the same time have plenty of overhead cover. Before the first picking the crop tends to be something of a jungle. Birds can be very difficult to flush at this stage, the lower leaves hiding each individual bird.

There can be continual disturbance when picking takes place between November and March.

Sprouts provide good holding cover for game in the late winter after many other crops have had to be ploughed in.

Insecticide sprays are necessary, but these should be carefully chosen and applied. 'Saphi-Col' (containing menazon) is an example of an effective low-toxicity spray. Organo-phosphorus insecticides, which can be particularly dangerous to game, should be avoided if at all possible.

Buckwheat *(Fagopyrum esculentum)*

It is quite a useful game crop, both in strips on arable farms and in open glades in or near coverts. In Spain and Portugal it is a favourite for redlegs. In the USA it is planted for mallard and pintail. Tartary buckwheat is, in fact, known as 'duck wheat', and all buckwheat is good for honey bees.

In southern counties buckwheat 'stubble' has proved very good for holding partridges and pheasants as late as January and February in mild winters. As soon as a few seeds are developed deer will find buckwheat attractive.

Buckwheat is not a true cereal, but a polygonum: there are a large number of species. A native of Central Asia, usually about 3 ft. (90 cm.) high, its main virtue is that it is reasonably quick-growing – maturing in 10–12 weeks – and the seed ripens over a prolonged period. It is, however, killed by the frost and cannot, therefore, be classed as 'winter' cover. According to Harold G. Marshall, 'Buckwheat is extremely sensitive to weather conditions – especially at blooming time. Drought and drying winds may cause severe blasting of flowers and result in a poor seed-yield.'*

It does not like cold, wet clay or chalk, and grows best on light, sandy soils, with adequate sunshine and warmth. It has a good tolerance to soil acidity. The crop is best shown in May – or when all danger of a killing frost has passed, at the seed rate of about 36–48 lb. (16–22 kg.) per acre drilled or 120 lb. (54 kg.) broadcast. A firm seedbed is essential and sow at a depth of 1 in. to 2 in. ($2\frac{1}{2}$ cm. to 5 cm.). It germinates rapidly and the dense leaf canopy soon smothers most weeds. In northern counties it should be sown in areas with a south-facing aspect, the annual growth being very uncertain from Yorkshire northwards.

Fertiliser should only be used on soils of low fertility.

Canary grass *(Phalaris tuberosa)*

Care should be taken to distinguish between canary *grass* which is a perennial and canary *seed* which is an annual. Canary grass must be planned as a medium- to long-term crop as it takes two years to establish sufficiently to provide good permanent nesting and shooting cover.

Once established it will last 10 years or more and can be used in the same way as Jerusalem artichokes – alongside wire fences, under pylons, around bare spinneys and shelter belts. The main advantages over artichokes are that the seed for canary grass is less than a tenth of the price of artichoke tubers, the

* 'Description and Culture of Buckwheat' (U.S. publication).

stems do not tend to break down so early in the winter and it is absolutely wind-proof. It will also tolerate a wider variety of soils, preferring light, dry ones, although it will grow on clay providing it is not too wet.

Canary grass will give good cover in upland areas for nesting in the spring and for holding in the early autumn. However, it does not like very cold, exposed sites and we are not certain how far north it will grow. In the spring of 1978 we heard of a crop being killed by hard frosts and very cold easterly winds.

Sown in an intensive arable area alongside wheat and barley, canary grass has shown no tendency to be a host for foliar diseases or to spread by seed into neighbouring crops.

The related species (*Phalaris paradoxa*) has recently caused worry due to being highly invasive, but canary grass has *not* shown this tendency and has been grown in Britain for at least twelve years.

A shoot in Hertfordshire has successfully grown canary grass between the rows in a young plantation to give cover while the trees and shrubs are establishing. Being a xerophyte there is some danger of planting the grass too close to the tree rows as it may compete with the young trees for nutrients and moisture, but this effect may be outweighed by the shelter it gives to the establishing tree seedlings. It would seem ideal as an alternative to Jerusalem artichokes in the 'instant spinney' layout.

It is not thought that the seed is of feed value, either to pheasants or partridges; canary grass can be regarded basically as a cover crop only and therefore to obtain the best results, especially where reared pheasants are concerned, a long ride should be swiped through the crop (and then strawed), in which birds can be fed by hand each day.

The crop can be sown with a root drill in March/April when it may grow up to 1 or 2 ft. (30–60 cm.) in height by the autumn. In the second year the seedheads will reach a height of 6 ft. (2 m.) or more. An autumn sowing has not been successfully established. It should be drilled in rows 28–36 in. (65–95 cm.) apart using a seed rate of 5 lb. per acre (5 kg. per hectare), and at a depth of approximately $\frac{1}{2}$ in. (1 cm.). Broadcasting seed is unwise as the crop becomes so dense that it is extremely difficult to control or use as game flushing cover.

One system of overcoming the long wait until the second season, when it has made sufficient growth to form nesting and holding cover, is to oversow in June of the first year with mustard. This should form some initial cover for the first shooting season and will then die away allowing the canary grass to grow on in the following spring.

Rabbits do not usually eat the establishing grass, unless present in very large numbers, and the crop does not require a deep, rich soil. It establishes well on dry sites.

The roots grow to a medium depth and the crop can be removed by spraying with 'Gramoxone' followed by rotavating or ploughing. Burning off the dry top growth and root trash may be necessary before cultivating.

2–3 bags per acre (5 to 8 bags per hectare) of ICI No. 2 fertiliser should be applied to the soil immediately before drilling. A top dressing of 1 bag per acre (3 bags per hectare) of Nitram in the first spring following drilling will ensure a good crop. Once established it is drought resistant and will tolerate most frosts.

Competition from broadleaved weeds may be controlled by spraying with Legumex Extra or, when fully established, with M.C.P.A.

Canary seed *(Phalaris canariensis)*

At one time this crop was a very good commercial proposition and when grown on Lincolnshire farms was found to be most attractive to partridges.

A proportion of canary seed is usually to be found in game foodpatch mixtures suitable for southern counties. Some Essex farmers are now mixing 6–7 lb. ($2\frac{3}{4}$–3 kg.) of canary seed with their lucerne. This attracts game and helps to provide shooting cover during the first season. It can also be mixed with cocksfoot to provide nesting strips alongside barbed wire fences.

It does not generally grow well north of the Humber–Mersey line, but for those who wish to try a few strips it should be noted that it is best grown on heavy land. Prepare a fine firm seedbed with a seeding rate of 28–30 lb. ($12\frac{3}{4}$–$13\frac{1}{2}$ kg.) per acre.

Carrots *(Daucus carota)*

Pheasants and partridges like the crop in dry weather, but when wet the leaves hold moisture for a long time and birds tend to flush badly. In the old days it was a shooting crop early in the season, but there can be a great deal of disturbance at lifting time (October/December). However, most crops are now harvested mechanically and therefore quickly. Later-sown crops provide good over-wintering cover into January. Both pheasants and partridges will feed on waste carrots during and after the harvest. Insect abundance is usually very low, as a result of spraying for carrot fly.

Usually drilled – sometimes in ridges – in light soils at any time between March and July. The seed rate is 3–5 lb. ($1\frac{1}{4}$–$2\frac{1}{4}$ kg.) per acre.

96 In certain counties carrots can make useful shooting cover

251

Cereal crops

The planning of the cereal crop acreage and its distribution on an intensive arable farm can have a significant effect on the welfare of gamebirds in terms of over-wintering cover, and chick survival linked to insect abundance.

When considering winter-sown cereals, the value of winter wheat for game is superior to winter barley. (Winter oats are of little value, and the acreage of the latter should be kept to an absolute minimum on any sporting estate. Where the land is suitable that is, of course, what happens.) Winter cover, feed preferences (green leaf shoots) – particularly for partridges – and insect production provided by winter wheat, is much greater than the alternative winter cereals. Winter barley is a poor second, but preferable to winter oats, which comes bottom of the table of cereals in potential insect abundance for the chicks the following summer.

In northern France a simple rotation of winter wheat interspersed with grain maize is at present in general use. If this practice were to become common in southern England it could greatly help wild game.

When considering *spring*-sown cereals, barley will generally produce a greater insect abundance suitable for partridge chicks than wheat or oats.

These generalisations on insect potential are obviously subject to overall management plans. The tenth barley crop in succession is not likely to produce as many insects as a white straw crop following potatoes or sugar beet.

Chicory *(Cichorium intybus)*

It has been known for many years that pheasants will eat chicory and it was often the practice when sowing a rearing field to put two pounds of chicory seed per acre with the grasses and clovers. Chicory will withstand frost and may last from 3 to 5 years, growing up to 5 ft. ($1\frac{1}{2}$ m.) high. It is a crop with a high insect potential. But providing salads for poults is something of a luxury.

The crop will grow on a wide range of soils and will tolerate both very dry and also very wet conditions. It is grown as a contract crop in Cambridgeshire and the Fens, and will hold gamebirds until a hard frost. It should be drilled in the spring at a seed rate of 10–12 lb. ($4\frac{1}{2}$–$5\frac{1}{2}$ kg.) per acre.

Clover, red *(Trifolium pratense)*

Used in one-year leys for cutting: even when dry and frosted it provides camouflage and cover for partridges. Red clover has an average insect abundance potential.

Diploid seed varieties last for one year but tetraploid varieties will crop for two years. Sow at 15 lb. ($6\frac{3}{4}$ kg.) per acre as a straight crop in the autumn, or 2–12 lb. (1–$5\frac{1}{2}$ kg.) per acre when used in a mixture.

252

Clover, white *(Trifolium repens)*

White clover is usually sown in grass mixtures – either in temporary leys or in permanent pasture mixtures – and is very rarely sown by itself. It provides good over-wintering cover and food for partridges; it also has an average insect potential. Wild white clover provides excellent greenstuff for rearing field poults.

It can be sown in the spring or autumn, or can be undersown beneath spring cereals. When sown pure the seed rate is 6 lb. ($2\frac{3}{4}$ kg.) per acre, or between 1 and 4 lb. ($\frac{1}{2}$–$1\frac{3}{4}$ kg.) per acre in a grassland mixture.

Cocksfoot *(Dactylis glomerata)*

Where hedgerows and other nesting cover for partridges are scarce, strips of cocksfoot can provide attractive cover when drilled alongside wire fences or in between two different crops. While a whole field of cocksfoot grown for seed can become a tussocky jungle and a death trap for any chicks that are hatched too far from the edge, a strip a few yards wide will be most beneficial. (Lucerne is an alternative.)

There will not be much cover for the first year while the strip is being established, and inter-row cultivation will be needed to stop the weeds growing.

A nesting strip, unlike a seed field, should never be harrowed after the first (establishment) year. Running a cultivator between the rows during the winter will help to keep the crop clean. Any cultivations should be aimed at keeping the sheltered furrows in between the ridges, a pattern which is attractive to a nesting partridge.

Where it is not possible to use a large drill, on banks and in awkward corners which can nevertheless be cultivated, a handful of broadcast cocksfoot will help to provide extra nesting cover.

Cocksfoot has a low insect potential.

The seed rate is 2–5 lb. (1–$2\frac{1}{4}$ kg.) per acre when drilled, or up to 20 lb. (9 kg.) per acre when broadcast. 3 lb. ($1\frac{1}{4}$ kg.) should be used on most soils, the heavier rates on poorer soils or when sowing conditions are bad. It is best *drilled* in April, usually with a corn drill. The drill spouts can be blocked off to give a row width of 18–24 in. (45–60 cm.), with 21 in. (55 cm.) being probably the optimum.

Where normally grown for seed the first crop will be taken during July in the year following establishment, and the seed is usually harvested by combine. If the seed is not harvested a small amount may spread to nearby crops, but this will not matter if the surrounding fields are to be ploughed. The cocksfoot strip will need 'topping' (grass-mower set very high, 1–2 ft. [30–60 cm.] if possible) in the autumn to clear some dead grass and promote new growth for the following year. It is also advisable to 'drag' grass harrows through the crop to complete thinning and cleaning. Strips can be left down for two or three years, as convenient to the farm cropping programme.

Coriander *(Coriandrum sativum)*

Pheasants, partridges and ducks seem to be attracted to the standing crop and are drawn to the stubbles after harvest. Dogs have great difficulty in finding birds because of the aromatic smell of the plant!

Coriander has been grown in Britain for over 200 years on a very small scale, although a large feed-and-seed business is currently experimenting with it as a potential break crop for cereal farms in East Anglia and southern England. The seeds are used commercially in the production of gin, pickles, chutney and curry! It is an annual crop sown in drills 12–14 in. (30–36 cm.) apart in April at a seed rate of 10–20 lb. (4½–9 kg.) per acre.

Fodder radish *(Raphanus sativus campestris)*

Experience over several seasons has shown very variable crop performances, both in growth and value to shooting cover. Pheasants and partridges do not like the crop when it is wet, especially if sown too thickly. On the other hand, good drives of partridges in October, and pheasants in November, have been obtained from the crops standing almost 2–3 ft. (1 metre) high.

The crop is probably of more potential value in the north, if sown immediately following a hay cut or early potatoes, in areas where the harvest is too late for mustard or fodder radish to be sown as an after-harvest crop. Trials with Siletina suggest that its seeds may not be the great attraction to pheasants that was first suspected. It has a tendency to flatten in exposed areas, but can be useful in a mixture with kale. The kale stems support the Siletina well, even if pigeons completely remove the tops.

Fodder radish grows rapidly but some varieties show a marked tendency to flower and run to seed after a relatively short growing period.

The crop is more susceptible to frost damage than rape and hence is more suited to early autumn than early winter feeding. Despite its rapid growth it often does relatively less well than rape from late sowings. Relative to rape, fodder radish has done less well in northern areas than in the south.

Early flowering varieties such as Rapide and Siletina are suitable for crops intended for ploughing in, but they are unsuitable for forage purposes.

In certain circumstances fodder radish has advantages over mustard.

1. The crop emerges rapidly and grows well, given the right weather at sowing time.

2. It is very palatable, and can be grazed off as an alternative to ploughing in as a green manure.

3. The crop will grow as an annual if sown early, but will also behave as a biennial plant if sown in late July or August. If sown late, the crop may run to flower and seed after a short growing period.

4. It has not as yet been attacked by mildew or clubroot, and it does not increase sugar beet eelworm populations as do mustard and rape. Because of this the British Sugar Corporation allows the crop to be grown on land which will be used for sugar beet.

The first strains of seed available were very frost-tender, but improved varieties have much greater frost resistance. Cullen's 'Slobolt' fodder radish has been sown as late as 1st October in the south and has withstood three frosts of −10° C. – while in mid-Essex another crop was still standing well at Christmas, having withstood eighteen frosts down to −5° C.

The sowing rate for game cover should be 5–6 lb. per acre (6–7 kg. per hectare) with a drill width of 21 in. (50 cm.). Broadcasting rate should be 6–8 lb. per acre (7–9 kg. per hectare). In the north of England the crop should be sown before the end of August. If fodder radish is grown after a cereal crop apply 3 bags per acre (7 bags per hectare) ICI No. 4. If sown after other crops which have been well fertilised this may not be essential.

Foodpatches *(mixed)*

Over a period of years all sorts of mixtures were tried at Fordingbridge, gradually eliminating out most cereals, pulses and other crops that at first sight looked as though they might be suitable. The compromise finally arrived at produced the following 'game mixture':

	Quantity per acre	
	(lb.)	(kg.)
Sunflower	3	1·4
Maize	4	1·8
Canary seed	5	2·3
Buckwheat	5	2·3
Caraway	1	0·5
American sweet clover (*Melilotus alba*)	2	0·9
Marrowstem kale	1	0·5
Nida rape	1	0·5
Sowing rate	22 lb. per acre	10·2 kg. per acre

Several shooting men have added up to 4 lb. (1¾ kg.) of linseed to the above mixture, cutting down slightly on the buckwheat and canary seed. Lupins have been tried on poor, acid soils. The sunflower seedheads should be knocked down so that the pheasants can make full use of the food available (see page 275).

While the standard mixture is very suitable for the southern half of England it requires modification as one moves northwards. From Yorkshire to the north better results will be obtained with ¾ cwt. (38 kg.) spring wheat, 1 cwt. (50 kg.) tick beans and 2–3 lb. (1–1¼ kg.) kale per acre. However, the disadvantage of this mixture is that it has to be drilled or broadcast in three separate operations because of the disparity in seed size.

It has been noted that where game food strips or patches are planted in the same place two years running, the pheasants will tend to work the piece of ground upon which they are accustomed to feed: this results in the almost complete disappearance of the sunflower! If possible, it is therefore better to change the site of the foodpatches from season to season.

255

97 Sunflowers are not often grown as a pure stand for game, but are useful in foodpatch mixtures in the south and Midlands

98 A useful game foodpatch sold by Miln Marsters Group Ltd, of Chester

256

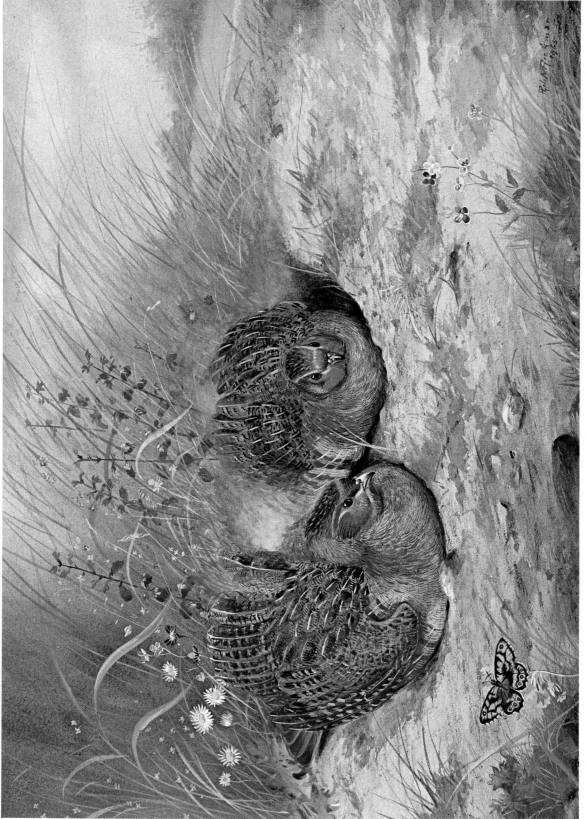

Grey Partridges *Philip Rickman*

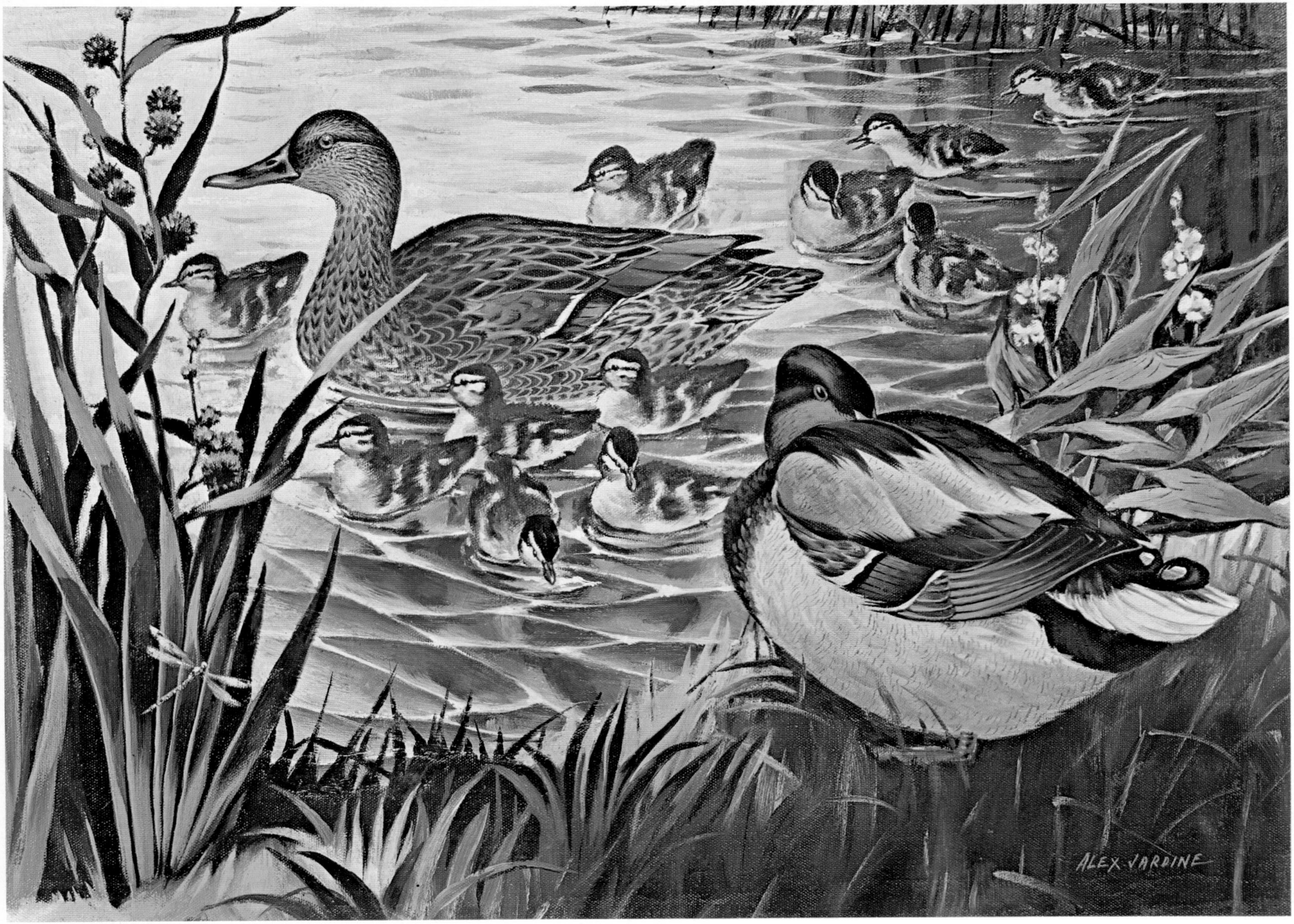

Mallard *Alex Jardine*

Most soils will produce a good foodpatch crop provided a reasonable seedbed is obtained. Sowing must be delayed until early May to avoid late frosts. The different sizes of seeds can lead to difficulties when the crop is sown with a force feed drill as opposed to being broadcast, in which case it may be necessary to order the seeds in separate quantities. The large seeds can then be drilled at the first pass, the smaller seeds being drilled at right angles on the second pass, thus enabling an even distribution. When a combine drill with cup feed is used the down spouts should be removed. This broadcasts well and avoids breaking or splitting the larger seeds.

Many farmers will be familiar with the problem of keeping rooks, crows and pigeons off areas of game mixture, maize or kale. Small areas are very vulnerable, and often the simplest solution is to plant a larger patch than will be required (say 10 acres [4 h.] instead of 2 [0·8 h.]), feeding or harvesting the excess crop for farm use.

Areas of 1–3 acres (0·4–1·2 h.) can be protected by stringing with black thread. (See also under Maize.)

Kale *(Brassica oleracea)*

Carefully sited kale can produce extremely high birds in the shooting season, and is a useful holding crop after the corn is cut. In the early part of the year, when the land is generally very bare, strips of seed kale serving the purpose of escape cover and protection from the weather have always been a wonderful investment for game.

Obviously there is little a shooting *tenant* can do about any kale there may be on the land he rents, unless he really has the goodwill of the farmer and can persuade him to site his crops in strategic places and in reasonable-sized blocks of 2–10 acres (1–4 h.). The owner-farmer, however, can certainly hold more pheasants and show better birds if he approaches his kale planting with a little forethought. For instance, a field of kale planted close to a thick, unbroken hedge can be a great disadvantage, as the birds will often steal out of kale and vanish into the hedge, from which they may be difficult to flush. A gap between the two can be helpful. Unless planted specifically to increase the size of a belt or small covert, kale should be kept away from woods, but preferably within driving distance. Size is not particularly important if the block is long and narrow (30 to 40 yds. [27–37 m.]) which means that a comparatively small team of beaters can manage it efficiently. In any case, fields of kale which are unwieldy at the start of season can usually be fed off or harvested to a better size and shape for end-of-season shooting. A good plan with a large, oblong block is to cut *diagonally* from one corner to another, enlarging this narrow strip daily until eventually a broad avenue has been cleared and one is left with two triangular blocks of kale opposite each other – ideal shapes for driving, as there is always a suitable corner to drive into whatever the wind.

Thousand-head kale is generally considered too wet to hold birds, but in the stone wall upland areas of the north it has proved a very useful shooting and holding cover. If drilled in June it will provide cover until the following April or May – but the drills should be 20 in. (51 cm.) apart to prevent the growth

257

getting too dense. Farmers cutting the kale in the late winter from January to March nearly always flush pheasants out of the standing crop.

Drilled or broadcast? As to whether kale should be drilled or broadcast, this seems to be a matter upon which opinions differ. The experience of the Conservancy advisory staff is that it is much easier to drive pheasants along drills. In broadcast kale they are inclined to spring up in all directions, though if there are two or three back Guns this may not matter. A disadvantage of drilled kale is that there is often a tendency for most of the birds to run forward and flush like a cloud of bluebottles right at the end of a drive. To some extent this can be prevented by more controlled – rather than merely exuberant – beating, and by standing the Guns well back from the kale so that if there is a big flush at least the birds will have had time to spread out and gain height and speed. To encourage the birds to flush a little way back, or at regular intervals throughout the beat, cross rides should be cut out by hand or with a forage harvester if one is available.

It has also been suggested that it helps to drill the kale at the flushing end at right angles to the rest of the field, or even to broadcast the end block or the headlands, but this presupposes that one is always going to drive the kale the same way and does not allow for alterations of plan due to a change of wind. The distance between the drills has some effect on the suitability of the crop for pheasants, 24 in. (61 cm.) between the rows probably being the best.

A technique that has been used successfully, though it would no doubt be frowned upon by the efficiency experts, is to stop the drill for brief intervals when sowing, so that the block of kale matures with a few open patches here and there. This also works well when sowing mustard as a partridge holding crop. The birds will often flush when they get to the bare patches.

Where Savoys are profitable, two rows of kale and two of cabbage – making four rows of each where the drill has turned round – produce a good pheasant pattern and keep the beaters happy. Turnips or swedes are often sown with kale, though if the kale is very heavy it will tend to swamp the turnips. Two rows of turnips to six of drilled kale are a useful standard mixture, though there are two sides to this question of providing a lane of turnips so that the beaters can walk along it dry shod, while the pheasants skulk about unharried in the neighbouring kale strips! Much depends on how well trained the beaters are.

A useful kale and clover mixture which is grown in Gloucestershire is as follows: kale drilled normally, with 2 lb. (1 kg.) per acre of American Clover added. In the first year there is little sign of the clover, but it seeds itself and in the second year dominates the kale. In the third year it is exclusively self-sown clover, which continues into the fourth and fifth year, by which time it dies out and the mixture has to be replaced once again.

This crop provides thick cover, and even in July it can be 6 ft. (1·8 m.) high, though hollow underneath, which makes it attractive to the birds. It stands well all winter and has a high insect population.

258

Roots for partridges. While considering kale for pheasants it might also be worth while briefly mentioning crops suitable for partridges.

Mustard (discussed later) is undoubtedly one of the best, but a field of thin kale can sometimes be almost as good. Thousand-head and rape are obviously better than marrowstem, but if the latter is thinned with swedes or turnips it becomes much more suitable as partridge cover. 1½ lb. (0·7 kg.) rape, 1½ lb. (0·7 kg.) giant rape, ½ lb. (0·2 kg.) marrowstem, ½ lb. (0·2 kg.) thousand-head, ½ lb. (0·2 kg.) swedes and ½ lb. (0·2 kg.) turnips, drilled as a mixture, is an excellent crop for both partridges and pheasants, the latter taking wing at regular intervals throughout the drive. The beaters have no lanes to escape into, and an electric fence can be used if wanted for stock.

Kale as release point for poults. From the information so far gathered, the results of putting reared birds out beside kale crops have been disappointing. A few estates seem to have managed to hold their birds in the kale, but most rearers did not. When released beside *large* areas of kale (25 acres [10 h.]) they gave a very poor return. Perhaps they got lost soon after release, before they were really acclimatised to the wild and able to fend for themselves? On two estates where this was tried the foxes in the kale made easy killings because the birds were forced to jug on the ground rather than roost in trees. On another estate, where very small acreages were chosen, the birds appear to have strayed out of the cover and never returned. The size of the kale area may therefore be an important factor, but there are probably many other considerations of equal significance, which makes this rather a complex problem.

On farms where releasing has to be into kale, planting blocks on each side of a central hedge will provide some shelter and roosting, particularly if the top growth of the hedge can be left untrimmed for several years. An open-topped release pen can then be built around the kale and through the hedge. Once established the kale should be left to go to seed. Feeding in and around kale fields is an excellent way of drawing wild and reared birds into them. Hoppers placed in the 'rides', or hand-feeding on straw, both attract birds. One keen shooting farmer always puts bales of straw in the clearings of the kale, and feeds nearby. The pheasants use these straw 'forts' as vantage points, getting up on top of them and looking out. This idea is commended to others, with the additional suggestion that a tunnel trap or rat-baiting point should be made in between the bales of straw. If these 'forts' are made as straw bale silos and filled with tail corn they will serve a double purpose.

Management on a shooting day. Although there are exceptions to every rule, there is little doubt that kale should never normally be driven after three in the afternoon, nor first thing in the morning if very wet from dew or rain. If the birds are accustomed to being fed at a regular time of the day, naturally the greatest weight of pheasants can be expected at this time. As a general rule midday is as good a time as any. If the same piece of kale is driven twice in one day it is wise to allow two hours before going into it for the second time. If birds

259

are driven into a block of kale from a previous beat, the field should not normally be driven immediately, but rested for about an hour. If taken through at once the birds are usually reluctant to fly.

By the time the shooting day arrives all that can be done to improve the size and shape of the kale for shooting will have been completed. Flushing rides and clearings will have been cut, and the only last-minute arrangement that may be helpful under certain circumstances is the provision of sewelling or wire netting for flushing the birds. The latter can be used in the following special way.

If there are not enough beaters to take a large block of kale through in one piece, it will be helpful to place the food hoppers just inside the kale down *one side only* and perhaps half-way round the two ends. This will encourage the pheasants to frequent one half of the field only. The day before shooting a temporary fence of wire netting should be run down the centre of the field, and the beaters put through the 'fed' half of the kale only.

As to the direction in which the kale should be driven – down the drills, of course – unless the wind dictates the day's tactics there invariably seems to be one way the birds want to go, and this can usually be discovered by disturbing them at feed some weeks before shooting. If there happens to be a home covert to which the birds are bent on returning, it is worth the risk of driving the birds *away* from the Guns and shooting them as they curl back over the beaters' heads. It doesn't always work, however!

Strips of kale as narrow as 15 yds. (14 m.) are successfully used on many farms. Relatively few beaters are needed. Birds can be driven from one strip to the next, and provide excellent shooting.

The beaters. Although everyone knows exactly what the beaters *should* do, it is rare to see the operation perfectly carried out. How rarely do they zigzag through the crop? How often do they stand and stare open-mouthed – forgetting to tap their sticks – when a shot bird is hunted for in the kale? However, the temptation to write a treatise on beating must be resisted, except perhaps to make the obvious comment that a 'waterproof' beater does his job better than a 'leaking' one.

It is of little use to discuss the ideal ways of handling kale, because for one thing it is a foregone conclusion that there will never be enough beaters. However many one has, one can always use more! Dogs can be a decidedly mixed blessing, except where half the Guns are walking and half standing, and there is virtually no escape for a bird flushed the wrong way by a wild terrier who has slipped his binder-twine noose. However, certain stratagems can be employed: beating should be *slow*, and reasonably quiet unless cheerful noises are necessary to keep the beaters' spirits up; all eyes should be on the headkeeper to see when to stop during a flush, or which flank should go ahead. The last 25 yds. (23 m.) are all-important, and if there are a lot of birds in the crop they are less likely to flush all together if only two beaters go forward to the edge of the field.

260

From the commercial angle, kale grown for seed usually pays handsomely about one year in five, when seed is in short supply. In other years it more or less holds its own – dependent on local considerations and January frosts. However, in this particular discussion we are considering kale solely as a shooting crop and not as a general-purpose item of cover.

After first siting his kale fields so that – depending on where the dairy is and similar considerations – the layout suits both his farming and his shooting programme, the owner will probably have ideas as to the type of kale to sow, whether to drill it or broadcast it, and so on.

Which type of kale? Most shooting farmers prefer marrowstem (or mixtures of marrowstem and other root crops), its only disadvantage being that it is more susceptible to frost than thousand-head. Where sheep are concerned thousand-head is the obvious choice, and if heavily fertilised will grow to almost the same height as marrowstem. Except in very sheltered areas it is wise to use up marrowstem kale before the end of the year, and on farms with very little woodland this lack of cover may affect the late shooting programme. Cholet kale has been known to continue growing throughout the winter in Scotland.

An important development has been the direct drilling of kale and other forage crops into grassland after silage. The grass sward is killed by spraying with 'Gramoxone' and 'Round-Up' and this gives a firm base for cattle feeding off the crop during the winter. Contract services now operate in most parts of the country to carry out this operation, known as direct drilling, and this has led to a revival of interest in kale on many farms where labour has become too scarce for traditional methods. This system is also helpful in retaining soil moisture more effectively than traditional methods, thus improving germination.

When to sow. As to when marrowstem should be drilled the present tendency in the game counties is to sow the kale on the late side, towards the end of June, as it is then more manageable in the shooting season. It should, however, be providing a little cover by harvest time. If it is sown early in the year, by the time the shooting season comes along it will usually provide nothing but top cover with a forest of banana stems (very susceptible to damage from snow and ice) growing from the otherwise bare floor. On the other hand, if June is a dry month there is a risk of crop failure, although sod-seeding has enabled later sowings of kale to be satisfactorily established.

The seed rate should be 2–4 lb. (1–2 kg.) per acre when drilled or 7–9 lb. (3–4 kg.) per acre when broadcast. If swede or turnip inter-rows are considered, the seed rates will depend upon the ratio of kale rows involved, but 3–4 lb. (1–2 kg.) of kale and 2–3 lb. (1–1½ kg.) of swedes per acre are usually required.

For real winter cover – apart from mixed foodpatches – strips of marrowstem kale grown for seed are about the best. When planting winter wheat, undersown with a one-year ley, a strip of two or three acres can be left in the same field, to be sown with kale the following spring. Kale grown for seed is approximately a fourteen month crop, and the whole field will become available for another crop after the kale seed and the clover have been harvested the following year. A field of undersown spring barley, with a strip of seed kale to one side, will give the same result, and the normal rotation of crops is not upset.

Mixtures. Some mixtures which have been used successfully are four rows of swedes and buckwheat to eight rows of kale, and four rows of marrowstem with two rows of thousand-head for the electric fence.

Linseed *(Linum usitatissimum)*

Not common nowadays, probably because it is cheaper to import oilseed than to grow linseed over here. It usually ripens early in September and holds birds well in the crop and on the subsequent stubble.

When growing this crop it is best to avoid extremely light or extremely heavy land. The seedbed should be as for roots, with sowing between mid-March to mid-May. Seed rate 80 lb. (36 kg.) per acre drilled or 120 lb. (55 kg.) broadcast.

Lucerne *(Medicago sativa)*

Although lucerne is a good cover crop for game, its usefulness tends to tail off rather early in the shooting season as the growth dies down. A group of Essex farmers have now found a way of prolonging its holding capacity. A mixture of barley and canary seed is put in with the crop to provide food and, providing pigeons are not present in too great numbers, it will last well into November and make excellent foraging for both pheasants and partridges.

As the grassland acreage declines in many eastern areas of the country, so the holding qualities of lucerne for partridges during the winter become important. A balance has to be struck between the beneficial overwintering facilities afforded by a field or two of lucerne, and the losses later in the year at grass-cutting time. Lucerne may not be such attractive nesting cover as many grass mixtures grown for silage, but unfortunately partridges will nest in the crop if alternative nesting cover is not available.

To counteract these disadvantages to some extent, lucerne has a high insect production to help chick survival. As the crop is mostly grown in the drier eastern counties, where the partridge stock will be highest, this is an important factor in predominantly cereal areas. Lucerne will continue to be grown in the east because of its deep rooting system. Efficient utilisation of the crop, especially a pure stand, is often a problem for the farmer.

The seeding rate per acre should be 14 lb. (6 kg.) of barley and 4 lb. (2 kg.) of canary seed (see first paragraph) added to the lucerne, sown at the locally recommended rate. If the mixture is drilled with the lucerne it will be too near the surface and very vulnerable to birds. It is therefore necessary to carry out a separate operation, drilling the mixture at the normal depth for barley before putting in the lucerne. Even though it will only be effective for one season, since barley and canary seed are annuals, it has been so successful in Essex that it is now a routine operation on many shoots.

Where grass drying is carried out lucerne is becoming increasingly important, as it can extend the drying season.

262

Lupins *(Lupinus* spp.)*

The value of the perennial tree lupin (*Lupinus arboreus*) as game cover has not, we believe, been fully explored.

Annual and perennial lupins are outside the range of normal farm crops, but the annuals grow well on acid soils, where they are used occasionally as sheep feed or green manure. There are two varieties of annual lupin offered by agricultural seedsmen – yellow (or sweet) which is said to have some value as a game crop, and blue (or bitter).

The seeds of lupins can be toxic to sheep, cattle and pigs when the crop is still growing, and after harvesting and drying. The Sweet Blue Lupin is comparatively free from the toxic alkaloids and this variety should always be grown in preference to the Yellow or Common Blue varieties. When grown as a game crop the plants will usually be ploughed in as green manure, but if stock are likely to be in the vicinity adequate fencing is an obvious precaution.

The sowing rate is high (80–100 lb. [36–45 kg.] per acre, in 7-in. [18 cm.] drills, seed sown 1–1½ in. [2½–4 cm.] deep), and the seed is relatively expensive. The seed, like lucerne, must be dressed with a culture if it is to be sown on land that has not previously grown the crop. Lupins will thrive only on extremely acid soils, and care must be taken to prevent the seedlings from being smothered by weeds in the early stages. The crop stands well even when dead, and will grow to a height of 2–5 ft. (60–150 cm.) depending upon soil and weather conditions.

Maize *(Zea mays)*

The most attractive crop for pheasants ever seen by one member of our staff was a modest-sized field of maize, which seemed literally to be moving with birds and provided fast shooting for practically a whole afternoon. This was before the war. Unfortunately modern strains of maize are usually harvested in October or early November, which is too early to be of any use for pheasant shooting.

In northern France it is not unusual to leave the maize stubble knee-high, which provides very good shooting cover. The top growth is then swiped off and ploughed in during December and January. This practice is recommended to shooting farmers in the grain maize areas of the south.

If a strip (preferably not less than 10 yds. [9 m.] wide) can be grown, or left from an existing crop of silage or grain maize in a strategic position (i.e. to widen an existing strip of cover) it will provide some of the best possible drawing and holding cover for pheasants. As the stems break down through the autumn a dry dense holding cover results, and the grain on the cobs will draw pheasants from far and wide.

When maize is grown in very large blocks it can become a danger for pheasant poults – particularly if intensively reared. If the release point is adjacent to the crop, the birds may find their way into it, get totally lost, and ultimately die of lack of food and water.

Some shooting men blank off the maize by sowing a few rows *across* the drills on the outside edge of the crop. If, however, the drills are left open – as opposed

99 Although the cobs may not ripen every year, maize nevertheless provides very good pheasant holding cover

to being sealed off – the poults will tend to work down them and eventually come out. It is also helpful if cross rides are cut in the maize, with a watering and feeding station sited in the middle.

Another method of managing maize is to grow the crop in three-acre plots and feed it up to early December. A narrow strip is then cut down one side of the plot with a forage harvester or a swipe. This will fell the cobs so that pheasants soon find them. This technique continues until late January, cutting a strip once a week. Such a maize plot attracts and holds birds very well.

Finally, a warning about maize! It is an absolutely first-class game crop, but it does need to be grown with care. Some shoot owners are tempted to 'try a strip for the pheasants', but give it less attention than a packet of radish seed. It fails and is never tried again – to the detriment of both farm and pheasants.

Maize is, incidentally the mainstay of most of the North American winter foodpatch mixtures – providing food and pickings for a long time, and shelter even during snowy weather. On the European Continent the cobs are often harvested on longish stems, stored carefully and taken out in bunches at intervals during the winter months to hang up just off the ground in the woods. Where a sizeable area of two acres or more is grown for game, another system is to run down a strip with a swipe or forage harvester each week. This breaks up the cobs and spreads them on the ground for the pheasants to feed on.

264

Its normal place in arable farming is as a one-year break in a mixed or mainly cereal rotation. With use of atrazine herbicide maize gives better weed control than other break crops that can be combine-harvested, and is not susceptible to any of the main hazards of continuous wheat or barley growing.

The time of sowing should be during late April when the *soil temperature at four inches depth reaches 10° C. (50° F.)*. Choose sheltered fields with a deep, well-drained soil at low elevation.

The young seedlings are susceptible to attack by the frit fly (*Oscinella frit*), particularly when the crop is late sown or if growth is adversely affected by the weather. Attacks by this pest may result in the loss of plants and poor grain production. The pest is best controlled by incorporating insecticide granules, such as phorate or chlorfenvinphos, in the seedbed.

Another pest that comes to most growers' minds is the rook, but if reasonable precautions are taken, attacks by birds can be minimised. The correct depth of sowing is 2 in. (5 cm.) and good covering of the seed is the first requirement. The most vulnerable stage is during seedling growth, particularly just as the crop emerges (usually 5–20 days after drilling). From immediately after sowing, rooks must be discouraged as follows:

(i) Dawn shot-gun patrols, particularly during the three weeks from emergence. The rooks must be deterred from settling in the maize field for their first feeding ground of the day.

(ii) Hanging up as many dead rooks as possible, suspending the birds outstretched with wingtips tied to two sticks, thus causing continual movement.

(iii) Stringing the field with black thread* at head height on medium-weight bamboo canes. Leave a droop of 18 in. (45 cm.) between canes to prevent breaking when wet. This need take no more than 1 man-hour per hectare ($\frac{1}{3}$ man-hour per acre). Thread in 40-yd. (35 m.) squares.

(iv) Agricultural bangers and even balloons – moved regularly – have proved successful in some areas.

Treating seed for bird repellance has been tried with varying success, Thimet probably being the most promising chemical to date. Much depends on whether there is an untreated field nearby.

New varieties are constantly being developed, but at the time of writing the following are some of the more prominent.

	Maturity class	
Silage maize	8	Dekalb 202, LG11
	7	Inra 240, Rubis, 'INRA 182'
	6	Aurelia, Circe, Eta, Fronica, Goal
	5	Campo, Solaris, 'UNCAC 242', Anjou 210, Caldera 535, Blizzard

* Cones of Coats Aptan No. 201, 40 gauge (black) are available from the Haberdashery Department of MacCullough and Wallis, 25 Dering Street, London W.1. Each cone contains 3,000 yds. (2,743 m.) – enough for 5 acres (2 h.).

Grain Maize early varieties that may be suitable for a grain crop in sheltered areas in the south and east of England below 300 ft. (100 m.) from Hampshire to Norfolk: Anjou 196, Anjou 210, Dekalb 202, LG7 and Maris Carmine.

Varieties in the Grain Maize classified list can be successfully used for silage, but generally result in lower silage yields than varieties in the silage group.

By selecting suitable varieties (i.e. those with a good standing ability) several farmers growing maize for grain successfully harvested the cobs from parts of the crop left for game cover in late January/early February. Yields are obviously considerably less than at optimum harvest time, but the excellent cover for game is considered well worth it.

Fertilise with 6 bags ICI No. 4 per hectare (2½ bags per acre) into the soil before drilling. The crop responds well to organic matter from a ley or an application of dung or slurry. After a heavy dressing of FYM or slurry apply 3 bags Nitram per hectare (1 bag per acre).

Mangolds *(Beta vulgaris)*

The acreage grown nowadays is a fraction of that grown 20 years ago, and is still diminishing. This is a pity, for it was one of the best crops for partridge driving and far superior to sugar beet in that respect.

Mangolds are of the same brassica family as sugar beet, the noticeable difference in the growing plant being that the larger mangold root – red or yellow in colour according to variety – is mostly above ground level. The crop is grown entirely as a cattle food, being pulled and carted (or stored in clamps) rather than grazed like swedes and turnips. On lighter soils the crop is usually carted to yarded cattle throughout the winter, but on heavier soils it is lifted in October and November before severe frosts and clamped, to be fed off in the New Year.

Drilled in April and May, the seed (10 lb. [4½ kg.] per acre) is put in rows 20–22 in. (51–56 cm.) apart on the flat, or 24–26 in. (61–66 cm.) apart when sown in ridges.

Millet

There has been a recent revival of interest in this crop, with newer Hungarian varieties available which are probably better able to withstand the British climate.

Millet was grown at Fordingbridge in trials during 1963–66 inclusive. The varieties then available struggled to survive and failed in average (i.e. most) summers. Improved varieties currently available are probably suitable for southern England and East Anglia only, and should be treated with the greatest caution in the midlands and North.

Millet does best on a reasonably light soil and should be drilled in rows 10–14 in. (25–35 cm.) apart at a rate of 20–25 lbs. (9–11 kg.) per acre.

Fertiliser application should be 2 cwt. of ICI No. 2 per acre, with Atrazin at 2½ lbs. per acre for weed control. The crop is particularly prone to attacks by rabbits.

266

Mustard *(Brassica alba)*

Grown as a normal farm crop it would be sown in early April, but for game it is commonly put in directly after the harvest, either disced in or broadcast with a spinner, together with the fertiliser.

For partridges the seeding rate – using the highest germination-rate seed – should be about 8–10 lb. ($3\frac{1}{2}$–$4\frac{1}{2}$ kg.) to the acre. Some landowners sow 8 lb. ($3\frac{1}{2}$ kg.) of mustard and 2 lb. (1 kg.) of rape to add some feeding value. Others stop the drill for a few seconds every now and then when sowing so as to create a few open patches in the crop. This pattern makes it even more popular with the birds and helps to provide flushing places.

Pheasants require a less dense crop, a seed rate of 4–6 lb. (2–3 kg.) per acre normally being sufficient.

Where a field is too large to drive, half of it can be rolled down the day before shooting. Similarly feeding rides – preferably not straight – are often made in the crop with a roller.

One idea for improving the shooting out of strips of mustard is that the last 10 or 15 yds. (9 or 14 m.) at each end of the strip should have an extra top-dressing of nitrogen at sowing time. This will provide dense, almost impenetrable stands which cause the birds to flush well before the end of the strip.

Probably the best dual-purpose crop on the farm, according to when and how it is cultivated. It grows rapidly, smothers weeds and when ploughed in (best done early in the year after frosting) improves the physical structure of the soil, and of course makes excellent game cover after the harvest is in.

It can also be broadcast (by hand or using a hand-held 'Fiddle') into a standing cereal crop, such as barley, ten days or so before harvest. This gains valuable time, particularly in the North where the harvest is later. It is best sown in mid-July and not later than mid-August. Deep drilling the seed will delay germination and growth.

Mustard will grow in almost any soil, the seedbed should be as for roots. Seed mustard is a good shooting crop and provides good food until the 'stubble' is ploughed in. This is normally sown at about 4 lb. to the acre (4 kg. per hectare) in drills 19 in. (50 cm.) apart.

Fertiliser application for a seed crop should be 12 bags ICI No. 2 per hectare (5 bags per acre) in the seedbed and top dressed with 5 bags Nitram per hectare (2 bags per acre). For green manure crops the fertiliser is reduced to 7 bags per hectare of ICI No. 2 (3 bags per acre) and only 3 bags per hectare of Nitram (1 bag per acre) applied as top dressing.

Oil poppy *(Papaver somniferum)*

The commercial market is limited, but wherever it is grown, from East Anglia to Herefordshire, the crop has been very attractive to pheasants.

If grown specifically as a game crop, the capsules may be out of reach of pheasants. However, it will usually be found that small birds break into the pods, and the seed is then scattered and made available for game. It is not certain whether the cover or the seed is the main attraction, but even a stubble after harvest still draws a lot of pheasants and partridges.

The cover provided by poppies is thin once the November frosts have cut down the foliage, but on several trial sites it was noted that pheasants were attracted to poppy patches. This was seen even where strips of mustard or other game crops had been unsuccessful on the same place in previous years.

A limited acreage of this crop – also known as opium poppy – has been grown in this country for a number of years. The actual opium alkaloids are not produced in our British climate. It does not grow well on heavy or wet soils, or in the north, and a really fine tilth on a level seedbed is necessary for the best stands. Although capable of withstanding a little frost, plants will be killed by a sharper frost below —2° C. (27° F.). March sowing is needed for commercial crops, but up to late April would be early enough where the poppies are being grown to attract game.

The seed rate is 2–3 lb. (1–1½ kg.) per acre in a drill width of 12–20 in. (30–50 cm.). Inter-row cultivations are necessary where the seed is to be harvested, but for game patches this will probably not be necessary. During the growing stage woodpigeons and hares may attack the crop.

The final crop height is 2–3 ft. (60–90 cm.) and it is ready to harvest when the capsule has turned brown and the seeds rattle inside when it is shaken. As the crop matures, the lower growth withers away, leaving stiff, hollow stems supporting the capsules.

Oilseed rape *(Brassica oleracea var.)*

Winter-sown rape is the highest yielding type, being drilled in September/October and harvested in the following July. After a mild winter September-sown rape can be 12–18 in. (30–45 cm.) high in February and provides good cover for partridges. For this reason the winter-sown varieties are much to be preferred in crop planning from the game point of view to the spring-sown varieties which are generally sown too late and harvested too early to be of great value in providing cover or food.

Oilseed rape crops in June/July are too thick for use by partridge chicks, but if a strip can be left unharvested in the autumn alongside a hedge it will hold pheasants.

Unfortunately oilseed rape is susceptible to several insect pests, and regular spraying with malathion to control pollen beetle, pod weevil and pod midge could cause losses among gamebirds in the crop.

Although a close relative to conventional rape, as the name implies, oilseed rape is grown as a cash crop with no stock feeding value at all. The acreage of the crop has expanded rapidly in the last few years as it has become established as one of the most viable break crops for the cereal grower.

Spring sowing is generally March/April, but can take place successfully as late as June in the south, harvesting normally being in September.

A fine seedbed is essential as both seasonal types can be drilled in row widths from 5 in. to 24 in. (13 cm. to 60 cm.), the wider spacing allowing for inter-row cultivations, if

268

100 Mustard, a popular and useful crop for both pheasants and partridges, right, until the end of the season

101 Following the harvest mustard makes excellent game cover until it is ploughed in early in the New Year, a job which is best done after frosting

269

these are required to clean the land. Seed rates are 6–8 lb. (2¾–3½ kg.) per acre according to soil conditions.

Parsnip *(Pastinaca sativa)*

This crop has been grown experimentally for holding cover, with good results. Many young pheasants have held to it, and partridges also feed on the falling seeds.

When grown in the eastern counties as a farm crop, parsnips can provide excellent cover for partridge driving. However, the tops are very susceptible to frost, so in many years there is little cover remaining by the end of October.

Sow in March, in drills 15–17 in. (40–45 cm.) apart at 4–5 lb. (2–2¼ kg.) per acre. The crop grows to a height of 6 ft. (1·8 m.) in its second year, when it runs to seed. If fallen seeds are allowed to germinate it can be regarded as a semi-permanent crop.

Peas *(Pisum arvense)*

When grown for *stockfeed* the crop provides very good game cover. The crop is cut from mid-July onwards and put on tripods to ripen and dry. While the peas are on tripods, they provide both food and shelter. However, chemical desiccation prior to combining is becoming more common. After the peas are cut the ground surface is often covered with small weeds which provide excellent food for young partridges. Additionally the crop has a high insect abundance to help chick survival.

On the other hand, when peas are grown for *freezing* the crop is a real 'killer'. Many partridges jug in the crop at night and are literally mown to death during non-stop, all-night harvesting operations.

Drilling on light land may start in January and continue until April on heavier soils. The seed is drilled in rows 9–12 in. (23–30 cm.) apart at a seed rate of 1–1¾ cwt. (50–90 kg.) per acre depending upon variety and seedbed. The crop may be sprayed with MCPB, which is not dangerous to game.

Being a leguminous crop, an abundant supply of lime should be present in the soil.

Potatoes *(Solanum tuberosum)*

Partridges prefer potatoes to any other farm crops, as they love to run up and down between the ridges. This particularly applies in July and early August when the weather is warm; it is usually moist under the haulm and there is plenty of insect life. When grown as a straightforward crop the potential insect abundance is probably higher than in most cereal crops. Indeed, when potatoes are grown for seed a strip of cereals – usually spring barley – is often sown around the headland as a weed control measure providing an ideal habitat for partridges. This practice is also being adopted around ordinary potato crops (usually maincrop varieties) as it gives a firm base for turning

270

heavy machinery on stubble should the weather deteriorate. The cereal strips are, of course, combined and cleared before the potato harvest commences. Partridges should always be driven *across* the ridges and never down them, otherwise whole coveys will run to the end of the field and flush together. After the haulm has been removed the crop is probably not as good for driving partridges as a good stubble, but good stubbles are increasingly rare nowadays!

Potatoes provide good holding cover for pheasants, although they do not drive out of them well. The crop is usually lifted before the shooting season, but is good for early walking-up days. Duck and geese will often flight to feed on potato fields long after the crop has been harvested.

The crop is planted from March to early May, starting with the early varieties and finishing with the maincrop varieties. The seed potatoes are usually sown in ridges 24–36 in. (60–90 cm.) apart, the tubers being 10–15 in. (25–40 cm.) apart in the ridge. In some eastern areas they are grown on the flat, but this practice is relatively uncommon.

In a bad blight year several sprayings of a fungicide such as 'Sanspor' will have to be carried out, and this will inevitably cause disturbance. In England the haulm may be chemically destroyed with 'Reglone' (previous trials have shown the chemical is not dangerous to game) or mechanically pulverised with a Wolseley Swipe or similar machine. In Scotland and the north the position is somewhat different, mainly because of the seed potato trade. It is estimated that approximately one-third of the Scottish potato crop (40,000 acres [16,200 h.]) is sprayed or pulverised. Much of this acreage is still sprayed with sulphuric acid, which can lead to losses of gamebirds.

Rape *(Brassica oleracea* var. *napus)*

It is a good crop to follow early potatoes, and mixed with turnips for sheep feed it makes good partridge cover. Another good sheep feed mixture which provides excellent shooting season cover is 6 lb. (2¾ kg.) rape, 4 lb. (1¾ kg.) turnips, 6 lb. (2¾ kg.) Italian ryegrass and 40 lb. (18 kg.) barley, sown during the first fortnight of August. This gives feed early in February with a second bite at the end of March.

Rape is normally grown as a forage crop for sheep and cattle. It can be sown from April to August, giving grazing from July to November according to the time of sowing. An improved variety, Rapide, has been sown as a shooting crop as late as September in the south and has provided good cover, under ideal growing conditions, growing up to 3 ft. (91 cm.) in six weeks. The crop does not generally grow as quickly as mustard, but it is more frost-hardy and will continue to grow throughout the winter. It can become rather thick (especially if broadcast) and is inclined to hold the wet.

Rape should be drilled at 4–6 lb. (2–2¾ kg.) per acre, or broadcast at 10–12 lb. (4½–5½ kg.) per acre.

It will grow on a wide range of soils, but prefers a soil well supplied with lime.

271

Raspberries *(Rubus idaeus)*

Raspberries offer safe nesting cover for partridges and also excellent sheltered holding cover during the winter. Partridges are often seen in the crop, but there can be continual disturbance during picking time – late June to August, depending on the locality.

About 5,000 acres are grown in Scotland, where it is very valuable for low-ground game. Pheasants and partridges are shot out of the crop, particularly after the roots and kale have been finally cleared. Showing the birds out of very large blocks is difficult without an army of beaters and dogs, as both pheasants and partridges tend to double back up the rows in between the beaters and are not always very easy to see.

Treated as a medium-term crop, on the same ground for up to ten years, the suckers are planted 18 in. (46 cm.) apart in rows 5–7 ft. ($1\frac{1}{2}$–2 m.) apart.

Savoy cabbage *(Brassica oleracea* var. *capitata)*

Good partridge drives can be made from Savoys, but the birds have to be blanked into them first – as for sugar beet. Pheasants will frequent the crop when it is not being disturbed by harvesting. Other cabbages grown on a field scale are of less importance as a cover crop because they are harvested earlier.

It is sown between April and June in drills 18–24 in. (46–61 cm.) apart, the plants being 8–12 in. (20–30 cm.) apart in the row. Savoys, being the most hardy cabbages, are harvested throughout the winter, starting after the first autumn frosts.

Stubble

Although stubble might not generally be thought of as a 'game crop', the present tendency for the plough to follow the combine in the shortest possible time will lead to a very rapid change in the wildlife habitat on many arable farms. Under such circumstances stubbles which can be left for any length of time become very valuable holding cover.

Immediately after harvest, and before any general stubble treatment commences, it is well worth while examining the weed distribution of individual fields in detail and 'zoning' general areas for different stubble treatments. If one block of several acres is free of couch and weed grasses, that stubble can be left untouched. Another area may need treating only with 'Gramoxone'; a further area may require cultivating – and so on. If selected areas or strips of stubble from one to five acres can be left preferably unbaled, then the holding and showing of birds – particularly partridges – can be greatly improved. Areas of stubble adjacent to game strips are particularly useful in holding birds, which can then be blanked into the main game crop to be shown.

General observations – the following guide is a reasonable 'order of merit' in providing the best game-holding capacity:

1. Undersown stubble.
2. Ordinary stubble, untouched. The longer the stubble length, the better the game-holding capacity.
3. Stubble 'dragged' with a harrow. On lighter soils recently 'dragged' stubbles seem to attract partridges, so that on farm shoots a man is sent off on a tractor on the morning of the shoot to drag a few strips in selected stubbles.
4. Ordinary stubble sprayed with 'Gramoxone'.
5. Stubble after one pass with a chisel plough.
6. Stubble after one pass with cultivators of one type or another.
7. Ploughed or rotavated stubbles.

Disposing of unwanted straw. Chopping and spreading is the best method of all, but machinery to do this has not, so far, kept pace with the density of straw swaths left by the larger combines.

Straw burning on top of stubbles will often leave strips of cover in between the burnt swaths, but stubble burning will leave little or no cover at all.

Apart from the disposal of unwanted straw there are other supposed benefits from burning. However, at the moment, these are the subject of considerable controversy. They concern weed and disease control and whereas one authority will claim that burning controls cereal fungus diseases, another will say that reinfection from surrounding unburnt areas will completely nullify this. It is possible that the value of burning in this respect is somewhat overrated. On the other hand, our partridge research unit considers that the damage to insect populations by burning may be considerable. In the interests of game and wildlife we suggest that burning should be avoided wherever possible. Where this is not practical, precautions must be taken.

Obviously it is better to burn the swaths of straw and leave the intervening stubble. To make this easier it is quite practical and cheap to use a machine to turn three swaths into one, so that as much stubble as possible is left.

It is essential to see that all those responsible have a copy of the Ministry of Agriculture's 'Straw Burning Code', which is an excellent guide to procedure. There are, however, two points which should be added to this. The Code advises ploughing firebreaks around the fields before burning commences. However it is important that these are not around the edges of the field, but at least 15 yards inside the perimeter. The reason for this is that if a fire becomes really fierce (as a result of a sudden increase in wind after lighting) it can jump the firebreak. If this is away from the field perimeter it does give a second chance to get it under control before it reaches valuable buildings, woodlands, hedges, etc. The Code mentions that fires may get out of control 'in strong winds' and 'in exceptionally dry conditions'. A further hazard should be added to this – in windless conditions. In these circumstances the fire will create its own wind but it will not be possible to know from which direction, and a runaway fire may easily result. The Code advocates that the straw around the perimeter should be burned one swath at a time in the early morning or late evening, when the dew is on the ground.

There are other points to watch.

Fields most likely to hold game (e.g. adjacent to woods where pheasants are released) should be thoroughly 'dogged out' before lighting. One frequently sees a man driving round a field with a burning torch setting fire to the entire perimeter. This is lethal for all wildlife trapped in the middle.

The advent of the chisel plough replacing the conventional mouldboard plough has produced a significant improvement in field habitat. Both pheasants and partridges appear to hold to the slight undulations created by the chisels, while a certain amout of straw and grain is still available on or near the surface. On many soils chisel ploughing in September/October followed by a mouldboard ploughing in December/January will be considerably more beneficial to game than an outright mouldboard ploughing or rotavating in September – with the additional agricultural advantage of a weed tilth being ploughed in effectively during the late winter.

Sugar beet *(Beta rapa)*

Sugar beet is attractive to pheasants. In one instance when it was grown very near some artichokes, most of the birds were found in the beet, only moving into the artichokes after the beet had been lifted. Pheasants flush well out of sugar beet and will often be found in the crop, unlike partridges. Partridges often have to be blanked into the beet fields before being driven over the Guns.

Although partridges are not greatly attracted by sugar beet fields, many thousands are – or were – killed out of this crop every year, because in a great number of areas it is the *only* cover in a wide expanse of ploughed land. After severe rain coveys often fly right over beet rather than drop into the crop, as it can be like a pond!

Spring cultivations often bring old crowns to the surface, and this can provide food for game at a time when many fields are bare.

Incidentally, sugar beet damage during the growing period can be caused by many birds (other than pheasants) and mammals. Specific counts on two estates with a high game population showed the damage to be about 1 per cent of the total crop.

The weedkillers used for this crop are not dangerous, but Metasystox 55, Didi-Col or other insecticides should be used with the utmost care after the end of May, when the first broods of wild pheasant chicks will be feeding in the fringes of the crop.

Sugar beet can only be grown under contract to the British Sugar Corporation. Sowing is usually staggered between late March and early May, being drilled on the flat in rows 18–20 in. (45–50 cm.) apart.

In the past much disturbance was caused by gangs singling and hoeing the crop from mid-May to the end of June. However, great advances in producing 'monogerm' seed

274

and chemical weed control, coupled with mechanisation, have drastically cut the labour requirement of the crop.

Sunflowers *(Helianthus annuus)*

These are very easy to grow as a pure crop – provided the rooks can be discouraged – and make a good food and cover patch; or the seedheads can be collected for hand feeding. Generally speaking, they are found to be of more use when grown as part of a mixture, with maize and other crops.

It was hoped that 'dwarf' hybrid sunflower varieties would enable the pheasants to reach the sunflower seedheads before finches and sparrows ate them first. Seed of four different varieties obtained from Canada was sown at Fordingbridge, but the heads were still a minimum of 3 ft. 6in. (107 cm.) above ground level – well out of reach of a pheasant.

The standard plant produces a seedhead 5 ft. ($1\frac{1}{2}$ m.) or more above ground level, so that small birds do take a proportion of the seeds. Some seed falls to the ground, to be eaten by pheasants, but the best practice is to knock down a few seedheads every day so that pheasants can make better use of the crop.

They will grow on quite poor soil and require no special treatment.

Swedes and turnips *(Brassica napus* and *B. rapa)*

The crop is fed to sheep during the winter from October to April and provides good holding cover for hill partridges and pheasants. Where kale growing is endangered by pigeon damage, swedes can be considered as an alternative. Even in good kale areas, inter-rows of drilled swedes between the kale will greatly help to show birds out of the crop.

Partridges prefer swedes to turnips – swedes generally produce more insects under the leaves – so that if there is a choice of crop made maybe swedes should be selected.

Swedes are an important root crop in the north of England and in Scotland where they are grown for sheep feed. It is often the only root crop in many areas and swedes, being more hardy than turnips, are also usually grown in hill areas. The crop is commonly grown on ridges 26–30 in. (65–75 cm.) apart, but can also be grown on the flat in rows 18–20 in. (46–50 cm.) apart. Swedes are sown in May and June at 3–4 lb. ($1\frac{1}{4}$–$1\frac{3}{4}$ kg.) per acre, while turnips can be sown later in June and July at a seed rate of 3 lb. ($1\frac{1}{4}$ kg.) per acre. Direct drilling into cleared silage fields after spraying with 'Gramoxone' is becoming popular in some upland areas, especially as a contract operation.

New varieties of turnips have recently been developed for late sowing in July–September for sheep feeding or ploughing in as a green manure. Known as 'stubble turnips' the three most common varieties are Debra, Vobra and Ponda. They can be broadcast at 6 lb. ($2\frac{3}{4}$ kg.) per acre or drilled at 3 lb. ($1\frac{1}{4}$ kg.) per acre. They could make a substitute crop for mustard after harvest, when this crop is not possible because of sugar beet. Stubble turnips may be a game cover worth developing.

Undersowing – general

This title will normally imply the practice of establishing a grass crop underneath a cereal crop, both being spring-sown, the grass growing away in the stubble after harvest. The main value of this practice for game is that it allows the valuable sawfly larvae – so beloved of partridge chicks – to develop in the soil. These sawflies are not pests.

Undersowing can also apply to a much newer technique of broadcasting quick-growing cover crops into standing spring-sown barley, wheat or oats. The faster-growing seeds such as mustard, fodder radish, stubble turnips and Rapide rape are most suitable. A seed rate of 6–8 lb. (2¾–3½ kg.) per acre is suggested for all these crops. The technique is to broadcast the seeds, either with an 'aero' seed fiddle-drill or by hand, into the standing cereals walking down between the drills of corn. The optimum time to do this is 10 to 14 days before the *anticipated* date of harvest. This allows time for the seeds to germinate and the resultant plants to be strong enough to withstand the combining and baling operations. If carried out too early the undersown plants may grow too tall and hinder the combining of the cereal crop – particularly if a short-strawed cereal variety is being grown.

This technique has proved successful under a wide range of crop and soil conditions, but it also depends upon the right weather conditions. Ideally, the undersowing operation should take place between rain showers or immediately before rain is forecast. There is usually enough shade and moisture under the cereals for the plants to establish, but if there is no rain within 7 to 10 days of the cereal crop being harvested, the growing plants will probably wither and die. After harvest it is *essential* to provide a firebreak around the undersown block or strip if the straw is to be burnt on the rest of the field.

Undersowing in this manner has been developed in the North of England because of the later harvest, thus enabling a catch-crop to be established *before* harvest, rather than following the south-country practice of getting an after-harvest crop established. Even in the south and in East Anglia undersowing may be considered for ensuring well-grown mustard strips for partridge driving early in the season.

Trials are at present being conducted to find out if undersowing is also applicable in other situations – for example establishing ground cover beneath a bare-floored crop such as maize.

Whole-crop cereal silage

Despite its rather grandiloquent title this fairly 'new' technique in the agricultural world is an up-to-date variation on the old crops of mashlum (in Scotland and the north) or dredge corn (in the south). The old-style crops consisted of a mixture of oats, barley or wheat with tares, beans or peas to give a nutritious, protein rich, cut of material for ensiling. The modern variation is to cut growing cereal crops – winter wheat or spring barley – for silage in the first half of July to provide a large tonnage of high dry-matter material in one cut.

The first, very beneficial, result for game of the resurrection of this technique is that cereal silage may help to reduce the peak mowing activity of grass silage in May/June which causes so much disturbance and loss to wild game. The

102 The artichoke is one of many valuable game crops which can be used on a farm

second effect is an indirect benefit in the possibility of increasing the winter wheat acreage. Because the cereal silage fields are cleared before the conventional harvest starts, cultivations can take place immediately and conditions are ideal for sowing wheat.

On the debit side, it must be noted that forage harvesters will be in use over a longer period on the farm. But in early July their effect on game will be much less than earlier in the season. Chicks and young wild poults will be about the fields then (as opposed to sitting hens in May/June) and can escape down rows of a cereal crop very much more easily than in a comparable grass crop.

The technique is likely to become accepted in the south and eastern counties, in predominantly cereal growing areas where the effect on balance will be more beneficial than otherwise.

Winter wheat *(Triticum vulgare)*

To gain the most advantage of the crop from the game point of view – and this particularly relates to partridges – the blocks of winter wheat should be well scattered around the farm. In predominantly spring barley country this dispersal of the crop is of the utmost importance: but in a more varied rotation the winter wheat should be sited away from root breaks and grass fields to have the most impact.

Although mentioned previously under 'Cereal crops', winter wheat is so important to game that it deserves separate mention. The wheat acreage has expanded since the late 1960s and much of this increase has been in winter-sown wheat, which spreads the labour requirement at both sowing and harvest and brings in a better gross margin return than spring-sown cereals.

The increasing acreage of winter wheat has led to some grain, treated with harmful seed dressings, being sown into poor seedbeds – particularly on heavier soils. This can lead to an intake of these poisons by gamebirds. (Aldrin, dieldrin and heptachlor are being discontinued.) Farmers should always *make sure dressed seed is adequately buried* and any spillages of dressed corn removed or buried as speedily as possible.

277

Table I: Growing calendar

The table is drawn for medium loam farms in the Midlands. Farms further north and south, or on different soils, will have different growth patterns.
Some crops, such as clovers and grass, have been omitted because of the great variety of management possible, which in turn affects the cover available.

Key

▬▬▬▬▬▬ Growing crop.

■ ■ ■ ■ ■ ■ ■ Quick harvesting—Possibly field by field (i.e. cereals).

▨▨▨▨▨▨▨ Slow harvesting in same field (i.e. sugar beet).

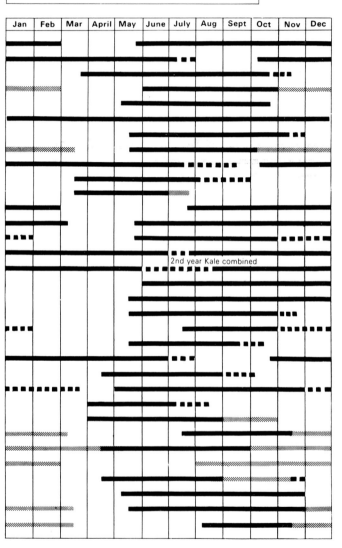

	Jan	Feb	Mar	April	May	June	July	Aug	Sept	Oct	Nov	Dec
Artichokes												
Beans — Winter sown												
Spring sown												
Brussels sprouts												
Buckwheat												
Canary grass												
Canary seed												
Carrots												
Cereal Crops — Winter sown												
Spring sown												
Cereal silage — Whole crop												
Fodder Radish												
Foodpatches (Mixed)												
Kale — Grazing												
Seed												
Lucerne												
Lupins												
Maize												
Mangolds												
Mustard												
Oil Poppy												
Oilseed Rape — Winter sown												
Spring sown												
Parsnips												
Peas												
Potatoes (Main crop)												
Rape												
Savoy cabbage												
Stubble												
Sugar beet												
Sunflowers												
Swedes/Turnips												
Stubble Turnips												

2nd year Kale combined

278

Table II: The impact of rotations and farming systems on insect production for grey partridge chick survival

Bad Insect Production
All-Arable Farm

SB	SB	SB
S Beet	S Beet	SB
S Beet	SB	SB
SB	SB	SB

Approximate rotations

SB	– Spring Barley
SB	– Spring Barley
SB	– Spring Barley
SB	– Spring Barley
S Beet	– Sugar Beet

Moderate Insect Production
Dairy/Cereals Farm

SB	SB	SB
DRS	DRS	WW
WW	DRS	SB
SB	SB	SB

Approximate rotations

DRS	– Direct re-seed (Grass 2–3 year ley)
DRS	– Direct re-seed (Grass 2–3 year ley)
WW	– Winter Wheat
SB	– Spring Barley
SB	– Spring Barley
SB	– Spring Barley

Table II (continued)

Excellent Insect Production
Beef/Sheep/Cereals Farm

WB	1st year USL	WW
3rd year USL	SW	2nd Year USL
SB US	SB	SB US
WW	1st year USL	WB

Assumptions

1. Same field size on each farm
2. Same field boundary types on each farm
3. Break crops excluded from rotations for simplicity
4. Equal (gamebird) predator control on each farm
5. Pheasant population low – wild grey partridges main game crop

Approximate rotations

1st year USL	– 1st year undersown ley (Grass)
2nd year USL	– 2nd year undersown ley (Grass)
3rd year USL	– 3rd year undersown ley (Grass)
WW	– Winter Wheat
SB	– Spring Barley
WB	– Winter Barley
SW	– Spring Wheat
SB US	– Spring Barley, undersown (ley)

280

Table III: An evaluation of different crops for game management

Crop	For shooting		Winter cover	Nesting cover	Food value			
					Pheasant		Partridge	
	Pheasant	Partridge			chick	adult	chick	adult
Artichokes	●●●		●●	●		●●●		
Beans								
Winter			●					●
Spring								
Brussels								
Sprouts	●●	●●	●●					
Buckwheat	●	●				●		●
Canary Grass	●●	●	●●	●●				
Canary Seed						●●		
Carrots	●	●●	●			●		
Cereal Crops[1]								
Winter wheat			●●	●			●●●	●●●
Spring wheat							●●●	●
Winter barley			●●	●●			●●●	●●●
Spring barley							●●	●
Winter oats			●				●	
Spring oats							●	●
Chicory						●		
Clover, Red								
Seed					●●●		●	●●●
Non-seed					●●●			●●●
Clover, White								
Seed					●●●		●●●	●●●
Non-seed					●●●			●●●
Cocksfoot			●●	●●●				●

[1] Cereals undersown with grass, one extra spot.
Cereals undersown with legumes, two extra spots (but beware use of DNPB).

Table III (continued)

| Crop | For shooting | | Winter cover | Nesting cover | Food value | | | |
| | Pheasant | Partridge | | | Pheasant | | Partridge | |
					chick	adult	chick	adult
Coriander								
Fodder Radish	●●	●				●		●
Foodpatches (Mixed)	●●●	●				●●●		●
Grass Silage						●		●
Pasture						●	●	●●
Kale	●●●	●				●		
Kale, Seed	●●●	●	●●●	●●		●		
Linseed						●		
Lucerne	●	●	●		●●●	●●		●●●
Lupins	●●		●					
Maize	●●●					●●		
Mangolds	●	●●●				●		●●
Mustard	●●	●●						●
Oil Poppy	●							
Oilseed Rape Winter			●●					●●●
Spring								
Parsnip		●				●		●
Peas[2]						●	●	●●

[2] Partridge chick food depends very much on spraying programme. Unsprayed crops 3 spots, unless very thick.

Table III (continued)

Crop	For shooting		Winter cover	Nesting cover	Food value			
					Pheasant		Partridge	
	Pheasant	Partridge			chick	adult	chick	adult
Potatoes		●						
Rape	●●	●●						●
Raspberries	●	●	●					
Sainfoin					●●●	●●●	●●●	●●●
Savoy Cabbage	●●	●●				●		●
Sorghum								
Stubble (unburnt)		●●	●●			●●●		●●●
Sugar Beet	●●●	●●●				●●		●●
Sunflowers						●●		
Swedes	●●	●●				●		●●●
Stubble Turnips	●●	●●				●		●
Undersowing	●●	●●						
Whole-crop Cereal Silage								
Winter Wheat			●●	●			●●●	●●●

When consulting the above table the following assumptions are made with regard to the food value for partridges: Insect pests, cereal and grass weeds are controlled. Further, the cereal crops are not too thick (crops which are liable to lodging are especially bad)

Chapter 19

Winter Feeding and Management

The term 'winter feeding' is a general one which covers two different aspects of gamebird management:

1. The continuation of covert-feeding reared and wild pheasants into the cold months. (Some of this has been dealt with in an earlier chapter.)
2. The provision of food for partridges and hedgerow pheasants, in hoppers and by hand, from October to March.

The first question that is usually asked about winter feeding is simple and straightforward: why is it necessary at all?

It must be remembered that farms today are certainly not as cosy as they were when Constable painted his landscapes. The kale and root acreage has decreased. There are fewer hedgerow berries, corn ricks, manure heaps, insect-ridden log piles and untidy corners. In the woods more conifers are planted, and as a result there is a decrease in the number of hardwoods with their welcome harvest of autumn seeds and fruits.

Modern farms can be hungry places for game and wildlife in winter. During the summer, weedkillers and insecticides may already have reduced the natural food supply, and by the time any stubbles are burned and ploughed in the landscape is frequently a bleak one for pheasants and partridges. The higher the stocks of game, the less food there will be to go round – not forgetting there will be more rooks and woodpigeons sharing the rations.

It is true that the ancestors of some of our European game pheasants were found in countries like Mongolia and Korea, where the winters are severe. Our native partridges are also very hardy and capable of facing European winter conditions, but if we expect them to survive in sufficient numbers to provide us with a *shooting* surplus we must actively help them in two ways:

1. Plan the farm crops so that they will encourage an even distribution of gamebirds on the land.
2. Supplement this planning by feeding grain and other foods by hand or in hoppers.

284

103 A modern farm, such as this area on the Sussex Downs, may be a very hungry place for gamebirds in winter and the problem is accentuated in snowy weather. Correct winter management and feeding will minimise losses

Farm crop planning

The distribution of crops in the recommended patchwork pattern really comes into its own in the winter. Large areas of bare plough should be avoided where possible.

Crops for game during the period of winter management can be divided into two types:

1. *The special game crop* that is sown mainly for the birds and may not be of much use to the farm. It is perhaps something of a luxury. Sunflowers and buckwheat are typical examples. (See Chapter 18.)
2. *Dual-purpose crops*, such as kale, mustard and clover, sown in the normal farm rotation, that can be sited to be of use to gamebirds as well. These crops fall into two sub-divisions:
   (*a*) Holding crops, providing cover in the right place during the shooting season.
   (*b*) Food and cover crops, sown primarily to give shelter, escape cover and food, although they can also be used for driving birds or holding pheasants.

They are particularly important during the late winter and early spring. Obviously the siting of all these crops must be planned several months in advance when drawing up the whole programme for the farm.

The farmer who shoots over his own land is at a great advantage. A little extra *trouble* may be necessary in planning the rotation and layout of crops, but there need rarely be any extra *expense*.

The man who rents his shooting over a farm and does not control the cropping pattern may think there is little he can do to improve the habitat. It is quite possible, however, that the farmer may be willing to make one or two small changes in his normal planning in order to help the shoot. He might, for example, sow mustard or a similar green manure crop after the harvest, if the seed is supplied by the shooting tenant; or perhaps split up a large block of kale into smaller units, some distance apart. It is often worth paying a charge per acre to have crops sown in the right places.

Finally a great deal depends on whether the farmer is invited to shoot!

One important use of both dual-purpose and special game crops is to provide escape cover in the late winter and early spring. The dead, tangled stems of such annuals as sunflower and maize give invaluable shelter. A few undersown leys and the verges of farm roads would provide early spring feed and the undersowing of some cover in the stubbles to hold the stock.

Partridges

The Game Conservancy scientists have naturally paid special attention to the problems of winter feeding and behaviour. Their investigations into the food of wild grey partridges in the late summer and early autumn show that they prefer to frequent stubbles – their main food being grain. Wheat is preferred to barley and barley to oats, but weed seeds and green leaves are also important. These account for a third of the dry weight of food intake. Both species of partridge have a clear preference for seeds of *Polygonum* spp., especially Knotgrass (*P. aviculare*) and Black Bindweed (*P. convolvulus*).

Before the widespread use of herbicides in cereals, the proportion of shot birds which had *Polygonum* seeds in their crops was just over 30 per cent. It is no surprise that this has fallen to less than 5 per cent on those farms where anti-polygonum sprays have been used systematically. The most important source of *Polygona* are now the stubbles of spring-sown beans. Simazine does not kill Black Bindweed.

Partridge survival does not, however, seem to have been reduced by the shortage of these autumn weeds. One reason is that a second preferred species, chickweed (*Stellaria media*) has not declined; another may be that a diet of grain combined with green leaves of the volunteer growth is probably just as nutritious as weeds. There is no evidence of an overall shortage of food, at least until late November, but it has been noticed how grey partridges often congregate on stubbles where Knotgrass is most abundant. It is the distribution, rather than the survival, that is affected by wild food pattern.

Supplementary feeding almost certainly holds the birds better on ground where the wild food has been reduced. Even in October wild grey partridges

286

readily take wheat which has been put out for reared birds, though they are not, of course, nearly so dependent on such food as the released stock.

Later in the season the food situation gradually deteriorates. For example in the third week of November 1973, 222 arable fields on the Game Conservancy's Sussex study area were assessed for the availability of grey partridge food. *In many of them food was practically non-existent* (see Table IV).

Table IV: Classification of post-harvest cereal fields according to the availability of adult partridge food in late November 1973, West Sussex study area:

Class I	good	22
Class II	poor	139
Class III	no vegetation	61
	Total:	222

However, the 61 Class III fields were still better for jugging than the intensive grass, and partridges did not leave areas with such fields, provided that the ones adjacent had food. In these neighbouring fields winter corn or clover leys were preferred.

Grain seed in the hay or straw put down for outwintered stock is highly attractive to both species of partridge. Clearly supplementary feeding (discussed later) is often helpful. This type of feeding is much more likely to occur on traditional beef and cereal farms, which are especially favourable to insect survival. It may be that the alleviation of insect shortages, by adopting sympathetic farm systems, would also hold the adults better in hard weather. On the other hand the very high losses in the winter of 1970–71 (see Table V) were not correlated with farming type, the losses being just as high on traditional farms.

Table V: Winter losses of wild grey partridges on the West Sussex study area. The key factor is the type of farming.

Ley farming				No traditional leys						
1961–62	62–63*	63–64	64–65	1965–66	66–67	67–68	68–69	69–70	70–71	71–72
29%	43%	33%	25%	39%	20%	58%	48%	47%	52%	30%
Average winter loss = 33%				Average winter loss = 42%						

* Hard winter 1962–63.

A widely held opinion persists that the exceptional winter of 1962–63 caused the lower number of partridges in the early sixties. However, on the study area the adult survival was good during that winter. *Food was provided.* And at least on keepered areas the low numbers in 1963 could clearly be attributed to the very poor chick survival in the previous summer of 1962.

Winter losses are high in grey partridges – they are much less in wild redlegs – and it is obvious that a reduction in these winter losses – most of which are due to dispersal – would mean that one could tolerate lower chick survival. However, all we do know about winter losses suggests that the rate is very stable. It is no more of a problem – and no less – than it was in the heyday of partridges.

Hand-feeding

Most of the following suggestions are applicable to pheasants.

The oldest method of feeding – and still probably the best one – is to scatter grain among straw spread on the ground. It is very important to keep this straw fresh. Wet, muddy litter trodden into the ground can encourage the growth of *Aspergillus*, which will sometimes result in fungus disease among the birds. On the other hand, fresh loose straw does much to prevent this and makes the pheasants work for their food. Feeding in fresh straw is quite economical, because it is difficult for small birds to get at half-buried food. Together with 'amusement centres', which consist of corn and seed silos made from straw bales, and other hoppers described in this chapter, this type of feeding keeps the birds busy and interested, but not overfed. An old keeper of our acquaintance called this part of each covert 'Tom Tiddler's Ground'. He included drinking fountains, a dry dusting area and traps, as well as hoppers. He knew, like many other pheasant rearers, that the birds would be kept happily occupied and would find less time to wander off and forage elsewhere.

It is very important, however, not to concentrate the feeding into a small area. Too often one sees patches of 20 yds. (18 m.) square with up to 150 pheasants hastily gobbling up food scattered on flattened straw. For this number of pheasants, feeding should be on a narrow swath of straw at least 50 yds. (42 m.) long. This reduces competition between the birds and enables them to take plenty of time over their food. Where they are too concentrated the birds tend to rush their feeding and eat too much. Overfed pheasants fly just as badly as overfed mallard.

Another traditional method of giving pheasants something to occupy themselves is the scratching heap. This is made simply by mixing grain or seeds into a trailer-load of sand which can be tipped beside a ride.

When hand-feeding in covert, a daily visit is essential and the birds should be whistled to come to feed – if they have previously been used to a whistle. Hoppers are certainly useful in covert, but hand-feeding should, if possible, be the mainstay of the programme. It is not possible to suggest a standard feeding technique for every shoot. Each poses its own problem and may require slightly

288

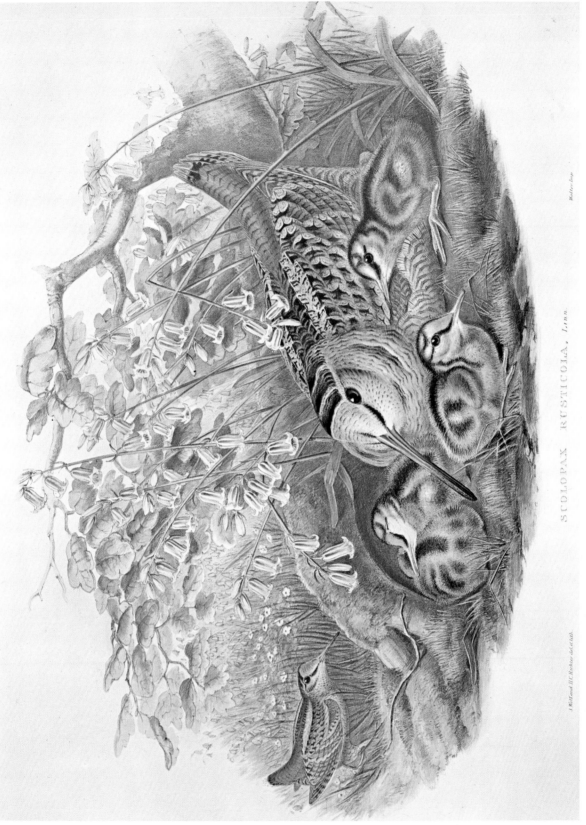

SCOLOPAX RUSTICOLA, Linn.

Woodcock lithograph from Gould *'Birds of Great Britain'*

Red Grouse 'Winter on the Moors' *David Binns*

different methods. In most cases effort should be concentrated where birds are released and this is usually in a small number of central coverts. Some of these pheasants are then encouraged by feeding to move into other neighbouring woods or crops. Whether this is done by hopper or by hand is a matter for local conditions. This is more a part of the releasing policy than the feeding policy.

In addition to careful planning of the covert feeding, it must be noted that many shoots carry larger stocks of wild pheasants than is generally supposed, and these birds should not be neglected. Although it is possible and useful to move a pheasant by feeding from one place to another, we do not think that 'longstop' feeding in outlying boundary spinneys will really draw out a great weight of birds from the centre of the shoot and induce them to step over the boundary. Feeding on the boundary is, on the whole, more likely to stop wandering pheasants than encourage them.

Hopper feeding

It is more than 30 years since we started trials on our experimental shoot with various types of hopper for the winter feeding of wild partridges. When we were satisfied that this system was not just labour saving but also efficient, we recommended it to shoot owners and keepers all over the country. Further trials followed with pheasants on small *unkeepered* shoots where it was not possible to feed daily by hand. Since this also proved generally successful, we extended the trials to wild pheasants in outlying spinneys and belts on *keepered* shoots. At this point hoppers began to be used on an ever-increasing scale by all sections of the shooting public, but often they were not used efficiently because their function and effect was not clearly understood.

One frequently heard the criticism that 'the birds get their food too quickly and then wander off, which causes straying over the boundary'. We repeat that the exact opposite is the truth! When hoppers are the cause of straying it is because there are not enough of them. This causes 'trough competition', as in poultry, because only a few pheasants can feed comfortably together at one hopper. Since the hopper is there all the time the birds will not concentrate their feeding times as they do with hand feeding. But it is no good expecting a single hopper to provide for 50 pheasants. Where this is done, a proportion will drift away rather than wait their turn. Similarly one aggressive cock can dominate a hopper and drive other birds off.

As a guide we would recommend one hopper per 12–15 birds feeding, the hoppers being spaced 15–20 yds. (14–18 m.) apart. The more hoppers there are the less often they have to be filled.

A network of hoppers can be serviced weekly by a vehicle or from strategically sited storage bins made from 40-gallon (182 l.) drums. On some shoots, filling these bins is the responsibility of a member of the farm staff, thus releasing the keeper for day-to-day maintenance of the hoppers.

Birds in cover crops such as kale, mustard and artichokes can also be efficiently fed with hoppers. If the crop has to be harvested during the shooting season, pheasants will quickly recognise other hoppers in the area as a source of supply.

One estate we know in Hampshire killed 7,000 pheasants off 5,000 acres. The number of reared birds put to covert was 4,000. The headkeeper said he could not possibly have held so many birds on this type of country without the use of a large number of hoppers (more than 100) on the *outlying* ground.

Another example is a Sussex Downland shoot where hopper feeding has been practised for many years. The routine here is to fill the hoppers *the day before the first shoot*. Up to this time the pheasants are held in the coverts and crops with hand feeding. Downland birds can fly very long distances when driven and tend to spread over a big area after shooting.

As we have said, partridges also benefit from a well-planned feeding programme. Although they are hardy, in exceptional circumstances they can suffer very high losses during the winter. The *average natural winter loss* is about 30–40 per cent between September and March. But on one estate during the severe winter of 1962–63, when the snow was deep and prolonged and no attempt was made to feed the partridges, we recorded a loss of 77 per cent. Of course, as has been stated earlier, owing to the poor chick survival of 1962 the stock was low. No supplementary feeding was the last straw.

Hand-feeding or 'trickle-feeding' of partridges is largely a thing of the past – not because it is inefficient, but because it is time-consuming. The hopper has taken its place and suits the partridge very well, because wild birds are not natural wanderers like pheasants. Feeding points can be near straw ricks or in the lee of shelter belts or hedges, in pits or uncultivated field corners.

Simple hoppers can be made for next to nothing from 5-gallon (23 l.) drums and are much used by both pheasants and partridges. Many other containers are also suitable. An anti-scavenger feed dispenser can be obtained from the Game Conservancy for use in hoppers. This will prevent food being pilfered by sparrows, finches, pigeons, rooks and others (see photograph 106).

A dual-purpose hopper for both pheasants and partridges (a hopper for pheasants only is discussed later) can be made by cutting three or four vertical slits on opposite sides of the drum near to the base and mounting the hopper on bricks (see Figure 104).

The slits (which can be cut quite easily with a cold chisel) should be about $2\frac{1}{2}$–3 in. (6–8 cm.) in height and between $\frac{3}{16}$ in. (4·7 mm.) and $\frac{1}{5}$ in. (5 mm.) across – just wide enough to allow the wheat to trickle out when tapped or pecked. The top of the drum should be cut out and replaced by a home-made clip-on lid. An old discarded disc from a harrow also makes a very good improvised lid, and its weight will keep it in place in a strong wind. A small piece of wood should be firmly driven into the central hole to ensure that the lid is absolutely watertight.

290

After filling, the hopper should be placed on two bricks, which must not protrude from under the oil drum or rats will use them as steps up to the feeding slots. It is then usual to hand feed around the hopper until the pheasants and partridges begin to use it. Once the birds begin pecking at the grain, the drums should be raised a further 4½ in. (11 cm.) by doubling up on the bricks, so that the base is now 9 in. (23 cm.) from the ground. This will stop rats and most small birds from getting at the grain, but will allow gamebirds to have access.

Some years ago hoppers had short slits on four sides and this is still the best feeder for partridges. In this case, if the hopper is placed right out in the open, where driving rain can beat against it, the grain in the exposed slits may swell up and jam, though a twig or a penknife blade will quickly clear any such blockage. In any case, the slits in the lee should still run freely.

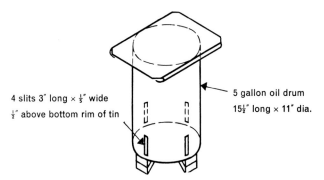

4 slits 3″ long × ⅛″ wide
½″ above bottom rim of tin

5 gallon oil drum
15½″ long × 11″ dia.

104 A dual-purpose hopper for both pheasants and partridges which is cheap to make, though not scavenger-proof

The most effective type for use only by pheasants, is where the food is extracted from the *bottom* of the container, set 15 in. (38 cm.) above ground level. This 'peck under' feeder, which can be fastened to a stake or a tree, has several advantages. The exposed food is well protected from the weather; it is much more inaccessible to small birds and well out of the reach of pigeons, rats and squirrels.

There are several methods of construction. The simplest form is an adaptation of the slit hopper (described earlier) but with one or two slits cut across the bottom of the drum. This leaves no protruding surface on which small birds can obtain a grip. They are thus forced to hover when extracting food – or to pick up the leftovers from the pheasants. To ensure that it is completely proof against rats or squirrels it is important to see that the slits do not run close to the supporting stake or tree. Another simple type has a small panel of wire netting in the base of the drum. The panel (about 8 in. by 2in. [20 cm. by 5 cm.]) is cut out of the base of the two overlapping layers of ⅜-in. (9·5 mm.) mesh – or some form of metal grille – and is fitted over the gap. The grain is more easily seen in this type, but some small birds (particularly tits) can cling to the wire netting or grille and feed fairly easily. An excellent form of this hopper is manufactured by Farm Equipment and Supply Company of Tumby, Boston, Lincolnshire. This is made of resin-bonded plywood and we have seen as many as eight pheasants at a time feeding from the 3-ft. (91 cm.) long grille. Two sizes are made, one with a capacity of $\frac{3}{4}$ cwt. (38 kg.) of wheat and the other $4\frac{1}{2}$ cwt. (230 kg.). Yet another successful type is the A.V.E.L. Mini-Feeder produced by Axe Vale Engineering Ltd, Axminster, Devon. This delivers the food on to a small plate beneath the hopper. It is fairly easily robbed by small birds, but it has one great advantage over the hoppers already described in that large grains, such as maize, can be mixed with the food.

Where oil-drum hoppers are used for the first time they should be pre-baited with a little grain scattered on straw beneath. *All* hoppers should have a rat bait point close by. This is most conveniently provided by a tile drain pipe using Warfarin loose or packed in polythene sachets.

One shoot owner on the Continent reported that he had to tie his pheasant hoppers to tree trunks with heavy wire because the grain attracted wild boar which rolled the hoppers for hundreds of yards in order to spill out the feed. This may seem to be a rather special problem, but roe deer and sheep can be almost as troublesome. Where this is likely it is wise to ensure that the hoppers are firmly fastened to their supports and enclosed in a small area by stakes and pig netting.

Cleaning oil drums

We are often asked about the best method of cleaning oil-drum hoppers before use. This can be done by putting a small quantity of paraffin into the drum (PETROL IS TOO DANGEROUS), swilling it around, dropping in a lighted match and retiring quickly! The drum should then be scrubbed with a *weak* detergent solution (too much detergent will taint) and then rinsed out with fresh water.

A thin film of old, congealed oil is surprisingly difficult to set alight and in such cases an oil drum may have to be cleaned out by scraping down and scrubbing.

Drums which have held toxic chemicals should obviously never be used.

Automatic feeder

The most sophisticated hopper is the Parsons Automatic Feeder, produced by E. Parsons and Sons Ltd, Blackfriars, Bristol BS1 2LS. Although more generally used for duck flight ponds, it can work equally well for pheasants. It is particularly useful for part-time keepers because it will reproduce hand-feeding at regular intervals, which is so important for reared pheasants after release. Regular feeding can be a great problem for the amateur keeper.

The Parsons Feeder has an electrically driven spinner, the power being supplied by an 80-amp. car battery, which can normally be expected to have a 4–5 month operating life before re-charging. The electric motor is controlled by

105 Pheasant pecks upward at a wire-netting food dispenser. Finches and sparrows cannot steal any quantity of grain and snow cannot block the outlets

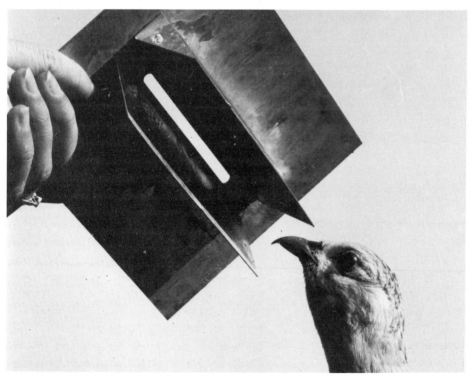

106 This anti-sparrow guard can be dropped into the bottom of any grain hopper and prevents the contents being pilfered by small birds

293

107 The size of the four feeding slots in this oil-drum hopper are determined by the type of grain in use. One slot across the centre is equally effective

a clockwork time clock which need only be rewound every 14 days. The clock has a number of settings so that the spinner can be made to operate several times a day, if desired, and at predetermined times. The amount of food delivered at each spin can be varied over a big range of settings from 21 lb. to 90 lb. ($9\frac{1}{2}$ kg. to $40\frac{3}{4}$ kg.). The hopper capacity is normally $2\frac{1}{4}$ cwt. ($114\frac{3}{4}$ kg.), but larger models are available.

An automatic hooter or bell can be used if the birds are accustomed to being called to their feed by this method. Among users there seems to be a preference for the bell, and it is said to work especially well with poults. A popular way of protecting the battery from the weather seems to be a covering of old fertiliser bags, but a wooden box with a lid is considered to be even better. Bad weather also makes it difficult to feed pellets. They tend to 'mush' in these conditions. Clean grain will give the least trouble; but if only tail corn is available, the functioning of the hopper may have to be checked daily.

Other feeding methods

Feeding grain 'in the ear' is an excellent idea. It keeps the pheasants busy and makes the grain somewhat less accessible to small birds.

Some shoots are therefore going back to this system by baling unthreshed corn at harvest time for covert feed. A small area of corn (preferably wheat) is left unharvested by the combine and allowed to stand for a few days until it is *thoroughly ripened*. A baler is then taken into the field to deal with combine straw.

294

As soon as it is seen that this operation is nearly finished, the standing corn is cut with a mower, and the baler continues straight on to it. It is important to see that the mown corn is not left lying for any length of time, since it is vulnerable to birds and the smooth swaths can quickly become sodden with rain.

The bales are then stacked near the feeding points in covert (protected by a Warfarin rat-baiting point) and covered with corrugated iron or a polythene sheet. Feeding is simple: the bales are merely broken open and spread out on staddles or feed rides as required.

The system is economical as well as practical. It is obviously cheaper to feed corn in the ear than to process the grain and the straw separately and put them together again on the feed ride. A useful game feeder which can be used both in covert and in rides in kale fields is a hollow 'silo' of straw bales five tiers high. With six rectangular bales for the base and reducing each layer by one bale, it will be found that 20 will be needed. The silo is best built on a sheet of black polythene. This should be trimmed so that none protrudes, otherwise it will trap rainwater which may run back into the centre of the silo. When the silo has reached the three-bale layer it should be filled with grain and covered with another small polythene sheet. The last two bales are placed on top of this to hold it firmly in place. Rat bait points or tunnel traps should be placed in holes made between the bales in the bottom row. The silo can be kept sealed up until the pheasants require the food, when more holes can be made between the bottom bales, allowing the birds to scratch the grain out.

The racks are usually filled with a mixture of cavings and grain and weed seeds so that the food can fall out only slowly when pecked. A dry, sheltered scratching yard soon develops all round the base of the hopper. Some types have slatted wooden sides, others are constructed of wire netting.

Incidentally, it is sometimes suggested that feeding weed seeds to game could spread 'noxious' weeds on the farm. We have carried out trials which show that, in a normal healthy gamebird, after the food leaves the gizzard the particle size is so small that it is unlikely that any whole seed will be secreted.

Dusting shelters and feed staddles

These are always appreciated by pheasants and partridges, especially in heavy land. The 'lean-to' type is suitable for both species but the commonest form used for pheasants in a covert is the 'staddle'. This is a platform at *least* 10 ft. (3 m.) square and 18 in. (46 cm.) above ground level. The platform should be made waterproof by covering it with straw sandwiched between two layers of wire netting (2–4-in. [5–10 cm.] wire mesh is suitable). The ground below should be turned over with a fork before construction begins and raked over at frequent intervals to keep the earth dry and dusty. A food hopper can be placed beneath.

The commonest faults in constructing staddles are making them too small and using small-diameter hazel poles often cut on site. These rot after a year or

108 An even
distribution of farm
crops will help
wintering partridges –

109 – but gamebirds
will suffer where
winter food and cover
are not evenly split up
across the landscape

296

two when the whole structure collapses – and it never seems to get rebuilt. The legs should be at least 6 in. (15 cm.) in diameter and preferably oak. Larch is second best but it must be cut in winter – summer-felled larch soon rots. The platform is again best made with oak or larch poles, 3–4 in. (8–10 cm.) in diameter. It always pays to make a good job of a staddle in the first instance to avoid repeated maintenance. Staddles are invaluable in western and northern districts where they provide shelter and food for the birds under severe weather conditions, particularly snow.

Grain

Pheasants prefer wheat to any other grain – but if they are not offered wheat they will readily take barley. Generally speaking, a mixture of these cereals should not be offered in hoppers, because the pheasants will pick out the wheat and scatter the barley on the ground for the sparrows. Maize, if available, is also favoured once the birds become familiar with it. Whole maize has the advantage of being too big for small birds to eat. Oats are not usually eaten for preference by pheasants, but where no other grain is grown they will take it quite happily.

Watering in covert

Where it is well known that *wild* pheasants will get along quite well without any water supplies, reared birds must be able to drink freely – particularly if they are being fed on dry grain and 'left-over' pellets in covert – until they are completely acclimatised to life in the wild. And, like wild partridges, wild pheasants will often take advantage of water if it is provided.

Polythene agricultural piping has simplified the watering problem on many estates, but where such facilities are not available, here are two suggestions which may be helpful: on a dry, sandy shoot in Holland, a network of shallow cement pools, rather like dewponds, has proved most successful for pheasants, wild boar and deer. They are situated at the lower end of a sloping ride so as to take up surface rainwater. Large stones should be placed in the pools as safety islands so that chicks cannot drown. Temporary pools can be made with thick polythene sheets placed in shallow depressions, weighed down with heavy stones round the edge.

The second idea is a home-made drinking fountain (see photograph 38 on page 123). The 2-in. (5 cm.) deep water tray is made from the base of a square 5-gallon (23 l.) drum. The round drum is filled with water, the tray placed on top and both are then turned over. The water will flow from the drum until it covers the cap when the flow will cease until the birds drinking from the tray reduce the level. The drinker thus uses the same principle as the old-fashioned jam-jar drinker – simple and cheap.

297

Chapter 20
Wildfowl Management: Flight Ponds

Introduction

The potential wildfowl habitat and the wild duck crop in Britain are at present under-exploited. In spite of the continued drainage of many of our natural wetlands, there are still hundreds of thousands of little streams, springs, marshy corners – as well as actual ponds, wet gravel pits and reservoirs – that are not producing anything like the wildfowl they could if the habitat and the ducks themselves were protected and managed to provide a shootable surplus. The main duck species which is managed for shooting in Britain is the mallard and it is this bird with which this section is chiefly concerned. Most of the advice does however relate to other dabbling ducks too.

Three main subjects are discussed: the construction of flight ponds; the rearing of mallard; the creation, improvement and management of breeding areas for wild duck; and our research programme.

Flight ponds are usually easy enough to make, given a suitable site. A little digging, damming, bulldozing or blasting will soon create attractive pools. Cover planting and the *regular* provision of food will, in due course, bring the fowl in, unless there are no flyways or natural feeding and roosting areas anywhere near. Although it is often surprising where ducks are to be found – in the middle of forests and on high moors – one cannot expect any weight of duck to materialise out of thin air.

If the weather is right and the hides are well sited, flighting can provide exciting, difficult shooting. Equally ducks can flop in like chickens and afford poor sport. Many pools are shot too often. Once a month is probably enough, or the future breeding population can become seriously depleted.

Some flight-pond owners rear and release a number of young mallard every year to replenish their stocks and to provide a 'lead-in' for wild birds when they begin to fly, exploring the area around the release point. This can be effective if the ducks are from a good wild strain, and if they are carefully acclimatised in a non-shooting area. Often, however, the 'replacement stock' – like duck that are reared for shooting – can become too tame, too fat, and too cossetted.

298

Duck which are reared in captivity and then released in unsuitable areas with insufficient food are very likely to starve to death. In such places they appear to find it difficult to change to a diet of natural foods. When hand-reared duck are released onto any area, they can be helped over the transition from artificial to natural food by careful supplementary feeding, with the amount being gradually reduced over several weeks. This will also hold the birds in the area until they are acclimatised.

The creation of wild duck breeding reservoirs, sometimes with the use of nesting baskets which can permit very high densities on small areas, is in many places the surest way of increasing duck numbers. But care must be taken to see that the environment is capable of supporting the ducklings which are hatched. Otherwise it would be better to let the ducks nest where they please.

Duck flighting

Mallard, and most other species of dabbling duck which find their way into wildfowlers' bags, fly to their feeding places at dusk and return to their resting places at dawn, often covering considerable distances between the two. Quite frequently where food is plentiful duck will return to their daytime resting places after a dusk feed, digest their meal during the night, then flight out for another feed before dawn, to return to the roost site again just after dawn. An evening flight intercepts duck on their way to feeding sites, and a morning flight those on their way to the roost site.

The British Isles are studded with small areas of water (half an acre or less) which provide, or can provide, good feeding places. The evening flight is, therefore, the one with which most shooting people will be concerned. Suitable resting areas usually consist of much larger expanses of water – lakes, estuaries, reservoirs and even the open sea – and are not so commonly found on the private shoot. A small secluded pond, however, will sometimes become a resting place. Even with generous feeding, it can then be difficult to make the ducks change their timetable and flight in at night!

The location of a flight pond is far more important than its size and excellent bags have been made on quite small flashes of water.

When excavating a flight pond the topsoil should be placed at the bottom of the excavated area to provide a source of nutrients for the fauna and flora. Good soil will also aid the establishment of marginal plants.

It is often possible to make a flight pond which will also be used as a breeding area. This means that suitable nesting cover, food and shelter for the young will have to be provided. However, we would recommend that such a pool or stretch of water be shot only lightly and less towards the end of the season. After that disturbances should be kept to the minimum, although feeding should continue for a few weeks.

299

110 A dragline machine is the best to use when creating fairly large areas of water

111 A hydraulic machine on tracks has a limited reach but works much quicker than a dragline and is much more accurate, particularly in achieving the correct depth

300

Siting a flight pond

On a small property there may not be many sites to choose from, and the owner may have to make use of any suitable piece of ground that is available. Where there is a choice, a study should be made of the flighting habits of the local wildfowl population. A river valley, for example, will usually be a regular flyway, though wildfowl will sometimes take short cuts across higher ground when moving between resting and feeding areas. Many flight ponds certainly draw in duck a long way from natural water-courses. In other words, it is not essential to be on a flight line, though it is helpful to be near one. An old farm pool that duck are seen to visit from time to time can often be made into a regular 'calling place' by careful feeding and a new flight-line developed for succeeding generations of wildfowl.

A good supply of water is obviously essential. This need not take the form of existing surface water, or even a spring, since the run-off from one or two fields is usually enough to fill a pond if the soil on the site is not porous. In temperate areas, where hard white frosts are not too frequent, the choice of a site is simplified because no great movement of water is needed to keep ice from forming. Digging down to the natural water table, or excavating an area that can be flooded, is all that is required.

Plastic sheeting (1,000-g. polythene or butyl rubber) *can* be used to line a pond – on the chalk, for example – but it is a comparatively expensive method of construction, involving not only the excavation of the site, but the extra cost of the material and the work of burying it. This has to be done to avoid damage by dogs and people. Even when it is placed 18 in. (46 cm.) below the surface of the bank, the plastic sheet will be exposed after a short period by quite a small number of ducks dibbling around the edges. Polythene is particularly vulnerable to degradation when exposed to ultra-violet rays and we therefore recommended at least 3 ft. (1 m.) of earth above the sheet at the pond's edge and 6–9 in. (15–20 cm.) in the centre.

Where frost is a problem, an appreciable flow of water through the pond will be needed to prevent it freezing over completely. Although it is sometimes necessary only to have a small area of water where the ducks can alight, if they have to climb out on to the ice they can be very vulnerable to foxes. In any case they will feel more at home on open water, and if they do not find any they may fly farther afield until they do. A pond with a strong spring in the centre will stay free of ice for longer than a pond with water flowing through it.

Shelter from wind and freedom from disturbance are other factors which should be considered. Exposure to some wind will help prevent the pond from freezing over. A quiet site which is already screened by mature trees or shrubs will obviously have advantages over one which is open to winter gales or too close to houses, roads and footpaths.

Once chosen, the site itself will largely dicate the most suitable method of construction, i.e. by excavation, building a dam, or blasting out a group of small pools with explosives. We shall examine these in turn.

A standard plan for excavation

Where practical a mechanical digger is always the most effective way of constructing a pond, because the planner has much more control over its shape, size and depth, than with damming or blasting.

The standard plan we have chosen to illustrate here has been very successful. The size is governed by the distance to which a drag-line operator can swing his bucket, normally about 39 ft. (12 m.) with the jib set at 45 degrees. The shape is designed to enable the machine to be operated with ease and speed, and the depths are also carefully calculated, since they can greatly affect the suitability of the pond for waterfowl. While 6–12-in. (12–25 cm.) depth is suitable for mallard and teal feeding areas, for *diving* ducks the water must be much deeper, 4–6 ft. (1·3–2 m.).

Fortunately the depth requirements for breeding and flighting ponds are complementary. They include a 'shallow-water' zone (1 ft. [25 cm.] or less) around the edge where a screen of sedges, reeds, etc., can grow, and a 'deep-water' zone (over 4 ft. [1·3 m.]) which will stay clear of emergent growth for longer without management and allow easy alighting for flighting ducks.

An attractive feature on any stretch of water is a low island clear of thick undergrowth, which ducks of all ages can use as a loafing spot for resting, sleeping and preening. It will be a deterrent to approaching ground predators except when the pond freezes over.

Duck do not like having to climb up a steep slope and it is important to see that all banks have a very gentle gradient.

The basic layout shown on the opposite page incorporates most of the features described above and includes an area of deep water 30 yds. (27 m.) square, with a 5-yd. (4·5 m.) square island in the centre. Surrounding the deep water is a series of shallow bays, each 5 yds. (4·5 m.) square. The bays are preferable to a continuous shallow area all round for several reasons. They limit the area of shallows to be dug, reducing the cost; they also provide brood territories; and they make it easier to hunt out each bay systematically with a dog when picking up after shooting.

Details of construction

The digging plan is simple. The dragline operator first takes out an area 30 yds. (27 m.) long and 12½ yds. (11·5 m.) wide, as shown in Figure 113 (A). He then turns at right angles and digs for a further 17½ yds. (16 m.) (B), turns again and digs 17½ yds. (16 m.) parallel to the first line (C). This leaves a small area to be

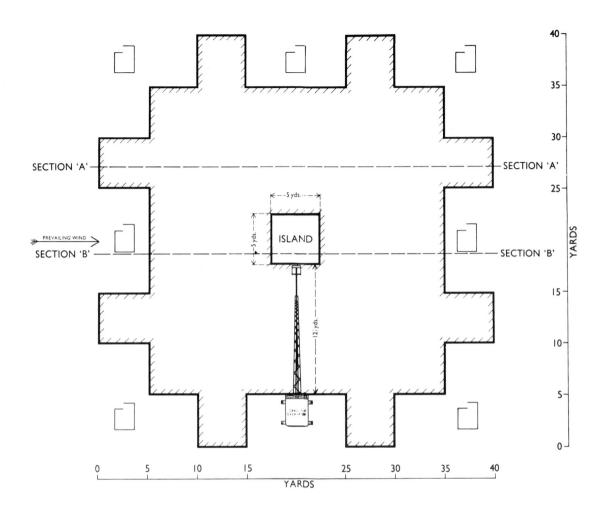

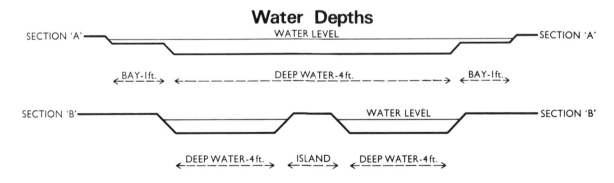

Water Depths

WATER LEVEL

SECTION 'A'

BAY-1ft. — DEEP WATER-4ft. — BAY-1ft.

SECTION 'B'

WATER LEVEL

DEEP WATER-4ft. — ISLAND — DEEP WATER-4ft.

112 Basic layout for wildfowl breeding and flight pond

303

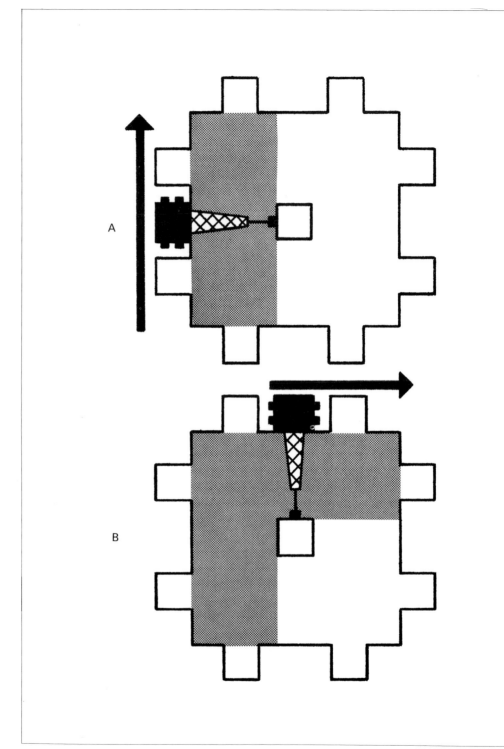

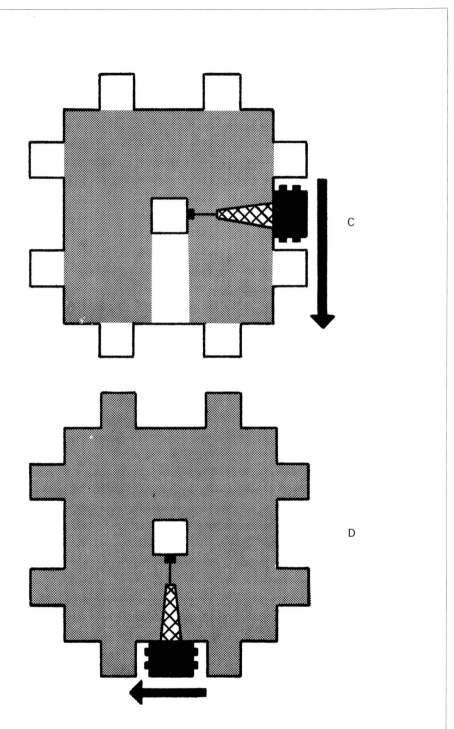

C

D

113 Digging plan for duck pond

305

dug to complete the square (**D**). The spoil should be thrown back from the water's edge as far as possible. The machine is then pulled back 5 yds. (4·5 m.) and taken round the pond once more to dig the 5 yds. × 5 yds. (4·5 m. × 4·5 m.) shallow bays. These should have shelving banks, so that ducklings can leave the pond easily and will not become separated from the parent duck, who can negotiate steeper slopes.

To carry out this plan exactly, it is necessary to have some level ground, not more than 3 ft. (1 m.) above the water table and free of obstacles such as trees. It is easy to vary the shape for less convenient sites. It can be made long and narrow, for instance, by increasing the length of the first and third digs. The overall size can be reduced by cutting down the distance to which the operator swings his bucket.

To assist him it will be worth while pegging out the first area to be dug and the central island. When the first two sections have been cleared it is only necessary for him to use the island as a pivot to complete the square.

Although we have given exact measurements they should be treated as approximate when carrying out the actual operation, otherwise a meticulous operator will waste a lot of unnecessary time. For example, it is of no great importance whether the island or the bays are 4 yds. (3·5 m.) square or 6 yds. (5·5 m.) square; it is the overall pattern which matters.

Similarly some bays could be eliminated to accommodate large trees or minor variations in the ground available for digging. The pond need not necessarily be made square or oblong – it could be the shape of a parallelogram.

Plants for flight ponds

It is a good idea to examine neighbouring ditches and ponds before choosing the plants which you wish to establish. This will reveal those species which thrive naturally in the area and will suggest a planting programme.

Select plants which are common and freely available. Plant them in the growing season preferably before flowering, i.e. April to mid-July for most species. The technique and the value of individual species are considered later in this section.

It is often desirable to leave one or two areas unplanted or kept clear as grain-feeding places for flighting duck. Ideally they should be accessible from the nearest field entrance to the pond and the island and ground between the pond and the spoil bank should be graded down. This gives additional space for duck to rest and preen, away from any thick cover which could screen approaching predators. The dabbling action of feeding duck can cause considerable erosion. This often produces cliff faces to the bank and increases the water depth to a point where food on the bottom is inaccessible. A simple way of preventing this is to dump a load of pea shingle into the feeding area and rake it down to just below the water surface. If the layer of shingle is 6 in. (15 cm.) or more deep it will effectively prevent this type of erosion and reduce loss of food.

A wind baffle on the top of the spoil bank can most easily be established by planting a double row of *Lonicera nitida*, which will eventually grow to a height of 6–8 ft. (2–2½ m.). Lawson's cypress, planted 2 ft. (0·6 m.) apart, and later lopped at 6 ft. (2 m.) would also make a good screen, but requires protection from rabbits and hares – unnecessary with *Lonicera*.

The area outside the spoil bank is best left to 'grow rough', providing food and cover for foraging ducklings in the summer. (It may also be used by pheasants.)

With this layout, each bay could accommodate a nesting basket or box during the breeding season. The shooting hides are sited on the land between the bays. Hides on different sides of the pond allow for all wind variations.

If cattle have access to the field it will be essential to fence the pond, or they will trample down all the marginal cover. Alternatively a small inlet can be dug to run out under the wire so that they have their own drinking pool, or their access can be restricted to certain areas where their controlled grazing on the marginal vegetation will provide another very attractive habitat – to snipe for instance.

Dam construction

Although on level ground a pond is most easily made by excavation, where the ground is sloping, a dam may be the best answer.

The most common fault when building a dam is haste! Water can be very powerful, and if care is not taken, a winter flood or even a few weeks' seepage may swiftly undo many hours of hard work.

The creation of a marshy corner or a primitive – albeit productive – pool, can often be achieved by putting a few sheets of corrugated iron across a sluggish-running ditch. But where there is any appreciable flow of water, a proper dam must be planned with care. The following points should be noted:

(*a*) The height of the dam and the gradient of the land upstream determine the length of the pond.
(*b*) The width of the valley at dam height determines the width of the pond.

A simple method of establishing the first point is to drive two sticks into the ground 6 ft. (2 m.) apart at the position of the dam: one stick at the pond face and the other at the downstream face. Then fasten a straight cross-piece between the two and line up with a spirit level. By sighting upstream along the cross-piece, a rough indication of the extent of the flooding can be obtained. The cross-piece may be moved up or down until the correct amount to be flooded has been estimated. A rifle with a telescopic sight can be levelled and used in the same way. This will give the approximate height of the dam required.

Design

Once the site of the dam has been chosen, the construction is usually fairly simple, if certain rules are followed:

 (i)   The width of the top of an earth dam must be at least equal to its height;
 (ii) The width of the base must be five times the height (e.g. a 4-ft. [1 m.] high dam must be 4 ft. [1 m.] wide at the top and 20 ft. [6 m.] wide at the base);
 (iii) A concrete or brick spillway must be constructed of sufficient capacity to cope with the maximum amount of flood water;
 (iv) The discharge from the spillway must be well away from the base of the dam to avoid any possibility of erosion. The water should fall onto a concrete 'apron'.

114 Dam and spillways

The importance of the spillway cannot be emphasised too strongly. We have seen many old ponds and lakes which are dry, due to the failure of the dam. Almost invariably this has been caused either by incorrect design of the spillway or failure to maintain it.

Where very heavy floodwater can be expected, it is advisable to have a second bypass spillway as shown in Figure 114. The alternative is to have a deep main spillway with hatches to hold up the summer level. These can be expensive and must be well maintained.

During construction the dam must be carefully consolidated by running the machinery back and forth, gradually building up the height in layers not more than 1 ft. (25 cm.) thick. If the construction has to stop for any length of time, the top layer must be scarified before continuing, otherwise water will seep between it and the new layers. Made-up ground is not as strong as natural ground which has had years to settle.

The vegetation should be cleared from the wings of the dam before starting to build as the layer of topsoil and decaying organic matter can create a line of weakness at each end of the dam.

Where possible, make the dam in an arc facing into the lake so that the weight of water against the dam face presses the end of the dam tight against the bank sides.

The middle portion of the dam should be built higher than the ends to allow for subsidence where the filling is deepest.

Vegetation should be established as quickly as possible to avoid erosion of the dam faces by rain and waves. One method of preventing wave erosion on the pond face is to make a baffle of floating logs. Grasses, reeds and rushes are suitable for planting on dams, but *never plant trees* as their roots allow the water to permeate through the dam and cause washouts.

The best machine to use for dam-building is a heavy bulldozer or tractor bucket – the heavier the better.

If the soil is light and quickly permeable, such as sand or peat, a core trench should first be dug and filled with clay or similar material. This trench should project into the bank on either side and be *deep enough to reach into impermeable subsoil*. On some sites it may be necessary to build a concrete curtain wall along the centre of the dam, projecting into the bank at both ends, and down into the subsoil.

The chief attraction of a dam is that quite large areas of water can often be impounded by a very short length of dam. With modern earth-moving equipment, however, it is advisable to weigh up the pros and cons of making a dam compared with digging out an area below the existing water level. This produces a maintenance-free pond. Many old dams were constructed before the days when powerful machinery was available. Apart from the cost of a dam, which can be considerable, there is a another disadvantage and that is the possibility of silting. A lake with a stream running into it has the same effect as a settling tank. The slowing up of the water-flow allows material in suspension to sink to the bottom where it accumulates over the years, gradually reducing the area of water as the deposits rise to the surface level. In shallow lakes with a large influx of storm water, this action can be fairly rapid and is usually followed by invasive vegetation.

There are two ways to avoid this problem. The first is to construct a deep settling tank where the stream enters with a low dam dividing it from the lake.

This will trap much of the silt before it enters the lake. The tank can be cleared with an excavator every few years. The second method is to construct a new channel for the stream, around the side of the lake, holding the water level to dam height, with a hatch at the lower end similar to Figure 115.

In flat country digging is nearly always the best method; among hills a dam is usually the easiest. In undulating country the decision as to which is suitable is often marginal and here we would advise digging for safety's sake. If the lake is also to be used for fishing, then a dam has a considerable advantage because facilities for draining the lake can be included in the construction. This is very valuable for fishery management.

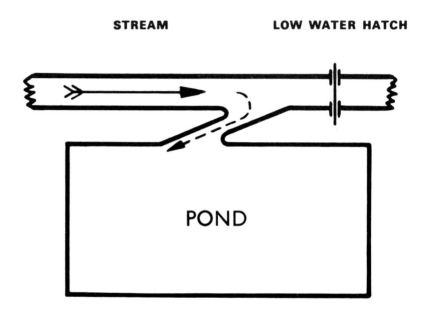

STREAM **LOW WATER HATCH**

POND

115 Pond beside stream

Precautions

The Water Resources Act of 1963 restricts the use of water in Great Britain. This not only concerns abstractions but includes impounding as well. Before constructing a dam it is always wise to consult your legal adviser and it is necessary to inform the local district engineer of your Regional Water Authority who will doubtless give much good advice, and who must sanction the construction of the dam before work commences.

Although we have given some general guidance on dam construction it is really essential to get professional advice from a chartered civil engineer before undertaking any work. For instance, without proper examination of the site, a dam might inadvertently be constructed over layers of peat, or where impermeable soil was not present. In both instances the dam would probably be unstable and possibly dangerous.

Explosives

Marshy areas are sometimes so soft they cannot support pond-digging machinery of any kind. Until now these places have been largely unproductive, except for an occasional snipe drive, but good wildfowl pools can sometimes be created on these sites with explosives. We would emphasise, however, that a mechanical excavator will always do a better job if it can be used and explosives should always be a last resort.

The site should be chosen with care. The water table must be at surface level or within a few inches of it. The reason for this is that all the holes we have blown – using a variety of explosives – are saucepan-shaped, with the depth roughly equal to half the width. Steep-sided holes are unattractive to wildfowl if only partly filled with water.

Another effect of the explosive is to produce a raised rim round the hole. The bigger the hole, the higher the rim and some sections of the banks should be sloped off by hand to provide easier access.

Since we first introduced this method into Britain in 1968, the use of explosives has become a recognised part of habitat improvement schemes. We would, however, strongly advise anyone wishing to use this method *to employ a qualified contractor, who will take all the necessary precautions.* In the right hands explosives are perfectly safe. In the wrong ones they are lethal!

Feeding flight ponds

If we were short of space we would restrict ourselves to saying 'feed regularly and shoot light!' But because correct feeding is the key to success we intend to go into a little more detail.

The following points are important.

Feed as late as possible – about half an hour before the first ducks appear – and *do not grossly overfeed.* Apart from providing a longer feeding period for unwanted scavengers, too much food can encourage ducks to stay late in the morning and flight late in the evening. In extreme cases they will stay all day without flighting at all! The quality of food put down can only be judged by experience. As a guide, the contents of a 2-gallon (9 l.) bucket (11–12 lb. [5–5$\frac{1}{2}$ kg.]) should be sufficient for 70/80 ducks, but this would be where the food is resting on a hard bottom, such as gravel. In a marshy area where the ducks are likely to lose some of the grain as they dibble down into soft mud, the quantity would have to be increased. If the *correct* amount of food is put down – varied according to the number coming in – it should be cleared up by morning. Any substantial amount left over will be a warning that the ducks have been disturbed during the night.

Ducks will eat almost anything, but barley is probably their favourite food in this country. In warmer countries, maize is often their first choice. Our native

311

ducks also enjoy this grain, but it sometimes takes them a day or two to get used to it. In fact any grain or mixture of grains makes a good food: split peas and beans attract them, also 'condemned' sultanas, raisins and bananas when obtainable. (Dock strikes can be a source of supplies.) We have also used sub-standard hound-meal with success.

Waste products from brewers can sometimes be obtained at a reasonable price and are much favoured by ducks. These include the 'coombs' or small broken barley, the 'culms' which are the sprouts after the barley has germinated and finally 'brewers' grains', left after the barley has been used in the brewing process. The last type is often used as cattle food, and can be more expensive than feeding barley. It can be profitable to shop around for bargains. Mouldy foods should be avoided.

Potatoes can be good value, especially when frosted and mushy. In this condition they produce 'worms' and other animal food. If they are split, pulped or mashed and mixed with seed or barley they are particularly attractive. If a large quantity of potatoes – up to several tons – are dumped in a pond, wildfowl will busy themselves excavating the soft material at the base of the pile. This will create small 'caves' and it not infrequently happens that these caves collapse, trapping the ducks' heads below water. To avoid this, fence in the potato pile with sheep or pig netting. This forces the ducks to make smaller excavations which, should they collapse, usually cause no harm to the birds. Beech mast and acorns are a great draw in the wild, and in good seeding years we have taken advantage of these free supplies.

Although rabbit paunches and dead sheep are often advocated, we do not recommend them. Unthreshed wheat and barley, floating on the water or tied head-down to upright poles – though a 'fiddly' procedure – can be a great attraction and will keep ducks busy.

By far the most productive flight pond known to us is sited in the Midlands. It consists of a carefully fed gravel pit, of $\frac{3}{4}$ acre (0·3 h.) surrounded by an 11-acre ($4\frac{1}{2}$ h.) field. The owner of the pond rents this field and puts most of it into barley every year, harvesting some for feeding and leaving the remainder as attractive natural food.

The food should be scattered mainly in the shallows, with only a small amount on the ground near the water's edge. It is often helpful to have some purpose-made gravelly shallows where the food can be scattered.

Food should be distributed over as wide an area as possible, and not dumped in heaps. Care must be taken to avoid feeding in places where damage to dams, drains, paths or valuable trees is likely to be caused by foraging ducks. Mallard can be fed very satisfactorily on rafts (about 10 ft. × 3 ft. [3 m. × 1 m.]). These should be moored to stakes well away from the banks. A running loop of rope should be used through a pulley (sailors will know it as an 'endless whip') and attached to the raft which can then be hauled to the bank. The food can then be put in the raft before it is hauled back to the stake.

312

116 A trial using explosives to create wildfowl pools. This wet marsh was incapable of supporting the weight of a mechanical digger. Nine holes were blown, each with a water surface area approximately 14 ft. (4 m.) in diameter

313

Although weed and grass seeds, grain mixed with straw, and other such refuse is useful, it will sometimes float too thickly on the surface and prevent the mallard from foraging underneath and getting the grain. These floating rafts of vegetable matter should be raked away from the feeding points.

During hard frosts, straw bales can be divided into 'slices' and fitted together to form a carpet on the ice – the grain being spread on top. Old sacks, chaff, shavings, etc., can also be used. Sheaves of unthreshed corn are still sometimes available in the north and will provide food that can always be utilised in frosty conditions. If the grain is thrown directly onto the ice it can become frozen in, particularly after a fine day when the surface may thaw slightly until the frost refreezes it at dusk. In really wintry weather quite thick ice can form during the day: this must be broken up and some areas raked clear, or it will soon freeze together again. The raking may have to be delayed until the last possible moment, even at the risk of being caught in the act by the first flighting duck.

If a flight pond is also being used as a trout fishery, then feeding hygiene is all the more important. Feed only 'clean' foods such as barley and not 'dirty' foods such as badly frosted potatoes, as these can cause pollution. Do not allow stale food to lie in the water by overfeeding.

Flight ponds are often sited in fairly remote areas and regular daily feeding can be a problem to the gamekeeper with other duties, or the amateur who can only visit the pond at weekends. The Parson's Automatic Feeder provides a very effective answer. It is run by a car battery which normally gives a life of two months or more before it needs recharging. A time clock, wound up every 14 days, determines the time at which the machine operates and the duration – which in turn controls the amount of food that is delivered. Food is scattered over quite a large area – up to 30–40 ft. (9–12 m.) from the machine. A special sleeve can be fitted to confine the feeding arc to 180 degrees, where the machine is placed on the edge of the water. On some pond sites the normal 360-degree arc can be used to feed pheasants on the bank as well. An automatic feeder will always give far better results than occasional visits to the pond with large quantities of food.

Most flight pond owners content themselves with feeding only during the shooting season. While this is understandable, it will never give the best results. Starting with a little bait-feeding as early as June and continuing as required until the following April, is the best advice we can give. Some duck fed in February and March after the shooting is over will always return the following year, with their friends, and may stay to breed.

Later in this section we mention the desirability of controlling rats, and crows, which can steal a great deal of food (page 345).

Call duck (though not the much-publicised white ones), tame mallard, or mallard hybrids can be useful in bringing in wild duck: they can eat large quantities of the food intended for the incoming wild ones. Apart from being expensive to feed, these resident ducks are sometimes aggressive to wild duck flighting in and are usually too fat from over-feeding to fly. Six or seven resident duck are quite enough on a small two-gun pond and can be augmented with artificial decoys.

Duck calls in skilled hands are also very effective – either blown, or hand-operated like the American 'Scotch' Duck Call. Mallard are chatty, sociable creatures and do not mind sharing a meal with friends. Of inexperienced duck callers an American friend once said: 'It's better to keep your duck call in your pocket and appear an amateur, than to blow it and remove any possible doubt.'

Morning flight

A good resting area for wildfowl must have adequate freedom from disturbance. This requirement can be met on large expanses of water where the birds can roost some distance from the shore, or it can be provided by a fair-sized lake (2 acres [0·8 h.] or more) that can be kept *absolutely quiet*. A useful feature is to have plenty of islands or large rafts on which the duck can sit about and preen. In this case it does not so much matter if the banks are used by fishermen, gravel-pit lorries or agricultural machinery.

A little feeding will always improve a morning-flight pond – particularly in hard weather – but no great quantity will be required. Natural cover and foraging areas are more important.

One of the Game Conservancy staff visited a lake where the whole central area was covered with mare's-tail (*Hippuris vulgaris*). On approaching, some 300 mallard rose from it and flew away. Previously, they had been quite invisible from the bank. Without shelter or safe places to roost duck will often be blown from one side to the other in rough weather and have little peace. Their only alternative is to roost on the bank sides, and this they will not do if constantly disturbed.

Unless it consists of a vast lake, a resting area must be shot less frequently than an evening-flight pond – say, three or four times a season.

A large expanse of water makes the problem of placing the Guns more difficult, and certain rules should be followed. Firstly, the host should study the actual arrival of the duck, since they very often favour one particular area to alight on. This will change depending on the weather, so it will be wise to have different hides to cover changes in wind direction. Shooting from the bank obviously tends to be more successful in rough weather, when the duck will usually land closer to the sheltered shore and within range of the Guns. Many lakes have a string of hides built out on islands or rafts.

Artificial decoys are always useful at morning flight to concentrate the ducks in the required places. They should be placed about 15 yds. (14 m.) from the hides in groups of three or four, with odd singles in between – about 15 decoys per Gun being sufficient. In choppy water, however, they can scare the wild duck away.

Making use of rivers

Many landowners with sizeable rivers running through their properties find that duck flying along the valleys are often too high to shoot except in very rough weather. They can sometimes be induced to drop in and feed along sheltered stretches out of the current. But in this case, if the visits are casual and take place intermittently during the day rather than at a well-defined evening flight, one hears the complaint that 'after one bang they all go!'

Flighting ducks on rivers can certainly be difficult, and our advice is often to get the ducks *off* the rivers to flight ponds elsewhere on the shoot. Before the owner does this, however, certain alternative ideas are worth trying.

Feeding duck in for an evening flight is worth trying – in spite of what we have just said – providing there really are suitable places available. These can consist of still backwaters (in Scotland sometimes pools in a spate channel which remain unfrozen in mild weather), gravel shallows where mallard can wade, or bays off the main stream. Artificial bays can usually be dug at little expense and without using any appreciable amount of land.

All these have one thing in common – they provide sheltered places where both ducks and food can remain without being swept away by the current. A big disadvantage of rivers is that heavy rains can spoil a month's patient work on one night by putting the food out of reach or washing it away, and directing the duck to freshly flooded feeding grounds.

Nevertheless if duck are observed dropping into the quiet stretches of a river even in small numbers, regular feeding can sometimes build up a good flight.

There are also times when duck will rest on a river during the day, using a run of shallows or a slow-moving stretch, and in such cases they can be flighted at dawn from hides on the bank.

When a river regularly floods its banks in winter, a very successful technique can sometimes be employed. Spring barley can be drilled along the bank in patches or strips of up to an acre or so. These are left standing right through the winter. Sometimes only half a crop will result, but when these patches flood, mallard and teal will flock to them and make excellent shooting. If the water is only a few inches deep, pheasants will also be regular visitors!

One of the best 'river shoots' we have ever visited was composed of a duck basin lying in a horseshoe bend of a river, but not actually connected to it. The wetland area consisted of about two acres of open water, tussocky marsh, rushes and bog bean, which was slowly beaten through like a pheasant covert.

The actual shooting of a river can present its own special difficulties. Chief among these is the problem of retrieving duck that drop into the water, particularly wounded birds. This has been overcome on our local river by stretching an old salmon net from bank to bank – downstream from the Guns – and stationing a man at either end with a dog and a torch. It is normally very effective, though when darkness falls it can sometimes be difficult to tell when a 'swimmer' reaches the net.

As a matter of interest, this shoot is one of the few successful ones on a river, with up to 500 wild duck flighting in to the shallows to feed. These provide a very calm area, which is in fact a ford only inches deep, and is probably the secret of its success.

Another problem is that duck, instead of pitching in at the same spot every night, will sometimes drop in farther upstream and *swim* down to the feeding point. For this no real answer has yet been found.

Where a main river proves to be unshootable, it is best to forget all about it and build a flight pond some distance away. (Water can sometimes be piped through from the river.)

Hides

Many hides are hastily knocked up – consisting of little more than a few branches tied round a rough frame – with the intention of constructing something more permanent later on if they prove to be in the right position. But the 'something more permanent' rarely seems to happen!

A well-made hide has two functions: to screen the Guns from the incoming duck, and if possible to indicate unsafe angles of fire. Even if the hides are carefully sited – with 'safety posts' on either side – this should not stop the host telling his guests exactly where they may or may not fire, particularly at a morning flight.

When making hides the following features should be considered:

Size. This is governed by the ability to reload quickly without feeling cramped or knocking the barrels of the gun when doing so. To achieve this would need a hide 6 ft. (2 m.) square, but this would be too large to screen the Gun adequately. The usual compromise is 6 ft. × 4 ft. (2 m. × 1 m.) with the long side facing the water.

Height. Visiting Guns come in all shapes and sizes. It is probably best to cater for the shortest guest – adding a light trimming of greenery along the top. A short man can remove it, and a tall one leave it in place. 4 ft. 6 in. ($1\frac{1}{2}$ m.) is about right for the minimum height. The top can be 'castellated' to indicate the direction of neighbouring hides.

Construction. If the minimum height is to be 4 ft. 6in. ($1\frac{1}{2}$ m.) the framework (3×2 in. [$7\frac{1}{2} \times 5$ cm.]) should only be 4 ft. (1 m.) high.

317

The frame should be covered by reeds or straw sandwiched between two pieces of large mesh netting (such as sheep netting). A permanent growing screen of privet or *Lonicera* can then be planted around the outside.

Footing. Constant use can turn the floor into a slippery quagmire, making it difficult or dangerous for the occupant. A slatted wooden floor – duckboards to most of us! is ideal: preferably covered with 1-in. ($2\frac{1}{2}$ cm.) mesh wire netting to give a good grip. A bed of dried bracken, brushwood, heather or other litter is sometimes put down fresh on the day of the shoot. The dogs certainly appreciate it.

Roofs. Some shooters favour roofing-in part of the hide, so that they can stay hidden while duck are circling. But this is not necessary if a Gun stays absolutely still and is properly dressed. It can also make it difficult to hear properly, and all good duck-shooters use their hearing to the full. Further, it pre-supposes that the duck will always approach from one direction. This is not always so – particularly in the case of teal.

Growing hides. These are best of all: privet or a thick wall of willow, carefully trimmed over the years, make ideal hides. Other suitable species are cypress, *Lonicera nitida*, laurel or spruce.

It takes time for them to bush up but if they are planted when the hide is finally sited, they usually grow sufficiently to cover the original framework before the initial reed-covering rots away.

Quite good hides can often be made by cutting out clearings in any evergreens that there may be near the water's edge. Rhododendron and laurel lend themselves well to this treatment. Dummies should always be put in the hides when they are not in use, to get the duck accustomed to seeing them occupied. Nothing elaborate is needed – just a sack of straw on a pole.

A number of refinements will suggest themselves to individual shooters, depending on the degree of comfort they require. For example, a ledge for cartridges or a torch will be appreciated and, for *some* dogs, a strong hook is desirable!

Shooting

Two points are of special importance – the weather and gun-safety.

The best pheasant, partridge and grouse shoots are always planned well ahead, but unfortunately the same routine cannot be adopted successfully with wild duck – or snipe. A change in the weather will greatly affect the flight and ideally one would delay making a firm decision about shooting in the evening until lunchtime on the day concerned. The only factors that can be studied in

117 Top: The framework of a new duck hide. Note the strong slatted floor covered with small mesh netting to give a good grip for the feet, the wooden batten projecting from the top to indicate an unsafe area for shooting, and the box with a wire-netting bottom for cartridges

Bottom: Cladding the outside of the duck hide with common reed. This is very durable and will last for a number of years

319

advance are the moon and – in coastal areas – the tides. A high tide in the early afternoon, coupled with rough weather, can force the duck to flight in earlier than usual. The time of flighting can most accurately be predicted during the dark-moon period, when there is no long drawn-out twilight due to a bright moonlit sky. Dense cloud cover will alter the situation and can keep ducks moving on schedule.

Shooting under a bright moon can be very successful but it is only possible with fleecy white cloud to diffuse the light and provide a background against which the silhouette of a duck is easily seen. Under these conditions the flight can last for a long time – several hours – and it is easy to stop shooting well before the last ducks are in. The need for the right cloud means that the decision to shoot must usually be taken at dusk before the flight is due to start.

Rain provides poor shooting conditions, but by contrast a really calm evening is equally unsatisfactory. The noise of shooting can be heard a long way away, sometimes frightening off the incoming birds. If the wind is too light the duck will not come in on a predictable line, though with a small pond this is not too important. Where heavy rain causes flooded fields and flashes of water everywhere, the ducks may prefer to go slugging and worming – or even just investigating new landing places – rather than homing onto the grain-fed pond.

A fairly strong wind or the approach of a stormy spell usually makes for good flighting conditions. A touch of snow in the air is also a good omen.

At evening flight the Guns are nearly always much closer together than when they are game shooting. As a result an inexperienced or thoughtless Gun can poach on his neighbours' birds all too easily, or even spoil the shooting of everyone taking part. The Guns must therefore *shoot as a team* and not as individuals.

Some hosts prefer to stand well back from the pond and observe the flights coming in – the Guns shooting only when they hear his whistle. In this way no one fires at a small trip of fowl or a single duck, when there are 20 others following behind.

Alternatively, the Guns can be placed in a circle or a semi-circle well away from the pond, shooting only at ducks that have first been allowed to settle – before being flushed by a man beside the water with a torch or a white flag. Picking-up then takes place away from the pond, and does not disturb the latecomers. Shooting should always stop before the last flights have come in.

The perfect guest – as well as shooting unselfishly and ensuring that his eager retriever does not collect any of the live decoys – will also dress unobtrusively. Clothes that are too dark are just as bad as those that are too light. We well remember a flight being spoilt by a Gun being dressed in a shiny black oilskin jacket that turned every duck away as surely as if it had already been shot at! A cap with a good peak or a hat with a wide brim is an essential item, even if the Gun has learned the art of *not* turning his pale face upwards until the last moment.

320

Strange objects left near the pond can also frighten ducks away. On one occasion a newly parked combine harvester ruined an evening's shooting.

Finally on a note of safety:

It may be worth remembering that at the first flight of the season, some or all of the Guns may be having their first shot since the previous January, and could be a little rusty on safety! It is therefore in everyone's interest for the host to brief the Guns carefully before they take up their positions.

Chapter 21
Wildfowl Management: Hatching, Rearing and Releasing Mallard

Wild mallard have a high potential for production which is in fact not often realised in practice, and it therefore follows that it is a species which will respond favourably to management which eases the constraints on its reproductive performance. Some ideas for this are considered later. While a high rate of natural production is desirable, it is advantageous to pick up early eggs for incubation (nest management, page 336) and rear the young ducks where they can be protected from natural hazards, to be released when old enough.

There are many reasons why rearing should be undertaken, apart from salvaging abandoned nests and picking up early eggs. Earlier we mentioned the replacement rearing by flight pond shooters who want to 'put something back'. Owners of lakes often wish to provide extra stock for shooting – using the water as pheasant shooters use the woods. And landowners or clubs, who are establishing breeding sanctuaries, will find that ducks will nest more readily inside the Dutch baskets and other artificial nests, *if the first generation has been reared in pens*, preferably from picked-up wild eggs. Why this should be so, we do not fully understand. But these ducks take to hole-nests quite quickly and then teach subsequent generations and new immigrants to use them. The ducks often take more easily to baskets placed close to the water surface. This can be achieved by means of rafts or, if you can be sure of a stable water level, by means of stilts.

Having presented the case *for* rearing, some of the possible disadvantages, where flight ponds are concerned, should be discussed.

When planning such an operation nearly everyone is tempted to 'rear a few duck' to put down as decoys to attract the wild duck in. Many people buy 50 eggs and finish up with 35 or 40 duck on the pond. This can have several harmful effects. In the first place, in order to ensure that plenty of food is available for wild birds flighting in, so much has to be put in that the decoys become grossly overfed and often quite incapable of flight. They then spend all day and night in the pond and cause considerable damage by eroding the banks and destroying all vegetation. Under certain circumstances they will actually harry and drive off incoming wild duck at flight time. On a pond the size of our standard layout half a dozen would be ample, and they should be pinioned or wing-clipped and confined to part of the pond with wire netting.

Catching-up and laying pens

Mallard eggs can either be bought from gamefarms or produced from penned birds caught-up* in local waters. This presents no difficulty, providing the birds are from a 'managed' strain, and not truly wild. It is unusual to be successful in obtaining fertile eggs from penned wild females in normal aviaries, and when we experimented with wild drakes (put to our own reared ducks) the fertility was nil.

A Dutch decoy-man with many years' experience gave us some interesting information on this point. To increase the number of 'lead-in' ducks, he occasionally takes wild mallard from the pipe, removes the flight feathers on one wing and releases them in the decoy. As long as they are immobilised, he finds that they invariably act in a very secretive manner, skulking in the reeds and only coming out after dark to feed. But by the time the new feathers have grown again and they can fly freely – after about one month – they are used to the regular feeding. They become tame and stay in the decoy. The decoy-man was certain that wild-caught mallard would not breed if they were restricted either by wing-clipping or pulling, or confined free-winged in a small pen, though success has been achieved in some cases.

The Game Conservancy is frequently asked to recommend a suitable catcher for waterfowl. Probably no one type is much better than another, but the model illustrated in Figure 118 works very successfully.

It is constructed of $1\frac{1}{2}$ in. $\times \frac{3}{4}$ in. (4 cm. $\times$ 2 cm.) framing, the floor planked with 6 in. $\times \frac{1}{2}$ in. (15 cm. $\times$ 1 cm.) boards, and covered in $\frac{3}{4}$-in. (2 cm.) mesh wire netting (except the sliding lids, for which $1\frac{1}{2}$-in. or 2-in. [4 cm. or 5 cm.] mesh should be used to allow small birds to escape). The catcher is separated into two halves by a partition.

Using 1-gallon ($4\frac{1}{2}$ l.) plastic cans or blocks of expanded polystyrene for buoyancy, the catcher is floated near the site where the duck are usually fed. Normal feeding is discontinued, the trap is baited (using barley) *and the sliding lids left off*. As soon as the duck are seen to be taking the bait freely (this may be after a day or so, but it can sometimes be only a matter of hours!) the catcher can be set by closing the lids. It is convenient to do this during the afternoon, removing the trapped birds early the following morning.

---

* The wording of the Wildlife and Countryside Act (1981) is not absolutely clear, but it seems that the practice of catching-up duck for penning for egg production requires a special licence from the Nature Conservancy Council. Individuals intending to catch-up ducks should therefore contact the Nature Conservancy Council at 19/20 Belgrave Square, London SW1, or their local NCC Regional Officer.

When carrying out trials on the river at Fordingbridge where the duck were fed daily, 28 mallard, 3 tufted duck, 9 coots, 15 moorhens and 1 water rail were caught in one week. At the gravel-pit wildfowl sanctuary, where the food can be put down only weekly, the duck were so keen to get to it that when the trap was set and baited it was sometimes full to overflowing in half an hour.

Larger 'walk-in' catchers can be used, similar in size and shape to crow cages (see page 53), but with funnel entrances at ground level. These are best placed on a sloping beach, partly in and partly out of the water, sited so that the funnel entrance faces the shore.

There is some difference of opinion regarding the ideal sex ratio in a laying pen, also the question of using immobilised birds as against free-winged, and whether deep water is necessary to enable the drakes to tread properly. The short answer is that we know of one breeder who pens 100 mallard ducks with 10 drakes. These are pen-reared birds, all wing-clipped and with only shallow drinking pans for water. This farm gets good egg production and excellent fertility.

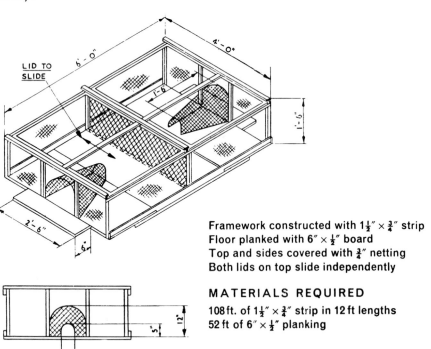

Framework constructed with 1½″ × ¾″ strip
Floor planked with 6″ × ½″ board
Top and sides covered with ¾″ netting
Both lids on top slide independently

MATERIALS REQUIRED
108 ft. of 1½″ × ¾″ strip in 12 ft lengths
52 ft of 6″ × ½″ planking

118 The Fordingbridge-designed wildfowl catcher can collect a large number of birds

The system we use at Fordingbridge with caught-up stock is equally satisfactory and has been practised for many years. The laying pen is 40 ft. (12 m.) square, roofed with plastic netting, and encloses a still backwater measuring 40 ft. × 5 ft. (12 m. × 1½ m.). Into this, 18 ducks and 6 drakes are put and these regularly produce 900–1,000 eggs, with over 90 per cent fertility.

324

It is appreciated that not everybody has a river flowing past his front door, in which case a sufficient number of drinking troughs will prove equally satisfactory, if not so picturesque.

Caught-up mallard should be fed on mixed barley and poultry *breeders'* pellets, gradually increasing the pellets until the barley is eliminated by the end of the second week. Some breeders prefer to continue scattering a little barley about (in the water if it is present) to keep the drakes busy and to discourage them from harrying the females. A hopper is needed for pellets, but grain can be scattered in the open.

A duck laying pen invariably becomes very muddy, particularly when any water is enclosed, and dirty eggs are the result. It has been found that duck will usually lay in artificial nests, if provided. Oil drums, lying on their sides with one end cut open and one third buried, have proved satisfactory and eggs laid inside them are cleaner.

Most eggs are laid before 9 a.m. and should be picked up soon after this, particularly in an open-topped pen where jackdaws and crows can be troublesome.

Incubation

Eggs from penned mallard should be collected daily and dry-cleaned with wire wool. All eggs should be washed for approximately 30 seconds in water at about 130° F. (54·4° C.), using a proprietary egg sanitant such as 'Nusan 2'. After the eggs have been allowed to dry, storage should be similar to that for pheasant eggs, in cool, humid conditions (50–55° F. [10–13° C.]). No turning is necessary for short-term storage, i.e. one week or less. Fumigating the eggs with potassium permanganate and formaldehyde will reduce the chances of impaired hatches due to bacteria on the egg shells.

A large broody hen can comfortably cover 14 to 15 duck eggs, which will usually hatch in about 26–28 days. Nest boxes should be kept damp or the eggs sprinkled with warm water from the 15th to the 24th day, and again at the commencement of hatching.

Although it is often stated that the first 10 days of duck-egg incubation are best carried out under a broody hen, reasonable results can be obtained by setting eggs in incubators for the whole incubation period (see Chapter 9).

Eggs set in still-air incubators should be turned twice daily for the first 24 days only. In cabinet incubators, transference to hatching trays usually takes place on the twenty-fourth day. The normal practice is to turn the eggs five times a day.

In dry regions, spraying the eggs each day with warm water from the tenth to the twenty-fourth day has given good results, but where atmospheric humidity is normally high – in areas of above-average rainfall – any additional moisture has been detrimental to the hatch. In the incubator room 70 per cent hatches have been obtained from fertile duck eggs in a Hamer P21 incubator, even when only one or two egg trays have been filled. With both water-trays full (except for the twenty-fourth and twenty-fifth days), it was not found necessary to spray the eggs.

Candling duck eggs is relatively easy, and should be a routine operation. It should be done at the ten-day stage and again before they are transferred to the hatching trays. There is some evidence to suggest that bad eggs left in the incubator may affect adjoining eggs.

Rearing techniques

Movable pens with broody hens or artificial brooders with wire-netting runs are commonly used for rearing. Raising birds on free range is possible but demands a rigorous degree of predator control that may be too time-consuming for the average person.

Although most *wild* ducklings will be afloat within a few minutes of hatching, it is usually safer to keep *penned* youngsters away from water – except for drinking and washing – until they are adequately feathered at about 6–7 weeks old. In bad weather they may get chilled and die, unlike their more waterproof or better insulated wild cousins. If reared on an exposed site they will sometimes suffer from chills and cramp. The grass on a rearing field should be kept short, so that the ducklings do not get their backs wet. A duckling's down becomes almost useless as an insulator when it is wet.

Compared with pheasant poults, ducklings soon make the ground on which they are being reared extremely dirty. Rearing in movable pens – provided they really are moved regularly – has considerable advantages.

Where relatively small numbers of ducklings are reared, the broody hens that have hatched the eggs make excellent foster-parents. On one gamefarm the mallard duck herself is allowed to hatch her eggs in a nesting box in a large communal pen, before being transferred to a movable pen in which to rear her brood.

If large numbers of mallard are required, they are readily reared in brooders.

The techniques and equipment needed for producing ducklings are similar to those used for pheasants (see Chapter 10). Young ducks are hardy and almost free from the vice of feather-picking. They also have the virtue of being flightless throughout the rearing period and can be kept in open-topped pens until released.

The equipment for rearing a batch of 80–100 mallard is much the same as for 120 pheasants. An overhead heater, using either electricity or bottled gas, is placed in a 5 ft. ($1\frac{1}{2}$ m.) square hut sited directly on gravel over grass. The heat at ground level should be approximately 90° F. (32·2° C.) for day-olds. This is decreased gradually as rearing progresses, the lamp being raised a few inches each week.

A run measuring 30 ft. × 10 ft. (9 m. × 3 m.) will be suitable for about 80/100 young ducks. The birds will, however, turn the area into a mud-puddle very

326

quickly and ideally one would move the pen once or twice during the rearing period.

With unroofed pens, precautions must be taken against climbing and flying predators such as cats and large gulls.

Ducklings will thrive on ordinary chick crumbs for the first three weeks. Water for drinking – and in which to dabble their food and wash their faces – must always be available a few feet from the feeding tray. It is surprising how much water ducklings will drink or waste, and where food is constantly available, topping up small water containers may be necessary several times a day. A hose set up to run water constantly down a piece of guttering is effective when rearing large numbers.

Management after release

Reared mallard are often disappointing to shoot because they sometimes fly badly. In extreme cases, they will not fly at all! Although this can be partly due to breeding from an unsuitable strain, it is more often the result of bad management after release.

Mallard tend to be the 'Cinderellas' on a shoot. Where 1,000 pheasants are being reared, a hundred or so duck are sometimes to be seen, squeezed into a corner as an afterthought and later released on to a pond without much idea of what is to be done with them. To show high, fast-flying reared mallard requires even more care than is needed for first-class pheasants.

One of the most fundamental mistakes that can contribute to poor flying qualities is overfeeding after the duck have been released. It is not uncommon for a hardworked keeper to throw down half-a-hundredweight of barley to 100 mallard every morning, on his way to the more important job of feeding his pheasants in covert. Mallard are extremely greedy and will accept such generosity with relish, but all too often this means that when the shooting season starts they are too fat and too tame to fly.

Using a small pond as a release point can aggravate the problem because the birds get little exercise, apart from an occasional walk in a neighbouring field and a short flight back to the water if disturbed.

One can certainly understand the keeper's dilemma. If he doesn't give his ducks enough to eat, they may desert him: if he is too generous they will become obese and immobile. The amount of food to give requires careful judgement. The keeper should aim to give just sufficient to keep them in good condition and hold them on the shoot. If in doubt, he should keep them a bit 'sharp'.

The time and place of feeding are just as important as the quantity. The basic thing to remember is that the food can be used to move the birds about, just as a donkey is lured with a carrot. This is easiest on a fairly sizeable area of water – an acre or more – particularly if it is long and narrow.

The feeding should be carried out twice a day, morning and evening. It is essential to whistle or call when putting the food down. In the afternoon the food should be scattered at the release point, but the morning feed (when reared duck are usually at their hungriest) should be moved farther away each day, until the two places are 100 yds. (90 m.) apart or more by the time the birds can fly (8–9 weeks).

From now on flying must be encouraged as much as possible by *varying* the morning feed point every day so as to keep the ducks guessing. If they know where it is to be, most of the birds will swim or walk to the area at leisure, and hang about waiting for their meal. An experienced keeper will choose half a dozen places which can be approached unseen, giving the duck no indication as to where they are to be fed until they hear his call. This should bring them *flying* from all parts of the lake.

Where there is more than one batch of birds of different ages, always feed the flyers first and then go back to the younger birds. This has the advantage of preventing bullying.

The same system can be used where ducks are released on a small pond, but the morning feed will have to be put down in an adjacent field, to get far enough away to make them fly. After they have cleared up the food it is advisable to make them take wing, otherwise they may walk back.

Where possible, gradual feeding on to higher ground some distance away will encourage duck to fly back – partly because they find it difficult to walk down a steep gradient.

Pinioning

Wildfowl breeders often wish to keep stock birds in open-topped pens, which makes it necessary to pinion or clip their wings. For short periods of confinement, pulling out the primary feathers of one wing will be sufficient and this is a useful technique when releasing ducks. Clipping the primary feathers of one wing will keep ducks grounded until the next moult (the eclipse period varies between June and August), while wing-pulling is temporary and can be used for periods of 4–6 weeks.

Pinioning involves permanent removal of the manus, or outer joint of the wing. This is a technique used mainly by breeders of ornamental waterfowl. The pinioning of adults is not recommended unless carried out by experts, but on downy ducklings the operation can be effected quickly and easily, the manus being removed with a pair of sharp nail scissors or, better still, an electric cauterising de-beaker. This is virtually a bloodless operation and does not seem to inconvenience the ducklings at all. It should not be done until they are feeding well at about 3 days of age, and not after they are 1 week old.

Pinioning adult birds should not be undertaken in summer when the scar may attract flies, nor should it be done during feather re-growth (for example, after pulling the flight feathers), or during the moulting period when arteries in the wing distend considerably. This operation should only be undertaken by a qualified veterinary surgeon.

Disease

Although mallard are easily reared they can be subject to many of the diseases of gamebirds, but it must be noted that the course of a disease may be different. Also, life in a watery habitat increases the importance of such diseases as those caused by the parasitic worms.

Healthy young ducklings grow rapidly on balanced poultry foods, but on poor diets deficiencies soon show themselves. It is surprising how often one meets the philosophy: 'Oh, ducks will eat anything.' Rations containing irritant materials can produce a form of enteritis whose symptoms may be similar to those of duck cholera and salmonellosis. Losses from this cause can be heavy. Poor diets are often deficient in vitamins, for example vitamin A. This lack results in a staggering gait, partial paralysis and whitish-yellow exudates in the eyes, and losses can be high. Too little vitamin A often predisposes birds to other diseases, including one known as 'white-eye' where the cornea of the eye becomes opaque simulating this condition.

Newcastle disease is not the killer that it is in gamebirds, but care should be taken if it is rife in an area, since mallard can act as carriers of the virus.

Salmonellosis is not especially common but where it does occur mortality may be high and since transmission can be via the eggs, the danger of incubating mixed species or batches from different origins is emphasised. While treatment with furazolidone in the mash is suggested, survivors may remain carriers of the disease.

Given the correct conditions, such as high temperatures and dirty stagnant water, poisons are produced by the bacterium *Clostridium botulinum* which cause muscular weakness and ultimate death. Clean water will prevent this problem.

Cyathostoma, a worm similar to *Syngamus*, is found in the trachea of ducks and causes respiratory disease but without the 'gaping' associated with the latter. Mortality can be considerable in feathering birds and treatment with tetramisole is suggested. Another worm condition is acuariasis (due to *Acuaria*, a parasite which invades the wall of the proventriculus causing the formation of capsules and a partial breakdown of the digestion). It reaches another duck while living inside the water flea, *Daphnia*, which when eaten by a new host releases the larval stage to begin invasion of the gut. Treatment is not practical, but the cycle can be broken by increasing the flow of water through the rearing pens to 'wash' out the *Daphnia*.

A parasitic fungus, *Aspergillus fumigatus*, can attack the respiratory system of ducklings, but since there is no treatment, prevention is of primary importance. Mouldy straw, hay and grain are frequent sources of infection. Dampness and warmth are paramount in the development of this fungus.

Prevention is almost synonymous with 'cleanliness'. If good-quality food is provided, and overcrowding, chilling, bad ventilation and the generally dirty conditions so often seen with ducklings can be avoided, diseases should present few problems.

Chapter 22

Wildfowl Management: Wild Duck Breeding Areas

It has been difficult to find a good name for breeding areas that are intensively managed to increase the mallard population. The word 'sanctuary' is not always apt, because in certain places the surplus ducks can be shot without affecting the value of the area for high-density nesting.

Our original experiment in producing more ducks by developing the right habitat, nests, rafts and management went through several stages. For some years trials were carried out on a flooded brick pit, badly overgrown with reed mace. The actual water area was very small, but, without rearing, the breeding population was raised from one resident pair to 28/30 pairs in five years. This breeding nucleus colonised at least half a dozen other small ponds in the district which had previously been untenanted.

Plenty of mistakes were made. The adults became too tame. And, because the experiment was only a spare-time venture, predator control and nest management were inadequate and the survival rate of young birds was very low. It did, however, show the potential of various forms of management, described in the following sections.

Artificial nests

Over 30 years ago one of the authors of this book visited a 12-acre (5 h.) lake in Holland where there were some 400 nesting baskets supported on stakes in the water and safe from all predators. At the end of the nesting season the baskets are washed, dried, dipped in wood preservative and carefully stored until the following year. Fresh lining material of short hay is put in every season. If properly maintained the cane baskets last 10 years, and the willow ones three or four.

The system was obviously so successful (each basket producing five flying duck, i.e. about 2,000 on one lake!) that a specimen basket was brought back to Fordingbridge and copied by a Wiltshire basket weaver. At first, difficulty was experienced in persuading the native mallard to adopt the new artificial nests, though within a few years we discovered how to adapt the original Dutch system to conditions in this country. Two radical changes were made: rafts instead of stakes were used to support the nests, because in most places our water level varied a great deal more than the carefully controlled conditions in the Netherlands: and *owing to an insufficiency of natural food, it was found necessary to feed the broods like reared duck.*

In Holland after the broods hatch off, the females take most of them away from the main breeding lake to the nearby farmlands which are intersected by a network of drainage ditches. In some places smaller lakes and reedlands abound, and there is rarely a shortage of natural food. It is a duck paradise. In England it was found that the broods either tended to stay on their home lake or move off to busy farms – in either case with unsuitable conditions and insufficient food for the extra numbers of growing broods.

The Dutch expert starts to feed his lake only when the broods are beginning to fly. First to flight in are the semi-tame *stahl* duck, and later the wild ones from nearby farms and polders. Gradually a big flight is built up, of which only the surplus is shot. Conservation is very well understood.

The plan at Fordingbridge has been to reverse the procedure, i.e. to feed the growing duck in and around the breeding areas until they are strong on the wing, then limit the food gradually, thereby encouraging them to forage farther and farther afield, visiting other ponds and perhaps colonising new areas.

In the early sixties it was decided to undertake some experiments with artificial nests on the River Avon and on 'the moat' at Fordingbridge – in reality a sort of backwater of the River Avon. The water was L-shaped and only measured 120 yds. × 10 yds. (110 m. × 9 m.) across.

These experiments showed that mallard which originated from released birds (bred from picked-up wild eggs) took readily to various artificial nest structures – nests on rafts being preferred initially to those supported on stilts. The use of these nests resulted in a marked increase in the number of breeding pairs over the three years.

Artificial nests on heavy duty rafts on the river were not successful – many capsized or broke free in heavy water.

Expanded polystyrene protected by heavy duty plastic sacks was found to be the best means of providing buoyancy for the rafts (see section on raft construction).

Various types of artificial nests or hole-nests have been developed.

The original Dutch nesting baskets are efficient as well as picturesque. The open weave is an advantage, allowing a duck to see in all directions while remaining unseen herself. Although the dimensions of the Dutch baskets vary slightly from one weaver to another, the diameter of the entrance hole remains constant at about 6 in. (15 cm.). This measurement is vital. These baskets are now obtainable from the Game Conservancy.

When placed on stakes above the water, the basket should be tilted upwards until it is at an angle of 20 to 30 degrees from the horizontal. This forces the duck to lay at the far end, as far from the crow's beak as possible. Coot and

119 Nesting baskets should always be supported on stakes sufficiently high above the water to avoid the possibility of flooding

120 Mallard returning to raft nest box (note leg ring)

332

moorhen also like the baskets to nest in and are predators of mallard eggs as well. It is a good idea to reduce the populations of these birds by shooting or trapping during the open season.

Over the years experiments have been carried out with various home-made nests, the best of which is like a traditional small bird nest-box, constructed from slabwood obtained cheaply from any sawmill. It is easy to make and n~ unattractive in appearance (see Figure 120).

The *inside* dimensions are 12 in. (30 cm.) square and 9 in. (23 cm.) high, with an entrance 6 in. (15 cm.) square. In their original form these boxes were subject to predation by corvids and the addition of a funnel entrance (to screen the nest) stopped this.

When fixing a nesting basket or box in position on a raft, it should be remembered that a parent duck sometimes likes to take her ducklings back into the nest the first night after hatching, so some form of step should be provided to ensure easy access. Cases are known where half a brood have struggled back inside the nest, while the weaker ones have been left outside to die. Where a nest is completely inaccessible, such as on stakes, no attempt is made to return.

Nesting rafts

Although nesting baskets on stakes above the water are very successful in Holland, in this country rafts are preferred for the two reasons already suggested: they allow for fluctuations in the water level and our native duck take to them much more quickly. Rafts are also very valuable as roosts on open water and in places where there is a certain amount of disturbance such as a working gravel pit. This is particularly noticeable in winter-time.

For small sheltered ponds a raft can be quite a simple affair – made from an old wooden door, for example. But for open waters the construction must be fairly heavy to make them stable and the moorings must be strong and secure. Various methods of providing buoyancy have been tried, such as metal drums of different sizes, but for preference pieces of expanded polystyrene scrap are used, packed in plastic fertiliser bags, since the duck like to eat it if it is accessible.

If metal drums are used it is better to have a large number of small ones rather than one or two big ones. Eventually they will rust through and obviously one or two small drums leaking will not affect the buoyancy so much as a big one. The small sizes are also more easy to replace. Plastic containers such as those used for chemicals and detergents are better.

We have found that old telegraph poles, usually obtained quite cheaply from British Telecom or local Electricity Board, provide the best basis for large raft construction, being heavy and pressure-impregnated with creosote. A simple framework or angle-iron fastened with coach screws makes a very strong, durable and cheap raft that will last for some years. Sloping ramps with 'footholds' or wire netting must be fitted to provide access for ducklings, otherwise some will be unable to follow their mother back 'on board'.

Raft construction

1. Cut a telegraph pole into two equal lengths and lay them out parallel, 5 ft. ($1\frac{1}{2}$ m.) apart and as close to the water as possible.

2. With a brace and bit, drill holes $\frac{3}{8}$-in. ($9\frac{1}{2}$ mm.) diameter where the angle-iron is to be fastened.

3. Before fixing, the iron frame should have $\frac{5}{8}$-in. (16 mm.) diameter holes drilled at each end for the fastenings and an additional hole in the middle of the angle-iron to take the mooring wire.

4. Place the iron frame in position and fasten with 6 in. $\times \frac{1}{2}$ in. (15 cm. $\times$ 1 cm.) coach screws driven into the prepared holes.

5. Turn the whole raft upside down.

6. Spread a length of 6 ft. (2 m.) $1\frac{1}{2}$-in. (3 cm.) mesh, 18-gauge wire netting over the raft and fasten with staples. In the event of a plank rotting, the wire netting will act as a safeguard to prevent rooted plants, etc., dropping through.

7. Nail planks across. These can be an expensive item (slabwood can be used as shown in Figure 125), but they can be spaced 6 in. (15 cm.) apart if used in conjunction with wire netting. Netting on its own would be forced up by the buoyancy material. Two planks should project 9 in. (23 cm.) beyond the poles on each side to form bottom supports for the duckling ramps. These boards should be 6 ft. (2 m.) apart and at roughly equal distances from the ends of the poles.

8. Secure the buoyancy material in position. The fastening need not be very strong (small-gauge lacing wire is adequate) since it is only to hold the material when the raft is launched, after which it will be held by its own buoyancy.

9. Turn the raft right side up, at the same time lowering it *slowly* on to the water. This can be done by running a supporting rope from a nearby tree or vehicle. It is important to carry out this manoeuvre gently and to see that there is enough depth of water to float the whole structure, otherwise the buoyancy material may break loose or be damaged.

10. Nail a board 6 ft. 6 in. (2 m.) long across the centre of the two telegraph poles and projecting 9 in. (23 cm.) each side. This will be the top support for the duckling ramps.

11. Fit the ramps, and nail in position to the top boards. The bottom boards will be below water level and the lower edges of the ramps will have to be fastened to them with wire unless the raft can be tipped over to bring the boards clear of the water.

334

12. Fill the space between the poles with straw and plant up with soft rush (*Juncus effusus*) or suitable reeds, and tow to the mooring position.

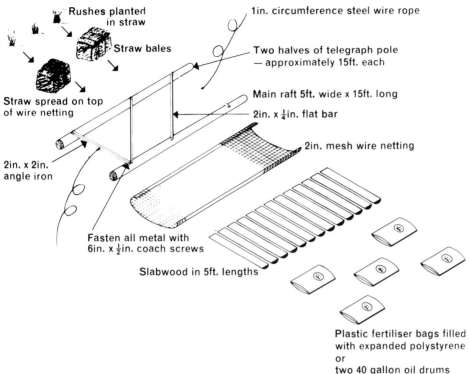

Rushes planted in straw

Straw bales

Straw spread on top of wire netting

2in. x 2in. angle iron

Fasten all metal with 6in. x ½in. coach screws

Slabwood in 5ft. lengths

1in. circumference steel wire rope

Two halves of telegraph pole — approximately 15ft. each

Main raft 5ft. wide x 15ft. long

2in. x ¼in. flat bar

2in. mesh wire netting

Plastic fertiliser bags filled with expanded polystyrene or two 40 gallon oil drums

121 Raft construction

It is important to see that the moorings are really strong. At Fordingbridge 1-in. (2½ cm.) circumference flexible steel wire rope is used with a breaking strain of about 4 tons (4,050 kg.). It is unlikely that this strain will ever be exerted, but deterioration must be allowed for. The rafts are moored in 'strings', usually with one end attached to an iron stake on the bank and the other to a mooring on the bottom. This is made up with concrete sinkers of convenient size (a 2-gallon [9 l.] can makes a good mould). One is fastened to the end of the wire and four more threaded on and allowed to slide down to the bottom – after which the end of the wire is shackled to the raft. Moorings must be regularly inspected. Chafe invariably occurs where the wire is fastened to the raft and the shackle must be moved to a new position further down the wire. For this reason there must be some slack in the moorings at first launching.

With large rafts it is possible to support the anchors on the raft while it is floated into position. If they are attached to the raft by a sufficiently long cable they can simply be pushed 'overboard' when the raft is in the desired position.

If more than three rafts are moored together, there should be additional moorings from rafts in the middle of the 'string' to prevent it from sagging before a strong wind and dragging the main moorings.

These rafts are illustrated in the diagram on page 335 (Figure 121). When planted with rushes they look most attractive. Some of the rafts at Fordingbridge showed no signs of deterioration after nine years afloat. By this time the wire netting and planking had rotted away but the rushes had formed a solid root mass which floated on the polystyrene and was held in place by the telegraph poles.

On these larger rafts, nests of Canada geese and tufted duck have been found among the growing vegetation, and on an unplanted raft a roosting pair of common tern have successfully nested for two seasons.

Nest management

It has been stated that it is advantageous to pick up early eggs.* We confirmed this observation during experiments with artificial nests at Burgate Manor.

[In a mild year we have found a first egg on 14th January; no fewer than seven artificial nests being occupied by the end of the month. With an average period of 40 days between the first egg and hatching, this meant that a duck starting to lay on, say, 25th January, would bring her ducklings off about 17th March. Their chances of survival would be poor at this time of year with little insect life available and the weather likely to be harsh. All the early eggs were therefore removed to see whether the ducks would lay again.]

The picking up was done between 14th and 23rd February, when the clutches were nearly full, a total of 91 eggs being collected. The experiment proved successful and all the nests were re-occupied by 20th March, together with two new ones. This has two effects. Those duck whose nests have been emptied tend to delay for a few days before laying again, and others who have not started and are undisturbed, do so after 1st April. As a result the first ducklings appear around mid-May. The main hatch is well spread out over a period of about a fortnight, eliminating the possibility of two or three cold, wet days killing a large percentage of the ducklings.

Habitat improvement and stocking with duck

Much can be done to improve existing wetlands and to create new habitat for wildfowl. In 1963 we decided to develop a wildfowl breeding reservoir on a 10-acre (4 h.) working gravel pit a few miles from Fordingbridge, where we could put our ideas into practice. The experimental gravel pit was very typical of the great majority of those found in the south of England. The biggest problems were deep water (8-12 ft. [$2\frac{1}{2}$–$3\frac{1}{2}$ m.]) and bare, cliff-sided banks devoid of vegetation. It was estimated that there were four breeding pairs of mallard in the spring of that year.

---

* The Wildlife and Countryside Act (1981) allows the taking of mallard eggs by authorised persons (owners or occupiers) up until 31st March, provided the birds which hatch are released no later than 30th September.

122 Collecting early-laid eggs from a nesting box

123 The ramp above the duck's head provides easy access to the raft for baby mallard

124 Launching heavy-duty nesting raft

337

125 Putting straw in the large telegraph pole raft. This will later be planted with rush

The first priority in the trial area was to create sheltered shallows around the edge of the gravel pit where a variety of water plants was introduced. A selection of rafts was constructed to make up for the lack of natural islands. The banks were planted with shrubs and trees such as alder and willow, some being planted on the water's edge to suppress marginal vegetation. Ducks need some areas of bare shoreline where they can rest and preen in comfort. Also they frequently roost on the branches of trees just above the water line and overhanging willows are ideal for this.

Once this habitat improvement was completed the area was stocked with mallard to form the nucleus of a breeding population. This can be done on any suitable water and the way to succeed is as follows:

An open-topped release pen of a suitable size, say 44 × 22 yds. (40 × 20 m.) must be constructed in a sheltered position, with at least one third of the pen built in the water. To keep foxes out, the wire should be 2-in. (5 cm.) mesh and 6 ft. (2 m.) high with 12 in. (30 cm.) turned out at the top and a similar amount buried (or turned outwards and firmly pegged down) at the base. The wire netting around the water area should also be 6 ft. (2 m.) high with at least 3 ft. (1 m.) below water – mallard are surprisingly adept at diving. This size of pen is suitable for 150–200 six-week-old mallard which should be fully 'hardened off' before being put into the pen. If possible, barley should be fed daily by hand; otherwise hoppers may be used. When they are approximately nine weeks old,

338

126 Planting up part of the south shore in March 1966, after levelling the steep banks

127 The same area in August 1968

339

the ducks will start to fly in and out of the pen. Feeding should continue in the pen, but the amount should be gradually reduced and more feed should be spread around outside. Later the birds can be fed at various sites as described in the section on flight-pond management. Light feeding should continue throughout the winter to hold the birds and to attract wild ones.

When this was done at the gravel pits near Fordingbridge the breeding stock built up to 55 pairs after three seasons. In the third year picking up early eggs for incubation boosted the total production to six fledged young per pair. In the fourth year there were sixty breeding pairs present, from an original population of four pairs in 1963. This success was partly due to the proximity of the River Avon and its water-meadows with the associated rich feeding grounds for ducklings. The survival of the broods which stayed on the gravel pit after hatching, however, was very poor in spite of the newly created habitat. For this reason it was found to be essential to provide food for the ducklings, and creep feeders which exclude adults are advisable.

The simplest form of 'creep' consists of an old broody coop placed a few feet back from the water with a 'trail' of corn leading up to the bars. Crumbs and cut grain can be put inside the coop, protected from the rain and out of reach of the adults. The more coops that can be made availabe, the less quarrels there are likely to be. Large 'creeps' can be made with 2-in. (5 cm.) square Weldmesh sides or wire-netting frames, raised 2 in. (5 cm.) above ground level. Both will admit small ducklings and exclude adults. 'Creeps' can also be housed on rafts moored just offshore, out of the reach of rats.

Breeding waterfowl as a group have certain requirements: safe nest cover for adult females; escape cover and shelter from wind for the ducklings. These are relatively easy to provide, and should be included as features of any habitat which is managed for the production of ducks. Our early work taught us useful lessons, but it became obvious that there was a great need for a better understanding of habitat creation. This was particularly so where the intention was to establish a completely wild breeding area with no regular management involved. The essential first step in designing this breeding habitat was to investigate the factors which control the survival of ducklings.

The Great Linford Wildfowl Project

This need for basic research was one of the reasons for the establishment of the Great Linford Wildfowl Research Project. This is a joint venture between the Amey Roadstone Corporation and the Game Conservancy, fully operational since January 1972, and funded entirely by A.R.C., a member of the Gold Fields group. Without this very generous facility we would have been unable to examine the problems in depth.

The aims and objectives of the Great Linford Wildfowl Research Project are two-fold. First, to take a part of a working gravel quarry in Buckinghamshire and to use this area for practical management trials to create habitat. To

128 Top: A newly excavated shallow lagoon in the Great Linford reserve

Centre: The same lagoon left to nature has only been lightly colonised by clumps of rushes even after 7 years.

Bottom: A similar lagoon alongside the one shown above. This was planted with a variety of plants after excavation and now provides excellent habitat for duckling broods in the summer and resting and feeding wildfowl in the winter

341

improve, diversify and maintain the habitat in such a way that it would cater for the needs of a high density of both breeding and wintering waterfowl, and waders, of a wide range of species.

Second, to carry out original applied research into the population dynamics of the waterfowl, and the problems of establishing and maintaining waterfowl habitat in these worked-out wet pits, so that management procedures can be based upon a sound scientific understanding of the general ecology of the new wetlands, and of the waterfowl populations which could benefit from them.

The work of the project in both habitat management and research is continuing. The following section outlines the basic habitat needs of waterfowl, and describes the ways in which these can be met by management of a new man-made wetland using examples from our reserve at Great Linford.

Site requirements

Where lake size is concerned obviously the larger the better, but even quite small areas can be made to produce ducks. Whatever the size, it is far better to have a long, irregular and gently shelving shoreline, and many islands, than it is to have a single large body of water with straight, steeply graded banks.

The water must have a range of depths, with a large proportion relatively shallow, i.e., less than 3 ft. (1 m.) deep. The water supply must be reliable and fairly constant, so that the levels are naturally stable. It should also be unpolluted, preferably alkaline, and rich in calcium and plant nutrients. The facility to control water levels by mechanical means such as weirs and sluices is of great value in various management procedures and should, if possible, be included.

All waterfowl have certain common requirements. Their habitat must be able to meet these needs if it is to be successful as a nesting area, a winter refuge, a safe place for the mid-summer moult, and as a year-round feeding site. The precise requirements vary with species and with season but the following are essential to all:

1. Seclusion, shelter and freedom from disturbance
2. Safe, quiet loafing areas
3. High-quality nesting areas with adequate ground cover
4. Good, rich, shallow-water feeding sites

These are dealt with in more detail below.

Seclusion and shelter

Freedom from disturbance is extremely important and it can be ensured in several ways. Obviously, public access and activities like fishing and sailing must be limited to certain zones or times, or must be prohibited completely.

In order to increase the seclusion of a breeding area, trees and shrubs should be planted to give screening cover and shelter from the wind. Willows, alders,

342

birches and poplars will grow close to water. There are very many willows and the following have proved useful, in our experience:

creeping willow; common osier; purple osier (good winter colour); goat willow; violet willow (good winter colour); white willow (large tree); crack willow.

The pin oak is also a useful tree which is tolerant of damp situations and produces acorns which are a great draw for mallard. The seeds of alder and birch are also enjoyed by duck. Where possible an outer belt of quick growing sheltering conifers should be planted on the drier ground.

Trees or shrubs must not be allowed to grow so close to the water's edge that they shade out marginal vegetation, except where some areas of bare shoreline are needed for preening.

The area managed for breeding waterfowl should be fenced to keep out grazing stock. This is to protect the planted material and to allow natural ground cover to grow up. However, it is useful to allow cattle access to part of the water margin where their trampling and manuring will make perfect conditions for waders such as snipe.

129 Marginal vegetation is a source of food for ducklings as well as providing protection from enemies

343

Roosting and loafing

Suitable places are needed to act as day-time roosts for ducks, and night roosts for geese, and a large expanse of water, above 12 acres (5 h.) fulfils this quite well. However, the birds must also have shore roosting areas where they can rest, sleep, preen etc., out of reach of predators, preferably in the sunlight, and sheltered from the prevailing winds. Such 'loafing spots' are of great importance to waterfowl and must be incorporated into their habitat. Wild birds prefer elevated banks, free from tall vegetation and with easy access to open water. At Linford this need can be met in a variety of ways. The ducks can have access to low grazed embankments, they will use bare loafing rafts moored in sheltered bays, and one area of our reserve contains a purpose built loafing spit. This is a long narrow peninsula, pushed out into the main lake, which is covered in black polythene sheet, topped with $\frac{1}{4}$–$\frac{3}{4}$-in. (6–18 mm.) gravel in a layer 10 in. (25 cm.) thick to suppress all vegetation.

Ducklings too have a vital need for some dry, bare areas for preening and sleeping. For this reason one or two islands can be kept clear of vegetation by the use of herbicides, or by physical clearance.

Breeding sites

A previous section described the use of various artificial nests for ducks, but breeding densities can also be increased in a more natural way.

The first need is for adequate ground cover to conceal the nests from mammalian and avian predators. This is quite simply provided by keeping out grazing stock, and by planting marsh and bankside vegetation. Island nest-sites are far preferable to mainland sites, and usually more successful too, so a profusion of islands is desirable to achieve greater production of young duck. Many small islands are better than one large one, but large ones can be 'hollowed out' to provide a sheltered lagoon in the centre.

Predator control

Early results from our studies at Great Linford showed that nest predation is an important factor regulating the productivity of a duck population and unless some form of protection is provided, such as safe nesting baskets on water, the ducks' enemies will have to be controlled.

In recent years the feral mink has become an important potential menace to ducks. Many cases of losses among nesting ducks along river banks have been recorded in which both the sitting duck and eggs have been lost. Fortunately, the 'catch'em-alive' cage trap, partly concealed with water weeds or bark, and baited with fish or offal, is very effective against mink when sited under the river bank or in an old willow stump.

Pike can cause havoc among young broods, and in enclosed water every effort should be made to remove them.

344

Egg thieves, such as crows, rooks and jackdaws, can be very troublesome, and the use of baited crow cages and shooting are recommended. Rats are always liable to appear, particularly when any feeding is carried out. They should be kept in check by tunnel-trapping and regular baiting with suitable rodenticides.

Tunnel traps will also control stoats which can cause havoc to a brood of ducklings foraging on shore. They are also egg thieves. However, present studies indicate that the fox is the most damaging predator because of the number of incubating females it can kill. Water is no protection and island nests can be just as vulnerable as those on the mainland. Fox control must be carried out, particularly in high-nest-density areas. (See Chapter 5 for details of predator control methods.)

Feeding sites

For a wetland habitat to hold and produce large numbers of ducks it must have sufficient sources of high-quality food. Requirements vary with the age structure of the ducks and season so a variety of foods and feeding sites should be available.

The primary requirement of dabbling ducks is shallow water, preferably less than 16 in. (40 cm.) deep because this is the maximum depth to which an up-ended mallard can reach, while a teal can reach down only 4–6 in. (10–15 cm.). Shallow water is also far more productive of plant and animal foods than deep water, and even diving ducks like the tufted duck and pochard prefer depths of around 6–15 ft. (2–5 m.) in which to feed.

Ducklings particularly need shallow rich waters where the invertebrates on which they must feed should be readily available. Such areas will also attract wading birds such as snipe, redshank, curlew etc.

The majority of aquatic invertebrates on which waterfowl feed live on and amongst water plants, and the water margin and shallows can be considerably improved by the introduction of food and cover plants (a subject covered in detail later).

In the spring and summer most of the dabbling and diving ducks will obtain food in and around the water in their breeding and moulting areas. In the winter the dabbling species usually use lakes or sea-shores as day-time roosts, while they feed away from water on cereal grains, the seeds of arable weeds, grasses, frosted potatoes, drilled seeds, acorns etc., and geese and wigeon will graze sprouting cereals. The proximity of such food resources is an advantage when choosing a site for development as a wildfowl refuge, but the adults of all species will fly quite long distances between their roosts and feeding grounds.

For most of the year, the grazing geese and wigeon (sometimes mallard and teal) require short, good-quality, growing grasses on which to feed. It is important that this is available in undisturbed places close to the nesting sites, so that juveniles do not have to travel far to reach their feeding grounds.

Suitable goose and wigeon feeding sites can be provided by allowing cattle access to a large part of the lakeside and by using sheep to graze selected areas to produce 'goose lawns'. This grazing is preferable to mowing as it is less labour intensive, and produces a much richer sward.

In the United States 'natural' feeding is an effective part of management and it would be possible to attract and feed relatively large numbers of duck by drilling a small block of cereal near the water.

Aquatic plants and other cover

Any wetland area, and in particular a newly made lake, can be considerably improved for waterfowl by careful management of the vegetation. The development of the marginal, emergent and submergent flora can be accelerated to a great extent by an initial planting of suitable material. This determines the vegetation pattern, and therefore the fauna, of a new lake for a very long period. It is therefore vital that the species are carefully chosen with due regard for their requirements and their intended purpose. Planting should be planned to establish a varied pattern of vegetation in and around the water to give cover, food and shelter and establishment of marginal vegetation can also reduce the erosion of unstable shorelines.

Different aquatic plants have different values to waterfowl, as well as those which they all share. For example, *all* plants provide a nutrient and energy input to the water when, on death in the autumn, the plant tissue enters the water and decays, thus the water plants are the beginnings of the food chains which end in the desired quarry species, be it fish, fowl or both. Selective planting and management of the vegetation, should encourage a variety of different species for particular functions. For example the sea club-rush, great pond sedge and bur-reed all produce food for ducks in the form of seeds, and while bur-reed dies down in the winter and disappears, the dead stems and leaves of the sedge and club-rush remain standing until spring providing valuable winter cover and shelter. Dense beds of emergent reeds of almost any species are of special value as escape cover and shelter when the ducks are in full wing moult.

The submerged parts of all aquatic plants provide a 'scaffold' on which the insect larvae, worms, snails, water boatmen etc., find cover and food. Some of our research has shown that the plants which grow most densely, such as the sedges, hold large numbers of animals of a wide range of species, while plants of less dense habit, such as the common reed, harbour fewer animals of a smaller range of species. This is apparently related to food and cover – the more dense the stems, the greater the surface area of plant available and therefore the greater the food supply and shelter that the plant affords. The densely growing

346

130 Top: The common reed can be very invasive and will grow in water as deep as 5 ft. ($1\frac{1}{2}$ m.). It can provide excellent marginal shelter on a lake

Centre: Large rafts of amphibious bistort have a damping effect on wave action and give excellent shelter for duckling broods. They are however not popular with fishermen!

Bottom: Water crowfoot is an excellent plant for harbouring aquatic invertebrate foods for ducklings especially in running waters

347

sedges, club-rush, bur-reed and reed-grasses therefore hold more items of food for waterfowl.

The totally submerged plants, and those with some parts floating or emergent (of which the more important are the yellow and white water lilies, amphibious bistort, broad-leaved pondweed, milfoil, crowfoots, starwort, sago pond-weed, and some other fine leaved *Potamogeton* species) are probably more important than wholly emergent plants for the provision of shelter and food for invertebrates. These too can be introduced and planted where suitable.

Site preparation and planting for habitat improvement

The factors to consider when embarking on a planting programme are the nature of the water body and the selection of species which suit both the conditions and any specific requirements. First of all, the existing vegetation should be surveyed at flowering time when identification is easiest using simple field guides. This will avoid the chance of planting species which are already present, and will facilitate planning any additions or removals. Similarly, it is advisable to identify a source of transplant material at flowering time, and mark the position carefully so that selected plants can be taken at the appropriate time.

The water quality and nature and profile of the bed of the lake are also important. Mineral-poor waters over hard sand or gravel, or acid peaty waters, will not encourage plant growth and may need treatment with topsoil, fertiliser or lime to improve them. The growth of plants in waters on sterile soils can often be improved by the addition of fertiliser and 6-8-4 NPK is suitable if enriched with either ammonium sulphate for hard water or nitrate of soda for soft water to give an 8-8-4 mixture. It should be applied in nine or ten 'doses', each of about 1 cwt. (50 kg.) per hectare. The first application may be made in April or May, and followed each week by another for a period of six weeks and then monthly until the autumn. The fertiliser should be broadcast from the windward shore on a breezy day and some should be spread on the margins to promote the growth of fringe plants. Waters with a high calcium content are normally best for plant growth and for invertebrates and fish, and should present no problems. Clay beds suit a wide range of plants, provided the clay does not cloud the water. Depths of more than 13–15 ft. (4–5 m.) will probably restrict growth or eliminate most water plants. The margins and shallows are therefore the best places to consider for planting, remembering of course to leave suitable open loafing areas, preferably on S. or S.E. facing island shores. In the case of deep lakes or wet gravel pits, it is often wiser to dig out shallow lagoons or wet shelves around the margin rather than attempt to establish plants in deep water. In small ponds it is a good plan to extend the shoreline by digging bays into the banks. The size of the duck population is governed more by the length and suitability of the shoreline than the area of water.

348

Sources of material and planting techniques

The way to guarantee success in planting is to introduce species which grow well in local natural water bodies. Invasive plants such as common reed and reedmace should be planted only where their growth is restricted by local conditions e.g., on a ridge surrounded by deep water or on a marginal shelf. Each species should be planted in a group occupying a stretch of shoreline sufficient in area to ensure it becomes firmly established before meeting competition from a neighbouring, perhaps more vigorous species.

Very shallow water, i.e., less than 12 in. (30 cm.) deep should be planted with low-growing marsh plants such as common spike-rush, brooklime, mare's-tail etc., which are easy to control and which are good low cover for ducklings and waders. Figures 131 and 132 demonstrate the various zones and suitable plants for them.

The most productive zone is invariably the interface between two different stands of vegetation or between vegetation and open water. Here, water and nutrients circulate freely, light can penetrate, and invertebrates have easy access, as also do fish and ducks. It is important, then, to create as much 'edge' as possible during planting. Most emergent reeds tend to form pure stands, and several small blocks of different species along a shore is much preferred to a few large stands of any one species. For instance, in some species the stems are so dense that ducklings and fish can only feed around their edge. For this reason the pattern to be aimed at is a number of groups of these high-production species in a matrix of less dense types such as reedmace, common reed, flag iris, bullrush etc., which allow access for feeding ducklings and fish.

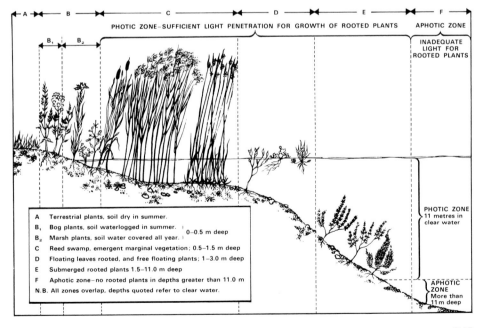

131 Typical zoning of vegetation

349

Plant Species	A	B₁	B₂	C	D	E
Alders	●	●				
Great willow herb	●	●				
Forget-me-not	●	●				
Woundwort	○	●				
Gipsy-wort	○	●	○			
Marsh marigold	○	●	○			
Sweet flag		○	●	○		
Flowering rush		○	●	○		
Spike rush		○	●	○		
Water plantain		○	●	●		
Jointed rush	●	●				
Willows	●	●	○			
Bur-marigold	●	●	○			
Sea club-rush		○	●	●		
Reedmace		○	●	●		
Brooklime	●	●	○			
Water cress	●	●	○			
Water mint	●	●	○			
Great water dock	●	●	●			
Mare's-tail	●	●	●			
Meadowsweet	●	●	○			
Hard rush	○	●	●			
Soft rush	○	●	●			
Reed canary grass	○	●	●	○		
Bog bean	○	●	●	○		
Marsh horsetail	○	●	●	○		
Pond sedges	○	●	●	○		
Purple-loosestrife	○	●	●	○		
Yellow iris	○	●	●	○		
Great yellow cress	○	●	●	○		
Bur-reed	○	●	●	●		
Reed grass	○	●	●	●		
Common reed	○	●	●	●		
Bulrush			○	●		
Arrowhead		●	○	○		

132 Plant species associated with marginal areas of lakes

350

Plant Species	A	B₁	B₂	C	D	E
Duckweed			●	●	●	●
Amphibious bistort	●	●	●	●	●	
Water lilies			○	●	●	
Quillwort			○	●	●	●
Water crowfoot			○	○	●	●
Water lobelia			○	●	●	●
Broad-leaved pondweed			○	○	●	●
Water parsnip			○	○	●	●
Lesser water parsnip			○	○	●	●
Bladderwort			○	○	●	●
Water soldier			○	○	●	●
Frogbit			○	○	●	○
Hornwort			○	○	●	●
Canadian pondweed			○	○	●	●
Spiked milfoil			○	○	●	●
Whorled milfoil			○	○	●	●
Stonewort				○	○	●

Key
● – species characteristically found in this zone
○ – species sometimes found in this zone

When collecting transplant material, treat it with care. Keep the roots wet and re-plant as soon as possible in the new site. Simply lift a small piece of rhizome or root of the plant by pulling or digging, in some cases taking the whole plant if it is small, and heel in the pieces in the required place. Rhizomes are best collected at the end of the plants' dormant period in spring, just as the new shoots appear. A piece taken with a growing tip will establish best. Autumn planting does work, but with a lower success rate, and many plants will wash out over winter. If autumn planting is necessary, cover the material well with soil or a stone, or hold it down with a wire arch, and remove all top growth to prevent swans and coots uprooting the plants. If there is a large swan or coot population, the plantings must be protected until they are established. Whatever the time of year, plantings on exposed shores will need protection with floating pole baffles to reduce wave action and erosion. If a current is flowing, plant in 4-in. (10 cm.) deep trenches and place stones on the top. If other species are found to be mixed with the selected transplants, leave them in and they will add to the diversity; undesirable species should, of course, be removed.

The non-rhizomatous plants which will transplant readily include most of the submerged ones, plus watercress, brooklime, great water dock, marsh marigold and starwort. Watercress grows well from seed, but the others need to be dug with a good root ball in late spring or early summer when growth is vigorous before flowering. Cuttings of milfoil and crowfoot can be pushed into the mud in shallow water, or into a clay ball which is sunk in deeper water, and the leafy tips of many submerged species, especially of the *Potamogeton* pondweeds, can simply be thrown into water where they will put out roots, but this is wasteful of material as success rate is not high and there is no control over where the plant grows.

Some useful food plants such as arrowhead, broad-leaved and sago pondweed produce tubers or winter-buds called *turions* as over-wintering stages, and these can be collected in autumn for broadcasting in the water, or they can be stuck in clay balls and sunk in selected spots.

Most submerged and floating-leaved plants should be introduced into 3–6 ft. (1–2 m.) of water, preferably on a soft lake bottom, while the emergent plants should not go into more than 3 ft. (1 m.) of water.

Plants which are useful to waterfowl can be considered in several groups:

a. Plants which are totally submerged or which have only their flowers, and perhaps a few leaves, above the water surface.
b. Free-floating plants.
c. Emergent plants which have leaves floating on the water surface.
d. Emergent (marginal) plants which have erect leaves held above the water surface.
e. Marsh plants.
f. Terrestrial plants giving ground cover and/or food.
g. Trees and shrubs giving shelter and food.

There is necessarily some overlap between these groupings, but they form a broad basis for clarification.

Plant species of value to wildfowl

(Extra-value rating: ★★ excellent; ★ good)

(a) Totally submerged plants with only their flowers and perhaps a few leaves above the water surface

★★*Water crowfoot (Ranunculus aquatilis)*. Will grow in swift streams or ponds, sometimes in moderately acid water.

Brackish-water crowfoot (Ranunculus baudotii). Coastal areas in brackish streams, ditches and ponds. The seeds of *Ranunculus* species often mature in early summer and their value may be higher than suggested by studies done during the shooting season.

133 Newly planted vegetation on an exposed shoreline can be temporarily protected from wave action by heavy floating logs

134 Experiments are being carried out at Great Linford using barley straw to enrich the base of newly excavated and flooded gravel pits

353

Ivy-leaved water crowfoot (Ranunculus hederaceus). A common plant on mud in shallow water.

Circular-leaved Crowfoot (Ranunculus circinatus). A locally common plant in ditches, canals, ponds, gravel pits and lakes with a high mineral content.

Tassel pondweed (Ruppia maritima). The American name for this coastal plant is wigeongrass. It grows on bottoms of fertile soil or sand in depths of a few inches to several feet. The seeds are eaten by mallard and other dabbling ducks.

★ *Stonewort (Chara spp.)* An abundant plant in still and slow-running water. Much favoured by pochard and teal.

★ *Canadian pondweed (Elodea canadensis).* A widespread submerged aquatic plant which can grow to a depth of 12 ft. (4 m.). It will often choke a pond to the exclusion of other species and then almost die away. The male plant is very rare in the British Isles and so seed production is usually nil. It does, however, carry a very rich fauna of wildfowl food animals including the Jenkins' spire shell *(Potamopyrgus jenkinsi)* which is an important food for young and adult tufted duck. This plant can be a great nuisance to fishermen because of its invasive habit. It can, however, be controlled reasonably effectively and safely with Casoron 'G' which is available from Duphar-Midox Ltd, Smarden, Kent (telephone: Smarden 541/2/3).

Horned pondweed (Zannichellia palustris). This is a slender, short species reaching a length of approximately 18 in. (45 cm.). Its seeds are eaten and it lives in fresh or brackish water.

★ *Fennel-leaved pondweed (Potamogeton pectinatus).* Grows in ponds, ditches, canals, rivers etc. Its seeds and tuberised lateral rhizome buds are eaten. It particularly likes alkaline water.

(b) Free-floating plants

★ *Duckweeds.* All are eagerly taken by wildfowl. Lesser duckweed, the commonest species, is found floating in all types of still water, often covering the surface. Thick duckweed, ivy-leaved duckweed – submerged species except in the height of summer. Value to wildfowl is fair to excellent. Ivy-leaved duckweed thrives best in moderately acid waters and lesser duckweed is also said to be best in slightly acid water, but tolerates a greater range than other duckweeds.

Frog-bit (Hydrocharis morsus-ranae). This is a floating aquatic perennial with thick kidney-shaped leaves, about $\frac{3}{4}$–2 in. (2–5 cm.) across. It rarely produces seeds in this country, but is useful for the food animals which it harbours. It is somewhat local in distribution, being found in ponds and ditches in calcareous districts where it can sometimes be common.

354

(c) Emergent plants which have leaves floating on the water surface

★★*Broad-leaved or floating pondweed (Potamogeton natans)*. This is common in lakes, ponds and ditches. Its seeds and roots are eaten by wildfowl. It lives in depths from 12 in. (30 cm.) to $4\frac{1}{2}$ ft. ($1\frac{1}{2}$ m.) but is usually found in shallow water less than 3 ft. (1 m.) deep and tolerates acid waters, favouring a highly organic substratum.

★★*Amphibious bistort (Polygonum amphibium)*. A widespread and common plant which grows a good crop of seed and makes excellent surface cover for ducklings, who conceal themselves in the emergent flower stalks. The flowers are scented and attract flying insects which provide food for the ducklings. It has a terrestrial form which lives on banks by water, growing between 12 in. (30 cm.) and 29 in. (74 cm.) high. Large mats of bistort floating on the surface of a lake have a very marked damping effect on wave action.

(d) Emergent plants which have erect leaves held above the water surface

★*Arrowhead (Sagittaria sagittifolia)*. This herb grows from 12–35 in. (30–90 cm.) in height. It perennates and spreads by means of small tubers called turions. These are readily eaten by wildfowl. It is characteristic of muddy substrata and grows best in shallow water about 6 in. (15 cm.) deep. The foliage proves good cover for ducklings, but it dies down quickly after the first frosts. A similar species in the United States is called the 'duck potato'.

★*Mare's-tail (Hippuris vulgaris)*. Cover plant, locally common in ponds, lakes and slow streams. On one breeding area that we visit regularly the emergent tips are often infested with blackfly, which provide very good food for ducklings. The seeds are also eaten by duck. It can withstand moderately alkaline and moderately acid conditions.

★★*Bur-reed (Sparganium erectum)*. Food and cover plant. Common and widespread by rivers, canals and ponds and has proved very successful on some gravel pits. It grows on mud and in shallow water, producing a crop of seeds. Spring planting of divisions is recommended. It is invasive of water up to 18 in. (46 cm.) deep in many favourable locations. Three closely related species are good food and cover plants for wildfowl.

★*Common spike-rush (Eleocharis palustris)*. Provides seed for wildfowl and is found in wet meadows, marshes, ditches and the margins of ponds. It grows in dense tufts 6–12 in. (15–30 cm.) in height. Favoured by teal.

★*Common bulrush (Schoenosplectus lacustris)*. Found in the margins of rivers, lakes and ponds, usually where there is an abundance of silt. It grows 6–$7\frac{1}{2}$ ft. (2–$2\frac{1}{2}$ m.) and its seeds are eaten by mallard and teal. (This species should not be confused with reedmace, which is commonly called 'bulrush'.) It

355

seems to be less common in Wales than other parts of the British Isles. It can be invasive.

Reedmace (Typha latifolia). The false bulrush. This is an invasive plant, not of much direct value to wildfowl, although the analysis of the stomach contents of ducklings collected from amongst stands of reedmace has shown that it can harbour much in the way of insect foods. It is often dominant, especially on inorganic substrate such as the bottom of newly dug gravel pits or where there is silting and rapid decay of organic matter. It is not usually advisable to plant reedmace unless at least 80 per cent of the area is more than 3 ft. (1 m.) deep. Its distinctive cigar shaped seed head distinguishes it from the true bulrush.

Hair sedge, hammer sedge (Carex hirta). Commonly found in damp grass and near ponds. The seeds are eaten by mallard and propagation is by division.

★*Lesser pond sedge (Carex acutiformis)* and *greater pond sedge (Carex riparia).* Common in the fringes of still or slow-moving freshwater or round ponds. Their seeds are eaten by mallard. They provide early cover.

Flote-grass or Manna grass (Glyceria fluitans). Growing from 6 in. (15 cm.) to 2 ft. (60 cm.) high and is common in stagnant or slow-flowing shallow water throughout the British Isles. The seeds, freshly produced, are readily eaten by wildfowl. Propagation is by seeds and by division.

Reed-grass (Glyceria maxima). A taller 3–6 ft. (1–2 m.) grass growing in similar situation to flote-grass but often in deeper water. Abundant beside most lowland rivers but becoming rare in Scotland. Seeds eaten by mallard. This species is highly invasive of shallow water, forming a very dense stand through which ducklings might find it hard to travel.

★★*Sea club-rush (Scirpus maritimus).* This plant has been proved to be a very important source of food for mallard during the winter in brackish-water areas where it is locally abundant in ditches, ponds and rivers. We have been successful in establishing it in alkaline-water gravel pits by means of division. It appears not to be invasive.

Common reed (Phragmites australis [communis]). A stout, erect reed growing to a height of 9 ft. (3 m.). It stands upright throughout the winter. It is very widely distributed in swamps and shallow water, but is absent from extremely poor and acid habitats. It provides winter cover and wind shelter, and is useful in preventing bank erosion in the most exposed places.

(e) Marsh plants

Great water dock (Rumex hydrolapathum). This stout perennial (3–6 ft. [1–2 m.]) is found in wet places beside and in ponds, lakes, streams, etc. Propagated readily by seed or division. The seeds are eaten by duck. The seeds of other dock species are also very important wildfowl foods.

★ *Creeping buttercup (Ranunculus repens)*. Typically found on heavy soils and in wet meadows, by rivers and ditches. The seeds are eaten by mallard and teal.

Water pepper (Polygonum hydropiper). Sometimes useful, being found commonly in marshy fields and in shallow water on the edge of ponds and ditches. Mallard eat the seeds.

(f) Terrestrial plants

Persicaria, redleg or redshank, black bindweed, knotgrass, fat hen, common orache. All these weeds are widely found on disturbed ground, arable land and the banks of ponds and rivers. They are all free seed producers over much of the year and the seeds are readily eaten by foraging duck.

Blackberry or bramble (Rubus fruticosus). The pips are eaten by duck and this is one of the best natural cover plants.

Summary

For those who are in doubt and wish to keep things simple, the three groups of useful plants which are available in most ponds and streams are:

1. Tall reed cover (bur-reed, reed grass)
2. Low marginal cover (common spike rush, brooklime, yellow cress)
3. Emergent plants (broad-leaved pondweed, amphibious bistort)

Game Conservancy research on wildfowl production

As this book explains, the techniques for improving wetland habitats to increase the breeding populations of waterfowl are well understood and are relatively easy to apply. There are, however, problems such as the low fledgling success rate of ducks breeding on many gravel pits. The production of young mallard can be very low due to an extremely high mortality rate early in life. This is just one of the areas of study covered by our research programme.

The study of wild duck breeding biology was intensified in 1979, the aim being to produce a reliable mathematical population model which can be used to predict the effects of variation in several important factors (such as weather, predation, food supply etc.) on the breeding success of mallard and tufted duck at different population densities. This will be an extremely valuable tool for management of waterfowl populations – for example, showing the cost-effectiveness of predator control programmes, and indicating the proportion of a population which could be shot without adverse effect.

One of the early projects undertaken was a study of the food taken by adult mallard. This emphasised the dependence of inland mallard on the farming pattern of the surrounding area for their food supplies in late summer, autumn and winter. At these times 90 per cent of the food of mallard in our study area is of agricultural origin. Cereal grains, mainly barley but including some wheat and oats, are taken from laid crops as early as July. However, most of the cereals taken are spilled grains, gleaned from stubbles after the harvest. This enormous food resource can enable the birds to build up their body fat reserves and the assessment of the conditions of shot birds shows a very significant increase in body weight and size of fat deposits over the autumn and early winter. The general condition and amount of body fat begins to decline in February and March – the time when food supplies are scarce. The investigation shows that the local pattern of agriculture should be considered in any plans to develop a breeding reserve for mallard. Success will obviously be easier to achieve in extensive cereal growing areas.

The study of the feeding ecology of the adult mallard was extended to examine the food taken in spring and summer. There is a change from a predominantly plant diet to one consisting chiefly of invertebrates, including many aquatic species. This change may reflect an increased need for animal protein for gametogenesis (reproduction) and feather replacement after the moult, and also the fact that there are fewer seeds and other plant foods available, the crop from the previous autumn having been eaten, dispersed, or germinated.

There is an obvious advantage to the species if juveniles and parents require the same foods. A parent bird which selects an insect-rich area in which to find food will also be choosing the right area for its brood and it has been shown that mallard with newly hatched broods at Linford select the areas known to be richest in emerging midges. Diet investigations have revealed that the very young birds depend on an abundant supply of aerial insects in the first few days of life, and ducklings do much better in areas which are very rich in insect life. A well fed duckling, with a large part of its diet consisting of high-grade protein will grow faster, and be better able to cope with hazards such as poor weather, than ducklings made weak through lack of food of the necessary quality. An experimental feeding trial confirmed the hypothesis that for satisfactory growth, the ducklings needed invertebrate material in their diet.

The majority of the necessary aquatic invertebrates live on or amongst aquatic plants, or in the sediments of the lake bed. Most of them feed on algae or on dead and decaying organic matter (detritus), and in a new gravel pit, with no inflowing stream, the accumulation of detritus takes a long time. We have therefore developed a technique for the enrichment of the sediments of newly flooded gravel pits using straw. We have shown in a number of practical trials that the addition in spring of about 10 tonnes per hectare (1 kg. per square metre) of barley straw to a suitable lake, i.e. one with alkaline water and a non-organic sediment, significantly increases the amount of invertebrate life present on the bed of the lake. Eventually, when the straw has decayed, it

358

stimulates the production of larger numbers of chironomid midges, which can then be exploited by the wildfowl. The increased production of aquatic invertebrates would, of course, also be of tremendous benefit to the fish in the water, which we believe may be in direct competition with waterfowl for these vital invertebrate food organisms. Current research at the Wildfowl Centre at Great Linford is concerned with the significance of this competition.

Incidentally, we have noted that the addition of straw in spring also helps to reduce algal bloom problems and it will help to stabilise soft lake silts, speeding up colonisation by aquatic plants.

The knowledge gained from this study should enable us to create the conditions needed to ensure that ducklings produced by the wild duck attracted to areas such as our reserve, have a better chance of reaching maturity.

In this way, breeding sanctuaries can be made to produce a surplus of wildfowl to improve the shooting potential of the surrounding area, and to replace those birds which are shot elsewhere. With the dramatic rate of loss of natural wetlands it is vitally important for the future well-being of European waterfowl that we manage as many areas of existing and new man-made wetlands as possible so that they can harbour and *produce* wild waterfowl.

Conclusion

To many of us there can be no more exciting sport than wildfowl shooting, and no more rewarding activity than the practical conservation that increases the shootable surplus and safeguards the breeding stock. We hope that this book will stimulate readers to realise the importance of the improvement of wetland habitat. Even a small effort can have really worthwhile results in terms of increased wildfowl production and those who apply in any way possible some of the practical techniques outlined here can be assured that the rewards are well worth the effort.

We hope that readers will use this book as a guide to their own activities in this field, whether as individuals or as clubs or conservation groups. We would welcome details of experiences elsewhere as also requests for further information from us.

The results of our research work are published as scientific papers and in the Annual Review of the Game Conservancy. Interim findings are used to increase the scope and value of the Game Conservancy's Advisory Service. One aim of the research project is to produce a blue-print for the restoration of suitable parts of worked-out gravel quarries as wildfowl and wildlife reserves in harmony with man and his leisure activities.

Chapter 23
Snipe and Woodcock

Snipe

If the number of old prints showing our ancestors shooting snipe were any indication of the popularity of the sport, there has been a sad decline in modern times. With the heavy demand for more shooting this is surprising, for there are thousands of farms all over the country where more could be done to encourage snipe – and at a low cost.

Evidence of snipe populations is difficult to obtain, but in this country it is generally believed that a decline in numbers was first noticed about the beginning of the nineteenth century. This decrease has been associated with the draining of marshland and the introduction of the breech-loader. More recently the icy winter of 1962–3 killed thousands, particularly in south-west England where they were most numerous. It is only now, after several years have elapsed, that in some – but not all – areas, snipe numbers are returning to the pre-1962–3 level. The overall picture, so far as we have been able to discover, is that snipe are not declining further. They are certainly shot less than in times gone by.

Migration

In the autumn and winter months the numbers of native snipe are greatly increased by immigrants from north-west Europe. These may stay with us or move on to more southern countries bordering the Mediterranean: some may reach the Equator. Before the evidence from ringed birds was available, it was (and still is) thought that our home-bred snipe moved south before the winter visitors and passage migrants arrived. It now appears that during August and September a local re-distribution takes place, and this accounts for the oft-reported scarcity of snipe in their breeding areas during these months. It is possible that some home-bred snipe may get caught up in the southward migration later in the year.

The passage migrants and winter visitors begin to arrive in September from Iceland, Scandinavia or other European countries, but the main movement takes place in October, November and December. This southward migration is often triggered off by the onset of a cold spell and is usually most marked during periods of bright moonlight.

Management for snipe

Snipe shoots can be divided into two groups, according to whether or not they depend for their success on the onset of hard weather. Where, for some local reason such as the emergence of springs or the presence of warm effluent from an old-fashioned sewage farm, relatively small areas of wet ground remain unfrozen, little or no management is undertaken. Weather lore and the ability to muster the Guns at short notice are all that are required. But in the milder climate enjoyed by the west and south-west of the British Isles, spells of cold weather cannot be relied on to concentrate the snipe, and the incentive to attract birds to really good feeding grounds becomes greater. In such areas it is worth while making an effort to provide the conditions they are known to like.

Their diet consists mainly of invertebrates such as earthworms – the long, pliable sensitive beak being designed for probing in soft earth. Bare patches of humus-rich soil are well favoured; cowpats are also worked over. Snipe dislike meadows that are choked with reeds and rushes, but such areas can usually be improved quite easily by eliminating a proportion of the dense cover, i.e. *in patches*. This can often be done by controlled burning, especially where there are reeds, which are usually inflammable in a dry October or November. Failing this, a swipe can be used to reduce the herbage. The dead stems can then be burned or raked off.

Years ago, the tethering of grazing horses in marshy areas provided ideal snipe habitat – the open patches among the taller vegetation being very much to the snipe's liking. The importance of these bare areas – whether of natural or artificial origin – has long been recognised in the U.S.A. where they are known as 'eat-outs'.

Those of animal origin probably have the advantage over man-made ones, since the animals' manure is believed to increase the amount of invertebrate food available. In the old days 'manuring' the cleared patches in the bogs or reed beds was reported to have been carried out – mainly with blood and offal. At present it is almost impossible to find anyone in England who has had first-hand experience of attempts to increase snipe food by spreading manure. Only in the Scilly Isles could we find a place where fish guano had been spread for this purpose.

Snipe prefer to feed and rest out of the wind. The bare feeding places should therefore be made in areas where the rough vegetation that is left standing can provide essential shelter. Cutting swathes through the cover, in a criss-cross or chessboard pattern, will also allow the birds to run to shelter in times of danger.

Another way of improving a snipe bog is to use small explosive charges to create a pattern of small craters. These will have a dry rim on which the snipe

135 In the foreground, a natural snipe bed in the Dutch reedlands

can stand – they do not always wish to be ankle-deep in water. The sides should be 'shelved' by hand. Feeding circles cut with a spade – leaving the upturned sods round the perimeter – give the same result.

In some areas of Holland snipe management is perhaps better understood than over here and this fact, combined with their extensive reedlands, has led the Dutch to develop special snipe beds – a technique that could more generally be used in our own country.

There are two sorts of snipe bed – natural and artificial. The former are cut out of the reedlands (the reeds being a valuable crop for thatching, bulb fields and potato silos). The original 'wild' snipe beds simply consisted of the first clearings opened up by the reed-cutters. It was found that these provided the right feeding conditions – part wet and part dry – with nearby standing reeds giving escape cover. When the snipe hear or sense danger they often run into the sheltering reeds. The open beds are used for feeding, resting and actual sleeping. In time these 'wild' or natural beds were rented out to shooters and gradually became more sophisticated, with butcher's blood and mud poured on to them to attract insect life.

The snipe flight into these beds in the early morning, and are shot from hides in much the same way as duck.

The artificial beds are usually made in patches of *open water* rather than cut out of a wilderness of reeds – partly so that the snipe can see them more easily, but also so that shot birds will fall where they can be retrieved by dogs.

They consist of 'mats' of cut-down reed stubble about 20 ft. (6 m.) square with a top layer of dug-out roots – in one area it was reedmace – dressed with

362

136 An artificial snipe bed in a flooded sand pit near The Hague

mud or manure. It is essential to achieve the right pattern of water and half-submerged, rotting roots, which form a 'raft'. During the season – September and October – the surface is raked over each week.

More ambitious still are snipe beds made in places such as sand or gravel pits. Here boards are used to enclose an area of about 20 sq. yds. (17 sq. m.), which is then filled with sunken faggots and mud, and finally *Phragmites* roots (or reedmace) turned upside down. Fresh mud and manure are added each week in the season and raked over.

The snipe bed undoubtedly provides interesting shooting, and where birds are found in substantial numbers but cannot be approached or shown satisfactorily, they are worth considering. Many a small rough shoot could well do with a morning snipe flight to spin out a day's sport.

None of these simple suggestions is beyond the capacity of even the smallest farm with a patch of undrained, boggy ground. Indeed, we believe that many a bog would never have been drained had the owner realised its potential sporting value.

Woodcock

In the course of a season most shoots manage to bag a handful of woodcock, but only in certain places like Cornwall or Ireland can they be relied upon to provide a full day's shooting, given the right weather. Unfortunately, woodcock habitat is deteriorating every year, largely because present-day

363

afforestation does not create the right conditions for them, and the old keepers who maintained the cock coverts are in any case dying out.

It would be quite possible to plant new woodcock coverts even today – but they would not be an economic proposition to the same extent as pheasant woodlands. Nevertheless there are many owners who at least wish to preserve what they have, and others who can afford modest changes in their softwoods policy.

Woodcocks are resident throughout the British Isles in fair numbers and breed in all counties, except perhaps Cornwall. The more southerly counties are less favoured.

Migration

The majority of birds that make up our winter population are migrants from northern Europe and their flight lines seem to follow a regular pattern. The movements of woodcock are more clearly defined than snipe, which move south and west on a broad front.

Migration, as observed in the Isles of Scilly, starts with the October moon. This is invariable, though the numbers involved depend on the wind strength and direction, as well as the severity of the winter. Like most migrants, they seem to know when bad weather is to come and keep ahead of it. The mild season of 1966–7 produced small numbers of woodcock in Cornwall, compared to the hard winter of 1962–3. It was interesting to note during that very hard winter the woodcock arriving in west Cornwall were not in such bad condition as the snipe: they monopolised all the unfrozen areas on the edges of running water, in some cases driving the weak and starving snipe away.

Good shoots are naturally on the main migratory routes. These include the promontories of our eastern, western and southern shores, also the Irish coastline. Here, near the coast, the weather is warmer and the fields less likely to freeze. It is in such areas that it would be profitable to plant and maintain suitable woodcock cover.

Habitat

Perhaps because woodcock resemble snipe in many ways, there is a tendency to think that they like only boggy or wet conditions, but nothing could be further from the truth. During the day, which is spent mainly resting – though in hard weather they feed voraciously all round the clock – they seek a dry, sheltered locality with plenty of open spaces at ground level and good cover overhead.

An all-important requirement is quiet. For this reason many experts will not allow pheasants to be released in the same area, though proof as to the success of this measure is lacking one way or the other.

Favourite sites are usually spinneys of alder, willow, rhododendron – when tunnelled and not too dense – gorse, hazel and sometimes bracken. The floor is comparatively bare and lawn-like or carpeted with dead leaves: the soil rich in

364

humus. American woodcock (*Philohela*) also favour alder groves as well as aspen plantations when not too high, and grey dogwood thickets (*Cornus racemosa*). Alder, sycamore and aspen are associated with high levels of nitrogen: so are earthworms.

The overhead canopy of the covert should be broken and not too high. The optimum seems to be about 10–15 ft. (3–4$\frac{1}{2}$ m.) for alder and willow and 5–10 ft. (1$\frac{1}{2}$–3 m.) for gorse and rhododendron. In coverts of any size this means a coppicing rotation that can involve a great deal of work. The open spaces, clear to the sky, are used by the birds for getting in and out. Such spaces can take the form of zigzag paths, circles about 10–20 ft. (3–6 m.) in diameter, and wide rides which divide the coverts into shootable blocks and provide good stands.

To be out of the wind is essential and this is why they usually frequent low-lying alder and willow scrub. To some extent this produces a conflict of interests for such places are often damp and boggy. If they are, the right conditions must be obtained by providing good drainage with a system of ditches and by keeping the ground cover – brambles, rushes, etc. – under strict control.

Given calm conditions woodcock feed mostly at night. Indeed they can be observed and counted at dusk leaving their coverts and flighting to nearby soft ground, plough or market-garden type of land. Well manured root fields are a favourite. Here they probe and listen for worms in the same way as snipe: in the woods they will excavate under the leaves for invertebrates. They tend to avoid clay, calcareous and sandy soils, which are low in humus, though in some good snipe areas in Cornwall and Tresco these particular soils present no clear-cut disadvantages. The key is the availability of earthworms, usually more common in pasture fields.

Shooting

Driven woodcock is a specialised art and produces superb shooting which, no doubt, is why in west Cornwall and similar districts there is less incentive to rely on pheasants.

Short drives of not more than 200 yds. (180 m.) are the order of the day and this means that the coverts must be split up into small blocks by wide rides in which the Guns stand. Probably the most important aid to driving and picking-up afterwards is a well-disciplined pack of spaniels. Woodcock will run before the beaters and when flushed will often fly in a predictable way. Year after year these birds can be found in the same places. They have a liking for flighting down tunnels among the trees or through gaps between tall species, and this can be employed to good purpose by the shoot owner. Artificial tunnels can be made and trees felled in strategic places to funnel the birds towards the Gun stands.

To sum up, woodcock require their own special day-coverts which must be kept quiet, while adequate night-feeding grounds should be available nearby.

A cock keeper can be a surprisingly busy man, with ground cover to clear, rides to maintain, gaps to cut in the canopy, new plantations to manage, top and coppice, ditches to dig and so on.

New information* on the breeding biology of the woodcock

Recent research into the breeding biology of the woodcock has shown that males, contrary to popular belief, do not maintain exclusive territories and are successively polygamous, mating with several females each season. The pair bond lasts only for the few days prior to egg-laying, and the male then plays no further part in the proceedings. Many nests are lost to predators, particularly foxes, but females can re-lay in as little as 8 days after losing eggs or chicks, although they usually move to another locality to do so (up to 6 miles [10 km.] away). Males return to breed in the same area every year.

* Research carried out by Dr G. J. M. Hirons, Game Conservancy.

Chapter 24
Grouse Management

The red grouse (*Lagopus lagopus scoticus*) is a uniquely British gamebird. It provides some of the world's finest shooting.

Grouse moors cover 3,000,000 acres (1,215,000 h.) of Scotland, nearly 1,000,000 acres (405,000 h.) of England and Wales and 1,000,000 acres (405,000 h.) of Ireland. This is a very large area so it is important, where grouse shooting is the predominant interest, to know how it should be managed to the best advantage, and to what extent other interests can be beneficially accommodated.

These moors consist of areas of hill land where the main food of red grouse – the ling heather *Calluna vulgaris* – is the dominant plant, or at least makes up a high proportion of the vegetation. Heather thrives on dry ground, and in the east of Scotland, England and Ireland it forms almost continuous stands over much of the moorland. In the wetter areas in the west, it is common only to steep, well-drained ground, and the hills tend to be grassy rather than heathery. In Scotland these wetter areas are used as deer forest. Broadly speaking, Scottish moorlands with 40–60 in. (1–1½ m.) of rain serve as grouse moor or deer forest, while ground with less than 40 in. (1 m.) is good grouse moor, where deer are regarded as a nuisance.

The lower moors were originally natural forests, which have been cleared by man. They are kept as open moorland by burning and grazing. If these processes are stopped the ground quickly reverts again to forest. Almost all grouse moors serve as hill grazing for sheep, and increasingly for cattle as well.

Although in southern Ireland some of the best grouse ground has been afforested in the past forty years, the economics of substituting forestry for grouse shooting on the better moors in the United Kingdom weigh in favour of continuance of the latter.

The reasons for grouse research

The main problem with grouse shooting as a form of land usage is that stocks periodically dwindle to a very low level. They normally recover, but in some places have failed to do so. A Committee of Inquiry, under the Chairmanship of Lord Lovat, was set up in 1904. Much of the research was carried out by Edward Wilson, who later died with Scott at the South Pole. The Committee discovered a great deal about diseases and parasites in red grouse. This, together with a lot of general information, was published as a two-volume work entitled *The Grouse in Health and in Disease* in 1911.

Grouse stocks dwindled on many moors in the late 1930s and did not recover. The bags plunged, and so of course did shooting rents. This situation continued without radical change until in 1956 the Scottish Landowners' Federation decided to support a three-year research programme by voluntary subscription. After the three-year period, the Nature Conservancy took over and set up a Unit of Grouse and Moorland Ecology attached to the Natural History Department at Aberdeen University. A moor at Kerloch, near Banchory in Kincardineshire, was rented for practical research. In 1968 the staff were embodied in the Conservancy, and the Unit's base at Banchory became a Conservancy Research Station. Later the staff became part of the Institute of Terrestrial Ecology and moved in 1981 to the ITE station at Banchory. The ITE grouse research team now works mainly on the moor of Rickarton near Stonehaven.

The main research problems are:

1. Why do grouse stocks fluctuate?
2. Fluctuations aside, why do certain moors have, on average, larger numbers of grouse?
3. Why was there a sharp decline on some moors prior to 1914, and subsequently on many others since 1930, from which grouse stocks have never recovered?
4. What are the best ways to manage different moorland areas in order to maintain good grouse stocks, and reverse declines where they have occurred?

More recently a management-orientated study has been started by the Game Conservancy in the north of England. This is investigating the major factors influencing grouse bags in an attempt to develop practical management techniques which will assist moorland management.

Requirements of grouse

Food

Grouse feed largely on the shoots and flowers of ling heather, which makes up nearly all the diet in winter and the majority in summer. In some places, grouse have little else available, but on many moors other plants are eaten.

Other favourite foods are the stalks and leaves of *Vaccinium myrtillus* (blaeberry, bilberry or whortleberry), the flowers and shoots of *Eriophorum* (cotton grass, drawmoss or moss crop), the seeds of the heath rush (*Juncus squarrosus*) and grass seeds. Many other plants are eaten in small quantities, including birch and willow buds and catkins, sheep sorrel, chickweed, bell heather, whinflowers, pine buds and so on.

The grouse biologists do not know any moor where there are plenty of grouse and no heather or blaeberry.

In autumn, grouse also eat berries and ripe oats, and will often move a mile or more to visit stubbles and berry patches. It was said in *The Grouse in Health and in Disease* that feeding on oats was harmful to the birds, but no evidence of this was given. Work with marked birds shows that grouse which visited oat stacks or stubbles almost daily for months, survived as well – and reared as many young – as other grouse that visited the stubbles only once or not at all.

In summer, the young grouse chicks eat insects, heather tips, moss capsules and various flowers, from the first day. The proportion of insects eaten is usually low compared with partridges. At ten days they are eating mainly plant material and at three weeks an entirely adult diet.

Adult grouse prefer to feed on the current year's growth from heather aged about three years.

Cover

Grouse need a proportion of old heather for shelter, in addition to young heather for food. Nests are usually concealed in long heather, with easy access to shorter heather. Broods often move for cover into long heather. As moulting grouse are probably more vulnerable in this condition to being caught by a fox or eagle, they spend a lot of time in very rank heather in July–August.

Although grouse in packs, territorial and non-territorial, are often seen on large areas of young heather in winter, none will take a territory consisting entirely of young heather. This means that such ground will be largely wasted in spring for producing *new* grouse. It is also why *over*burning, which results in extensive areas of very short heather, is wasteful. The whole practice of muirburn is discussed in detail in the next chapter.

Territorial requirements

Grouse need good cover in a territory but will abandon growing conifer plantations after the trees are about 10 ft. (3 m.) high. They are completely absent from mature closed stands of pine, even though the ground has a good cover of heather and blaeberry. But if these are felled, grouse will soon re-colonise the area and breed.

An area of moor on which grouse have declined, due perhaps to overgrazing or overburning, will recover its numbers within two years of being fenced, ploughed and planted. Under these conditions, competition from livestock is eliminated, ploughing improves drainage, makes grit available, aerates the soil, and may thereby increase the nitrogen content of the heather. The upturned furrow slices are usually colonised rapidly by seedling heather and the adjacent vegetation is sheltered and grows better. The effect for a year or two is an ideal burning pattern in miniature. All these factors are important for a territory.

Grouse are often more abundant, and occupy smaller territories on well-broken ground, than on flat expanses, open hillsides or wide gently shelving basins. The cocks show less aggressive behaviour, possibly because the irregularities of such ground give them greater seclusion from each other.

Territorial behaviour breaks down at hatching, so grouse do not need any special nursery areas for their chicks (e.g. with plenty of insects) within their individual territories. The families move freely about the moor, often a quarter and sometimes over half a mile, from the nesting site.

Water

Grouse drink every day, but their water requirements do not restrict their territories. Most territories have some water during the spring when the grouse are on their breeding areas all day. They will drink from streams, pools, dewdrops, frost or snow. Otherwise, the birds make a quick flight to the nearest water, take a drink and then return to their own ground. Even in summer, dew is nearly always available in the early morning.

Grit

Grouse require grit to grind up the hard fibrous heather in their gizzards, and can retain the grit they already have in their gizzards for weeks if no new grit is available.

On most moors there is plenty of natural grit, even in deep peat, where the birds find it in stream-beds. The decline of grouse on most moors cannot be blamed on a shortage of grit. There are more new hill roads, with surfaces and roadside banks made entirely of grit, than in earlier decades. Grit is also spread on public roads in moorland areas during snowy periods in winter. However, grouse may experience a shortage in areas of continuous deep blanket peat or of soft shale rocks, where it may be advisable to supply grit.

It is not known if the supply of extra grit will increase grouse stocks on continuous peat. But it seems unlikely, because in such areas there appear to be no more grouse along the roads, where grit is freely available, than away from them where it is scarce. Supplying grit should come very far behind heather burning as a priority in terms of money and labour, and if it is done, it should be spread on blanket peat, not near roads. Poultry grit is far too large for grouse and is a waste of money.

Populations and behaviour

Behaviour – general

In every case so far recorded, August stocks were higher than in the following spring. Only in one case did a large number of grouse move on to an area in

September, and remain there for several months, but even here the spring stock was lower than in August.

The resident stock on a moor does not gradually decrease over the winter. It drops in one or more sudden steps, separated by periods of fairly stable numbers. These changes are determined by the habits of the grouse themselves, so it is important to have some understanding of their behaviour.

Grouse are territorial birds. The cock has an area or plot of ground on the moor which he defends against all intruders. This is done by attacking them and forcing them from his territory. Much time is spent on favourite mounds or stones which act as look-out stations. From here, their territory is surveyed, and if necessary an advance made to attack intruders. The size of individual holdings on any area varies according to the aggression of the cock and the topography. Hens move from one territory to another until they find a cock with whom they want to breed. The cocks court the hens on the territories and eventually pair. Most cocks have only one hen, but a few with large territories may have two hens which will both nest within the territory. Other cocks with very small territories may have no hen. In spring, the hen nests in the territory while the cock looks out for predators.

Seasonal changes in behaviour and numbers

On every piece of ground grouse numbers decrease at least once each year, and possibly twice or even three times. The first drop in the resident stock usually occurs in September, but sometimes in August or October. This may be followed by a second decrease in January or February, and on very high-lying moors a third has been recorded in April.

June/July: The young grouse are with their parents and move in and around the old territory. There is very little aggression between adults and from a distance a moor can appear empty of grouse. The only sign of birds may be the odd display call at dawn and dusk, and occasional clucking from a hen as she calls her young through the day.

August: The old cocks start to become aggressive and noisy, and are seen in the early morning on some prominent piece of ground. They rejoin their families later in the day.

September/October: Threatening behaviour and fights among both young and old birds result in the dispersal of the family unit. The less aggressive birds group together, forming packs, while the most aggressive individuals take territories in the morning. Later in the day they join the other birds. Obtaining good bags becomes more difficult because so many birds are packed together and may all fly over the butts at once. They are also much wilder, sitting less tight than the territorial birds. The 'pack birds' are often driven from the moor by the latter, and spend a lot of time visiting stubble fields, scrub, bogs and grassy areas, usually within a mile of where they came from.

Early October: There is a complete reshuffle in the shape, number and ownership of territories. The advanced young cocks threaten and fight the old ones on their territories and sometimes evict them. Young hens also move on to pair with old or young cocks, on occasions displacing old hens. Many young of both sexes fail to get territories or to pair, and these join the surplus packs on the moor. Territorial behaviour by those birds 'in possession' is still shown only in the morning as mentioned above, but this is enough to prevent non-territorial birds from settling permanently and showing aggression or courtship at any particular place. Neighbouring territory owners parade together along the boundaries. Cocks often make a parachuting display flight, culminating in a steep descent to the ground accompanied by the well-known cackling or becking call. All birds tend to pack together in the afternoon. They may stay packed all day during gales or snow, especially later in winter. Although the pack birds are not usually allowed to feed on the moor in the morning because they are continuously 'moved on' by the territory owners, by the afternoon all birds feed together with little or no strife. This situation continues from October until a new phase of behaviour begins, usually in the New Year.

January/March: Now territory owners defend their areas all day, and surplus birds which a month previously were allowed to feed on the moor in the afternoons, are no longer permitted to do so if they are observed by the territorial birds. This results in a second seasonal decline in the resident stock on the moor, leaving only the territorial birds.

Early April: About a fortnight before the start of egg-laying, the pairs become very secretive. Territorial behaviour and display flights become more uncommon, being confined mainly to dawn and dusk.

Fate and function of the surplus

There are thus three 'social' classes of grouse on the moor during autumn and winter:

1. The territorial residents which rarely leave their chosen patch in the mornings, and which will be the breeding population the following spring.

2. The early-season surplus, evicted by the stronger members of the family in September or October. These almost never challenge territory owners and do not show courtship: they stay in packs even in the early morning in autumn.

3. Late-season surplus, which are non-territorial residents pushed out in January–March when the territory owners defend their areas at all times of the day. These may often challenge territory owners in autumn and winter

and are often seen singly, but are almost invariably sent fleeing from the territory if discovered there by the owner.

Classes 2 and 3 do not breed because they fail to get a place on the moor where they can nest and raise a brood. They are often the victims of accidents, such as flying into overhead wires, fences and trees, and they are also subject to heavy predation.

It seems likely that Class 1 grouse know every 'stick and stone' of their own territory and are well able to look after themselves. On average, it has been found that only 4 per cent of them die from predation and accident during the winter. In the event of something happening to a territory owner, its place is usually taken by the most aggressive surplus bird in a pack, who therefore elevates himself from Class 2 or 3 – a destined non-breeder – into Class 1 – a probable breeder. All the available places are kept filled until breeding time by this method. However, during some years of declining numbers, many of the territorial birds also give up their territories and die or disappear – thus steepening the decline.

Members of Classes 2 and 3, if they escape predation and accident, become so poor in condition by late winter that they succumb, and are nearly all dead by April, from a combination of social stress, starvation and parasites.

Length of life

Grouse are short-lived birds. On average, nearly two birds out of every three in August are dead before the following August, irrespective of whether shooting takes place or not. Most hens therefore nest only once. Although a grouse has been recorded living in its eighth year, only one did so out of 1,267 recovered in a national ringing scheme covering most counties in Scotland, and only 5 per cent lived beyond 3 years.

The short life of the grouse is mainly due to the severe competition for territories each autumn. Even if old birds are not shot, they will have to compete again for territory in October. If they fail to retain their territory, they will die. Thus, many birds which would get shot on a well-driven moor will live on an undershot moor for an extra month or so, only to become surplus and die later in the winter.

Consequently, the turn-over of a grouse population is very rapid. Each year, every living bird has the opportunity of becoming a member of the breeding population the following year, and there is usually no bias in favour of either young or old birds. The important factor affecting their life expectancy is how aggressive they are. If they are aggressive enough, they will get a territory and usually a hen, and subsequently breed. They are then almost guaranteed a year of life. If they lack aggression they will die before they are 11 months old. Annual mortality varies, but on average is about 65 per cent.

Movement and migration

Adult grouse frequently make local movements of up to a mile (1½ km.), for water, to feed on oat stubbles or berries, and especially so when they are in packs. Such movements are quite commonplace after disturbance by birds of prey or by man. Occasionally grouse will move 2 miles (3 km.) ahead of an eagle, and even 3 miles (5 km.) in front of beaters at a grouse drive.

It is highly probable that many of the reports of supposed grouse migration that occur are movements of birds disturbed by predators. When a large pack is seen moving over some distance, a predator, such as an eagle, is a common cause.

At high altitudes, areas may be deserted if the snow becomes deep and continuous, and grouse will then move downhill. Similarly, areas at low altitudes may be deserted if the snow falls deeply without drifting. The grouse then move up to live on the higher ground where stronger winds may keep some of the heather clear. In this case, people conversant with the low ground may well think the grouse have left the low moor, but a reconnaissance on skis to the otherwise inaccessible higher ground will usually show that the grouse are up there. If the snow is continuous for long periods, these high – or low – areas may be deserted for weeks or even months. Usually, the grouse will be found within a mile, but in very deep snow they may exceptionally stay 3–4 miles (5–6½ km.) away for several months. Nevertheless, as soon as the snow melts, they normally return to their old haunts. In severe winters grouse may be recorded (as in east Yorkshire in 1963) in packs on farmland, miles from the moors. Indeed, they have been seen out at sea! Upon such occasions it is sometimes alleged that the birds do not return, but this has never actually been confirmed. However, in such circumstances if large numbers do move on to farmland for a long period, heavy mortality is likely to occur, which amounts to the same thing.

Ringing results

Out of 818 young grouse which were ringed in June and July for several consecutive years, as part of a national scheme, and subsequently recovered in the following shooting season, 773 or 95 per cent moved less than a mile (1½ km.). Only 2 per cent had gone more than 2 miles (3 km.), i.e. farther than a day's grouse driving, before their first shooting season a month or two later.

More extensive movement was recorded among 457 ringed birds recovered by shooting in later seasons; 82 per cent had still moved less than a mile (1½ km.) but 7 per cent had gone more than 3 miles (5 km.), and 4 birds (1 per cent) had moved 15–26 miles (24–42 km.).

It is claimed, though without any factual evidence, that grouse sometimes migrate en masse over long distances to settle in new areas. As already

374

mentioned, temporary migrations are common. But if grouse do migrate to settle permanently on other distant moors, the ringing results to date indicate that this is very uncommon. Nevertheless it is quite common for individual pairs of grouse to leave an area with a high stock just before egg-laying and move to a nearby area with a lower stock.

Areas with high or declining stocks can also lose grouse emigrating with their broods after hatching. The birds return in autumn without their young. This kind of emigration can leave parts of a moor empty on 12th August, even though it had been well stocked in spring. Similarly, grouse pairs with young sometimes emigrate to parts with low numbers, and this speeds up the population increase there.

Breeding success

In a good breeding year grouse will lay on average 8–10 eggs and in a bad year 6 or less. The usual incubation period is about 22 days. Normally the peak hatching date is about the end of May on low ground and in early June on higher ground. The average hatching date can be 10 days earlier in a good year than in a poor one on the same ground. In a good year, most of the eggs hatch, infertility is rare and few hens desert. In a bad year, hatching is poor, with more infertile eggs and more nests deserted. In such a year if the hen is also in poor condition, a second clutch is seldom laid if the first nest is lost. She will usually lay again in a good year, unless the eggs are robbed during the last few days of incubation. Second nests usually have smaller clutches and the chicks seldom do as well, but in an exceptional year the average brood from second nests is as good as that from first ones.

The differences in breeding success from one year to another are attributable to clutch size, hatchability, and the survival of the chicks after they hatch. In very good years, most of the chicks live, and a young:old survival ratio of up to 3·3:1 may be recorded in July–August. In the worst years, and on the poorest ground, only 1 young per 10 old birds (0·1:1) may be recorded. A survival ratio of 1 young to 1 old must be regarded as poor, and 1 young to 2 old as very poor. Anything over 1·7 young to 1 old is likely to be followed by an increase in the spring stock next year, and anything less than a ratio of 11 young to 12 old by a decrease.

Most chicks die during the first 7–10 days, with an occasional bird dying 2–3 weeks or so later. In poor years, when the brood is often seen with only one parent, the hen does not usually show a normal sense of protection when disturbed, i.e. no broken-wing trick or loud distraction call, and she may fly straight off. Such broods may show variation in size, with some well- and some poorly developed chicks, in appearance 7–10 days younger.

	GOOD YEAR	BAD YEAR
Clutch size	6–13 eggs	2–9 eggs
Hatching	early	late
Proportion of eggs that hatch	92–95%	70–80%
Nest desertions	Few	Many
Parental care	Good	Poor
Number of young reared per old bird	2–3 young	0–1 young
Change in breeding stock in the next spring	Increase	Decrease

Examples of *'breeding success'* in the wild and in captivity in good and poor years:

	GOOD YEAR	POOR YEAR
Number of young per 10 adults in the wild	27	8
Percentage of hatched young reared in captivity, from eggs taken in the wild	100	25

The quality of the eggs, of course, stems back to the condition of the laying hens. After a warm, dry summer the previous year, providing good conditions for heather growth, a winter with little or no heather browning and an early spring with good new growth, the grouse hens tend to be plump and healthy, and will breed well. The opposite happens after poor summers, severe browning or late spring growth.

Chicks do occasionally get drowned in thunderstorms or chilled by heavy rain at 3–4 weeks when they are too big to be covered completely by the hen, but this is unusual. Odd though it may seem, the young are no more likely to die in cold, wet, sunless summers than in warm, dry, sunny summers. In this respect grouse seem to be very different from partridges. But there is one important habitat difference in that heather dries out extremely quickly after rain, even without any sun or wind, whereas crops and herbage may stay soaking for many hours. This can be demonstrated by walking through both heather and grass an hour after a heavy shower. Recent research shows that grouse chicks eat far less insects than partridges, and commonly take a lot of vegetation even when only a few days old.

Radio tracking
Results from the radio tracking of broods demonstrate that grouse broods selectively visit insect-rich areas, in particular the wet sphagnum bog flushes. In some areas it is possible that the additional nutrients the chicks gain from these insects could be beneficial to their growth and subsequent survival.

Annual fluctuations
The size of autumn stocks depends on the number of territory holders in the previous spring and the number of young birds reared. Spring stocks depend on

the number of grouse that succeed in gaining territories in the previous autumn. The main objects of moor management should therefore be to create conditions which encourage small territories, and favour production of large broods.

On any given moor, both spring and autumn stocks vary from one year to another. Usually, growth or decline in numbers lasts for more than one year, but some records show ten years between a peak and a trough on one area, and as little as 3–4 years on another. Certain years tend to be generally good or bad over a large region, such as Sutherland or Ross or north-east Scotland. Sometimes this is true over the whole country (e.g. 1922, 1934 and 1957 were generally good years). Even in years of wide uniformity under average conditions, some beats will hold higher grouse stocks than their neighbours, a situation which may be reversed 12 months later.

The highest fluctuation we have recorded was at the Sands of Forvie on the coast, a few miles north of Aberdeen, where spring stocks varied from 2 to 29 birds per 100 acres (40 h.)! Although autumn fluctuations are, on average, slightly greater than those in the spring, the figures are remarkable. There are some moors where there is little difference in either spring or autumn stocks, as at a study area in Deeside where numbers have fluctuated only one and a half fold in 12 years.

The following table shows changes in breeding stocks after good and poor breeding, when the parent stock is high, medium and low:

BREEDING STOCK IN THE PREVIOUS SPRING

		HIGH	MEDIUM	LOW
Breeding success	Good	No change	Small increase	Big increase
In previous summer	Poor	Big decrease	Small decrease	No change

The spring stock is based upon the results of a re-shuffle of territories during the previous October. Following a poor breeding season one year in Glen Esk, the young that secured territories were more aggressive, obtaining larger areas than old birds. Next year in the same locality it was a good breeding season, and the young cocks were less aggressive, taking smaller territories. In some areas, as all the moor is occupied each year, any changes in spring stock are due to the average size of territory taken by the young cocks.

As the spring stock is higher when more young are reared in the previous year, the quality of food available to the adult birds in that year can be used to forecast the number of grouse twelve months later. It thus becomes possible to predict grouse numbers one – and sometimes two – years ahead, when a warm, dry summer and good heather growth will enable the birds to get into really good condition for the next breeding season.

Often, however, a late spring or severe winter browning can upset a forecast, particularly on the Scottish hills!

Grouse numbers are influenced by the weather in the following sequence:

377

Weather → Condition   Condition → Quality → Number of ────→ Number of
        of heather of parents of eggs   young reared   breeding grouse

Differences between moors

In places with heavy rainfall – as in much of western Britain – and where heather is sparse, grouse numbers are unlikely to be high. Conversely, a dry climate will encourage good heather growth and grouse will thrive. This, of course, partly accounts for the first-rate grouse moors of the eastern half of Scotland.

Climate apart, the two main reasons for differences in grouse stocks are the fertility of the soil, and man's management of the heather. Soil fertility is important because it affects the nutritive value of the heather. Heather growing on rich soils contains a higher percentage of nitrogen, phosphorus, calcium and mineral trace elements, which are important in animal nutrition. It is not possible to tell the nutritive value of heather simply by looking at it. Fresh-looking heather shoots may in fact be poor value, and poor-looking ragged ones very good. Heather often looks poor because it is heavily grazed by grouse, hares, deer or other animals, a sign that it is attractive as food. Only chemical analysis will accurately show its nutritive value.

Effect of underlying rock on red grouse

What determines the quality of soil is complicated. One important influence is the type of underlying bedrock. If this is 'base-rich' (i.e. relatively rich in lime content or some other minerals) the soil will be fertile, particularly if the rock breaks down easily and forms fine particles. If it has a low lime content, the soil will be poor, especially if it breaks down into large gravelly particles such as in granite debris. The list below classifies the various rocks into their 'base richness', category 1 being most infertile and 5 most fertile.

1. Granite, Gneiss, Quartzite, etc.
2. Shales and Sandstones
3. Diorite
4. Epidiorite
5. All Limestones

To find out more about a particular moor, the Ordnance Geological Survey sheets that cover the area should be obtained, and, with a plastic gridded rectangle, an estimate made of the percentage of ground that lies over each type of rock. With the help of the table, it is possible to work out an average value for the moor. For instance, if 50 per cent of the ground is over category 1, 20 per cent category 2 and 30 per cent category 5, the average for the whole place is

$$\frac{50 \times 1 + 20 \times 2 + 30 \times 5}{100} = 2.4$$

378

If required this can be done beat by beat. An added interest lies in calculating the same thing for a neighbour's ground!

Heather does not always thrive abundantly on the most base-rich areas, as some limestone hills may be completely grassy and therefore support no grouse. However, it is often surprising how a large number of grouse can be supported by a small quantity of high-quality heather when it does occur in these areas.

Sometimes peat is so deep in places that the heather's feeding roots, which penetrate only to about 6 in. (15 cm.), are unable to draw nutrients from the mineral soil below the peat. The heather is then largely dependent on nutrients deposited by the rain and the atmosphere. It does not matter how rich the soil is underneath, if 3–6 ft. (1–2 m.) of peat form an impenetrable layer in between. The underlying rock is therefore of no consequence on areas of thick blanket peat, as in parts of north Scotland, the Pennines and Ireland. The only exception is where springs and flushes coming from the underlying soil and rock carry nutrients into some small areas of heather alongside streams and boggy places. Where the peat has eroded with extensive haggs, the underlying soil will be exposed in places, which will influence the heather's fertility locally. Quite small areas of lime-influenced heather will be enough to counter the effects of deep peat.

In some areas, where former glacial debris known as 'drift', a mixture of soil and boulders, lies upon the bedrock, it may be difficult to give an accurate forecast of the potential for grouse. Sometimes the replaced surface material contains a high granite content, upon a bedrock of limestone. In such cases the fertility will be reduced although it will be higher than if both drift and bedrock were derived from granite. Water can carry nutrients from an area lying over a different bedrock, and a boggy stream coming from a limestone area miles away can fertilise a moor overlying granite.

The type of plant life present on an area will also give a good indication of its fertility. This allows for all the complications mentioned above, because each species of plant has its own requirements. Some plants will not grow at all except in base-rich places. Fertile moors support a greater variety of plant life, and certain plants are much commoner on the base-rich moors, than those not so well endowed. The abundance, or otherwise, of these fertility indicator plants on a moor enables a general assessment to be made. Plant life varies a good deal locally, and so a predominant indicator plant on one moor may be replaced by another a short distance away. Where grazing pressure is high these 'indicator plants' should be looked for inside fences, among stones and in other places inaccessible to animals.

Molehills can often provide useful information, for moles do not generally occur unless there are fair numbers of earthworms, which in turn depend upon a fertile soil. If there are no molehills, the moor is probably acid and poor. If they are widely distributed over it, the moor will be base-rich.

A shooting man might use these points with advantage in evaluating a grouse moor with a view to purchase or tenancy. They will provide an indication of the moor's potential, when the annual bag records may indicate possible mismanagement.

Predators and 'disease'

Predators

It is common sense to suppose that if a grouse is found that has been killed by a fox or harrier, it means one less bird for breeding or shooting later on. This is usually the case with domestic livestock kept in good conditions on a lowland farm, but with wild creatures, it is different. There is so much competition in the wild that, if some of them die, it may improve the chances of survival for the rest. After a catastrophe, when stocks are low, wild animals tend to rear young successfully with a high survival rate. In periods of high stock densities fewer young are reared and less survive.

Surplus grouse will die from either disease, predation or shooting, and if one cause declines another will assume the dominant role. The non-territorial surplus grouse are heavily reduced by predation. Research at Glen Esk with tabbed grouse illustrated that one *territorial* bird was killed for every seven surplus birds. Their poorer condition may not enable them to escape as well as the territorial grouse, and as they move about much more they may not be aware of the escape routes and hiding places known to those inhabiting a territory. As already mentioned many are killed from hitting fence, telephone and electricity wires, possibly because they are not conversant with these local obstacles.

On most moors, predation is very low in summer and early autumn, and a walk of many miles may not reveal signs of a kill. But from September/October onwards, when there are packs of surplus grouse, the rate of killing increases. Kills are common through the winter, tailing off in March/April and becoming scarce again from May to August.

Winter predation

The main predators during the winter are foxes, hen harriers and golden eagles, but wild cats, buzzards, rough-legged buzzards, peregrines and stoats also take a few. Many additional birds of prey, particularly hen harriers and eagles, move on to grouse moors about September and away again in March. Evidence of many kills in winter means that the earlier shooting was not hard enough and a big surplus was left. As the surplus birds are in many cases destined to die of 'disease' (page 382) if not taken by predators, and as the very occasional territorial grouse that gets killed is replaced from the surplus group, winter predation usually has a negligible effect on the final stock that breeds in

380

spring. It would, however, be foolish to claim that winter predation had no effect on spring stocks every year or in more marginal areas like Ireland and Sutherland where stocks are very low.

Even on well-stocked moors, predation can occasionally depress spring stocks. At Kerloch one year, hen harriers stayed later than usual, and this coincided with a winter when few surplus birds were left after January. The harriers killed a number of territorial cock and hen grouse, which were not replaced. So in this case they did reduce the breeding stock. More research is being undertaken in areas where harriers, eagles or foxes are resident, to find out *how much* they depress spring stocks. So far, subject to the exceptions above, the evidence is that they usually have a negligible effect or no effect at all, but the work has to be continued over a number of years to see whether predation might not in some years be heavy enough to have an appreciable effect.

Summer predation

Predation in summer from May to August mainly hits the territorial birds and their eggs or young and so reduces production for the shooting season. Predation on adult grouse in summer is mostly by foxes, harriers and other birds of prey (all protected) taking the hen grouse on or near her nest, but occasionally a stoat will take the nesting hen. Few cocks are killed by foxes or birds of prey. The hen and particularly her young, are more vulnerable.

At Rickarton (study area) where foxes are common, predation is much more serious, and so it is in Western Ireland.

Where foxes and crows are very numerous on the hill, the predator pressure is increased and may become important. On one moor in Ayrshire, in a year when grouse were doing very well at just below a pair to 5 acres (2 h.), 44 dead hen grouse and a number of cocks were found at a fox den in a peat runner on the hill. Fox numbers here were exceptionally high and 28 adult foxes were killed on 2,000 acres (800 h.) between January and May.

Additional research is being undertaken in areas with resident eagles, foxes, peregrines and harriers and it is hoped to get more information, which is badly needed in this field, where personal prejudice and opinions based on little evidence are strongly held on both sides.

Even if summer predation depresses the August stock by 5–10 per cent, which in any case seems to be a rare event on the bare heather hills in the north-east, its effect on shooting is the important question. On most moors grouse are greatly undershot and it is usual for a large surplus to be left. In such cases the small depletion due to summer predation is of doubtful significance. However, it would obviously reduce the bag if this were big enough to remove the annual surplus – i.e. an average of 45 per cent shot per year. Nevertheless in some years a small depression of the August stocks due to summer predation, could affect shooting for the reason given more fully on page 387. For grouse driving is effective in showing all the grouse on the moor *only* if densities are high. Below a certain threshold a small drop in the stock present could mean a very much larger drop in the number coming over the butts.

Egg predation

Grouse eggs are taken mainly by carrion and hooded crows (grey or hoodie), and to a certain extent by foxes and stoats. These usually take the entire clutch. A few eggs are also lost to hedgehogs, common gulls and the larger herring and black-backed gulls.

In some years certain grouse lose all their young because the chicks are in poor condition and die naturally. In seasons when adult grouse are in poor condition, more eggs fail to hatch. More hen grouse desert their nests in such years.

On moors where crows are numerous, nest-robbing is common, but desertion is rarely recorded – presumably because a deserted nest is quickly robbed. By way of confirmation, grouse on an experimentally fertilised area raised big broods, despite having a pair of crows rearing young alongside. It seems clear that well-fed grouse in good condition are better parents, desert less and are not so likely to be robbed.

A high crow population, particularly when nesting on the moor, can appreciably depress the success of breeding grouse and the crows in such cases should be reduced or eliminated.

Predator disturbance during shooting

Many grouse drives have been spoilt by the appearance over the moor of a golden eagle or a hen harrier. The grouse will quickly take a flight of up to a mile and naturally the drive will be ruined.

Conversely, there must be as many first-class drives which have been attributed to a good season, but which were in fact the result of an eagle quartering a drive a mile away on a neighbouring ground. There can be little doubt that these birds of prey, without being noticed by the shooting party, provide additional grouse on as many occasions as they are *seen* to drive them away.

It is unfortunate that when perhaps only one day can be spent shooting grouse, it should be spoilt by an eagle. However, over a few day's shooting, the bag reduction due to disturbance by these magnificent birds can be discounted.

'Grouse disease' or strongylosis

So called 'diseased' grouse are usually found either dead, or in such a weak condition that they are unable to fly. Their bodies show evidence of extreme emaciation, and on post-mortem the caecum, or blind gut, is found to contain large numbers of Trichostrongyle threadworms. These may number anything

382

from 1,000 to over 26,000. Severe infestation causes inflammation of the wall of the caeca, with possible rupture, and consequent haemorrhage and infection.

Nearly all grouse carry some strongyle worms. In any given circumstances those in poor condition will normally exhibit a higher infestation than others in good condition. But it has been found that birds in poor condition one year may carry a lighter worm burden than those in good condition another year. It has also been discovered that some grouse, which have died with all the symptoms of emaciation associated with 'grouse disease' and been submitted to laboratory examination, have had no strongyles at all. As the strongyle threadworm is only visible with the aid of a magnifying glass or microscope, it is quite possible therefore for death to be attributed as a result of superficial investigation to 'disease', when in fact it is not.

'Grouse disease' and strongylosis have come to be regarded as synonymous terms. But recent research has given rise to doubts as to whether strongylosis plays the decisively fatal role previously attributed to it. In some cases, particularly where non-territorial birds are concerned, social stress and straightforward starvation can be contributory factors. This is very evident in the case of old cock grouse evicted from their territories. Observation has shown that they rapidly lose condition, and die within the week, despite a prevailing abundance of food enjoyed by other surplus birds.

If in the breeding season hens are found dead on the nest, or on the ground with their dead chicks scattered pathetically round them, 'disease' is almost invariably blamed. However it has been found that this state of affairs usually coincides with years in which the heather was badly browned in late winter, and the birds have subsequently been unable to find the green heather shoots in the quantities required for proper nourishment, and so have died of a combination of disease and starvation.*

Unlike pheasants, grouse will not come to communal feeding points, and so hand feeding and the administering of antibiotics by this means may have to be ruled out.

Other diseases of grouse

Fortunately coccidiosis is by no means such a scourge among grouse as it can be among pheasants. Chicks are occasionally affected. It is rare in adult birds, which usually recover and only exceptionally die from it.

Grouse may sometimes contract tapeworms in their intestines, which in cases of severe infestation may result in complete blockage of the intestine, and death. They may occasionally suffer from a number of bacterial diseases, such

* The Game Conservancy biologist, Dr Peter Hudson, suggests that recent research in field and laboratory indicates that strongylosis may be a contributory factor influencing the body condition and so breeding production of some birds.

as *Escherichia coli*, which may variously attack the liver, or cause pneumonia and ultimately death.

Grouse in poor condition may often be found infested with feather lice especially about the head. But the presence of these parasites is likely to be because the bird is weak, and there is no evidence to show that they are themselves the cause of such sickness.

Ticks are another parasite from which grouse, both young and old, are liable to suffer. They have been held responsible for the decline of grouse on a number of moors in the past, but declines on most moors occurred without tick infestation. Ticks are therefore not a problem for grouse management nationally. Nevertheless there is a severe problem on some moors, notably in Morayshire, and ticks do transmit louping ill, which can kill grouse chicks and adults. A detailed study of the problem has been made in Morayshire. Red grouse have been found to be very vulnerable to louping ill, and most grouse that get the disease die. Tick-borne louping ill has made several once-famous moors useless for good shooting, and as a result they have been sold and afforested. (See also 'Sheep ticks and their effect on grouse' page 393.)

Grouse counts

It is clearly useful to know the number of pairs of grouse on a moor at the beginning of a breeding season, and subsequently the number of birds and proportion of young to old, at the start of the shooting season. Spring and autumn counts of partridges are now increasingly a normal part of good lowland shoot management, recognised as playing an important role in enabling schemes for improvements to be properly evaluated. An equally good purpose can be served by censuses in grouse management. It has already been pointed out that a considerable surplus of birds over and above the necessary breeding stock for the following year is left on most moors at the end of a shooting season, and that this surplus is largely 'wasted'. Counts can help to reduce this wastage by indicating how many birds should be shot.

Reliable counting of grouse requires the use of trained gundogs, as otherwise birds may be walked over. It is immaterial whether the dogs in question are pointers, setters, retrievers or spaniels so long as they cover the ground properly and drop to flush.

Weather is an important factor, and a mild, fine day with good visibility and a steady breeze is desirable.

The area selected should be about 200 acres (80 h.) in extent, and bounded by easily recognisable features such as streams, fences, cairns, paths or other clear-cut demarcations. It should as far as possible be a representative sample of the whole moor or beat. In order to permit a clear view, gently sloping, open ground is preferable.

A spring count should normally be made around the end of March, and an autumn one in the same period of July.

The actual count should be conducted as follows. The person making it should start at one corner of the down-wind side of the area chosen. He should take a beat across the wind with his dogs ranging either side of him. On reaching the opposite boundary, he should turn and take a fresh beat back immediately adjacent to the one he has just completed, and carry on in this fashion until he has covered the whole area selected. When a bird, or birds, are flushed, he should halt and watch them to make sure whether or not they have flown clear of the area so that they will not be counted twice. At the spring count most pairs of birds seen should be a cock and a hen, but this cannot be taken for granted. Occasional 'pairs' may be two birds of the same sex. Sometimes a cock may have two hens, and in some years there may over all be three cocks to two hens. As this will make a difference to the expectation of broods and chicks, it is important to know the precise state of affairs. Binoculars should be carried and used by the person making the count to determine these things.

The success of a count depends a great deal on it being conducted with minimum disturbance of the moor. Thus the dogs should be reliable workers, that can be handled with as few commands as possible. If two men undertake the count together they should avoid unnecessary chatter.

The weather can complicate matters. If the day chosen for the spring count turns out to be an idyllic sunny one with no wind, it is quite likely that the cock will be flushed but the hen sit tight. So every time a single cock is put to flight, the dogs should be called in to make sure that he has not left his mate behind. On such days scent is often poor, so it is doubly important to cover the ground slowly and methodically.

The reliability of counts conducted on snow-covered ground, or ground which has only recently become snow-free while other ground in the vicinity is still snow-covered must always be suspect, because extra pairs may have taken temporary refuge thereon.

Experience has shown that the number of old grouse on a moor in July/August usually differs little from that in March/April. This fact can be utilised to facilitate the autumn, or pre-shooting season count. Taking the same area as was counted in the spring, it will suffice for our purpose to see a sample of at least ten coveys. The total birds flushed in each should be counted, and the old birds noted separately. Any barren pairs, or single cocks, must be included in the count. The final figures will show 'X' old birds and 'Y' young. The ratio of young to old birds will then be Y/X.

The state of development of each brood can be noted during the count, and a good indication obtained of whether shooting can properly start on or about the 12th August, or be delayed for a week or two. The following table gives an approximate indication of age.

Age	Description
1 day	Egg tooth often on the bill tip. No feathers or quills on the wing.
4/5 days	Wing quills well grown, feather tips just showing above quills.
1 week	Feathering complete in lines on the back. Flights over 10 yds. (9 m.).
10 days	Feathers beginning to appear elsewhere on the body. Flights of up to 5 yds. ($4\frac{1}{2}$ m.).
2 weeks	Feathering complete in lines on the back. Flights over 10 yds. (9 m.).
3 weeks	Feathering coming in heavily on back, head, flanks. Good-sized wing.
4 weeks	Almost complete body feathering has replaced the original down.
5 weeks 6 weeks	Body growing rapidly. Pointed, light coloured rudimentary tail (i.e. tail coverts) is growing, and is fully developed by 6 weeks.
7 weeks	Dark tail feathers beginning to show. Fluffy down around vent beginning to disappear.
8 weeks	Tail well grown.
10 weeks	Tail almost full grown. Cocks begin to give high-pitched becking call when disturbed. Dark feathers growing thickly on the flanks. Fluffy down around vent has gone.
11/12 weeks	Young cannot be told from old when observed in the field, except at close range (arrow-shaped bands of light pigment on the back feathers, compared with transverse bands in old birds).

Shooting report

As has already been described in the section on grouse behaviour, the covey or family unit normally breaks up in September/October, when the non-territorial birds form into packs, which may spend a lot of their time away from the moors. It is again stressed that in some years, due to special circumstances, this change in behaviour can occur earlier, and exceptionally even in the first half of August.

It is therefore important in all years to shoot hard and early in order to harvest as many of the surplus birds as possible before they 'pack' and become too problematical to shoot, and so largely a wasted asset. However, there are certain factors which affect the attainment of this aim. In years when the density of grouse on a moor is high, i.e. one or more birds per acre at the July/August count, 45–50 per cent of them may frequently be shot. But when the density is low, i.e. one bird per 3–5 acres (2–3 h.), the percentage shot may drop to as little as 5–10 per cent. This apparently paradoxical situation is due to the fact that when a moor is full of grouse, disturbance by the beaters instigates a chain reaction; the alarm calls of flushed birds alert their neighbours, which in turn get on the wing and pass on the warning to those next door, and so on. But when densities are low, breaks occur in the sequence, birds get taken by surprise, crouch in cover to escape detection and are walked over.

Another seeming contradiction is that in a poor breeding year the percentage of birds which will become surplus is actually higher than in a good one. Thus to avoid shooting or to shoot only lightly in such a year, in order to leave more birds to improve the spring breeding stock, will fail in its purpose.

To remove most of the surplus birds in an average year, 45 per cent of the grouse on the moor in August should be shot. As a guide in other conditions, 25–30 per cent ought to be shot when stocks are increasing from low numbers after a good breeding season, and 50–60 per cent when stocks are decreasing after a poor one. However, to achieve this higher percentage is difficult, not only because birds are harder to flush, but because it becomes uneconomic to employ beaters to obtain numerically small bags -- the sale of which does not cover their wages. Further, good Guns who can make the most of the limited opportunities may feel they are wasting their time.

On any reasonably well-stocked moor it is indisputable that driving grouse to the Guns is the only effective means of harvesting the surplus in the requisite numbers. But when the stock of birds is too low for driving to be a viable proposition, shooting over setters or pointers can be a satisfactory alternative, if it is early in the season. Walking up with the aid of dogs, i.e. retrievers or spaniels, is another alternative, but is generally rather less effective.

There used to be a prevalent belief that it was desirable to kill off old cocks at the back end of the season, a task normally delegated to keepers, and which occupied a good deal of their time. It was thought that the old cocks were more pugnacious and therefore occupied unnecessarily large territories thereby depriving younger and more virile males of ground they could use to better effect. Research has produced no evidence to support this idea. Further, actual experiments have shown that if the most vigorous territorial cocks are removed in November/December, they will not all be replaced. So apart from the practical difficulty of determining an old cock from a young one by its outward appearance, it is felt that this custom is one to be discouraged as, contrary to popular supposition, it is likely to do more harm than good.

Sexing and ageing grouse

A host normally wishes to give his guests a brace of young, not old, birds at the end of a day's shooting, and a dealer to whom any surplus may be sold always gives a better price for the former than the latter. So the advantage of being able quickly to sort out young from old grouse by sexes is obvious.

Sexing old birds is fairly easy. Cocks have a large red comb and hens a smaller, pinker one. Additionally the plumage of the hens is usually of a generally paler hue than the rich reds, dark browns or Titian bronzes of their mates. The feathers of a hen are more heavily barred with light pigment, and those of a cock finer grained with thinner, more wavy lines and spots. (See Figure 137.) Hens also have more brown or yellow mottling on the dark tail and wing feathers.

In young birds, where the differences in the comb may be less distinctive, the cocks have chestnut feathers under the chin and on the throat with little or no black barring, while in the hen these feathers tend to be more yellowish in colour, with more pronounced black barring.

Should these means fail to provide conclusive identification when it is required, recourse must be had to post-mortem examination. When the bird is cut open, a cock will have a pair of abdominal cavity testes lying against the back stomach wall below the kidney, and a hen a single ovary in the same position.

As regards ageing grouse, many traditional methods have their limitations. If a grouse is held up by the lower mandible and it breaks, it will be a young bird. But this procedure is very unreliable, and may fail with well-developed young birds of the year even as early as the 12th August. It is thoroughly misleading by mid-September. Likewise testing the strength of a bird's skull by trying to crush it with the thumb will, if it succeeds, be indicative of a young bird, but can be completely misleading even at the start of a season.

A more reliable indicator is that many young birds have the third outermost primary wing feather shorter than the rest. But with advanced young birds this distinction will have disappeared by late August. Also some old birds, due to a characteristic of their moult, can have a third primary shorter than the rest.

The simplest, and most reasonably accurate, 'field' guide to age is to compare the shape of the two outer primaries with that of the rest. If they are all of a kind with rounded tips, then it is an old bird. If the tips of the outermost two are pointed, and clearly differ in shape from the others, it will be a young bird.

 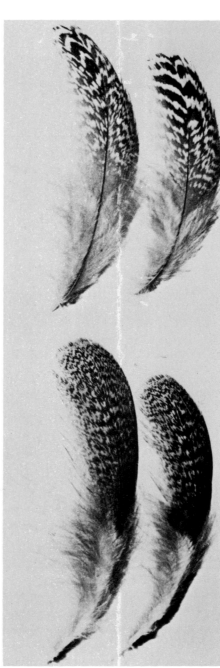

137 Flank feathers from adult grouse in summer and winter

Upper: Summer flank feathers of a hen grouse (left) and of a cock (right)

Lower: Corresponding winter feathers of a hen (left) and of a cock (right)

Note the more barred effect in the hen, effect in the hen, especially in summer plumage

389

However, a bird of the previous year, which has not yet moulted these two primaries, will exhibit the same features, except that in his case the two outer primaries will look tattered and faded in colour. Some of these points are illustrated in Figure 138.

138 Primary feathers from an old and a young grouse
  Left: The tip of the outermost primary of an old grouse
  Right: The more pointed and buff-spotted feather of a young bird

A further indicator is that when the first or second primary is growing, i.e. it has a sheath or pigment around the base, and the third is full grown, the bird is old, and when the first primary is full grown, and the third growing, unless any primary is bleached and well worn, the bird is young. This holds good until mid-September.

Another guide to age is that adult grouse shed their toenails in July–September. When a nail is seen in process of becoming detached it is a sure sign of an old bird. A transverse ridge or scar across the top of the nail, where the old nail was attached, may persist for a month or more after it has been shed, and so is indicative of an old bird.

390

The only really infallible method of ageing grouse is to examine the vent for signs of a blind pouch, or bursa, just above the actual vent itself. To do this the vent should be expanded or slit open, when the bursa can be easily seen, and a matchstick or quill inserted into it for a distance of nearly half an inch. An old bird has no such cavity.

The sex and age ratios of birds in the bag at the end of a day's shooting should usually be a fairly accurate reflection of those of the grouse population on the moor. However, when shooting over dogs early in the season an excess of hens and young birds is common, as these lie closer, and so are more easily shot. When driving early in the season, especially in a late breeding year, a high proportion of old cocks may be shot as these are the strongest fliers most readily flushed by the beaters, and come forward singly to the Guns. But by September such factors should have ceased to count for anything, and as stated the bag should normally show a representative sample by age and sex of the birds on the moor.

Restocking with reared or wild birds

The practicability of restocking a moor with hand-reared or caught-up birds is bedevilled by the grouse's peculiar characteristics. To date virtually no success has been had with methods traditionally used with pheasants and other gamebirds.

Thus grouse reared for release on a moor prior to the shooting season, and given the usual diet of chick crumbs fed to young pheasants and partridges in similar circumstances, have been found unable to adjust sufficiently quickly to the tough all-heather diet after release, due to their caeca being too small and their gizzard too soft. As a result they die.

Reports from attempts made elsewhere at this form of restocking also suggest that reared grouse can become so tame that they are unshootable in the same season.

If extra birds are released in late autumn with a view to building up the breeding stock for the following spring, the resident territorial birds have been found to drive them off to swell the ranks of the existing surplus. It is conceivable that if exceptionally heavy winter predation among territorial birds reduced these to an artificially low level, released birds might find territories and breed successfully, but there has been no opportunity to prove this in practice.

Wild grouse have in the past been caught up and introduced into areas where the species was either scarce or non-existent. Such of these instances as have been documented show that they have generally been failures, and that scarcity or extinction of grouse is usually indicative of something wrong with the environment, rather than the birds.

Grouse survive comparatively well under widely differing conditions of climate, altitude, topography and plant life in the British Isles. But birds reared in one type of environment become accustomed to it, and if transferred to another materially different, their chances of survival are placed in jeopardy, even though they are all among their own kind. Ecologists are generally agreed that in principle transference of birds from one location to another is unlikely to have any beneficial effect, and may more often than not simply result in the early demise of the birds concerned.

Checking mortality

What are the main causes of death in grouse?

Shooting

The number that die from shooting can usually be assessed fairly exactly. Even on grouse drives where scores of birds are shot, research workers have found that few birds that hit the ground are not picked up later. Some 'picked' birds fly on and die later, but their number must be small, as very few grouse are found dead on the open moors during the shooting season.

Apart from shooting, approximately half the grouse that died from other causes were located. Fifty per cent of the adult territorial grouse marked with back tabs were later recovered. Probably 80–90 per cent of grouse killed by predators or dying from accidents were found (where the birds lose a lot of feathers), but only about 33 per cent where the grouse died without injury.

Accidents

Grouse are found dead under fences or overhead wires with many scattered feathers. Subsequently, the body may be removed or eaten on the spot by a predator.

Predators

A fox often removes the wings or sometimes the outer 4–6 primaries in one piece, and may then carry the bird elsewhere to its den, or half-bury it in the moss or eat it on the spot. If eaten, many feathers are scattered, some of them attached to pieces of skin stuck together with saliva. The whole body is usually devoured, except for a small central piece of the breast bone; occasionally the bill and feet are rejected, and the intestines and gizzard are usually uneaten. (See also chapter 5.)

A golden eagle sometimes carries off the carcase. If it eats on the spot, numerous feathers are scattered by careful plucking. The feet and bill are generally left and the intestines rarely eaten. Eagles eat most neck bones and ribs, taking large bites out of the keel of the breast bone.

392

Occasionally a head lying separate from the body indicates a peregrine killing, by a blow high in the air. These falcons and hen harriers usually leave similar marks, carefully plucking many feathers. The skeleton is normally left intact except for a few broken ribs, but occasionally the wings become separated. The neck vertebrae and the back are also neatly picked. Scavenging crows leave similar remains, although they do not pluck as many feathers.

Deaths without injury

Here the grouse weakens, has difficulty in flying well and eventually dies. Symptoms: generally thin without any signs of violence, and feathers are not scattered unless by scavengers later. Post-mortem analysis usually indicates many parasitic worms in the gut, and sometimes other diseases are located.

Sheep ticks and their effect on grouse

Since the last edition, our North of England Grouse Research Project (Dr Peter Hudson) has been undertaking a great deal of new work on grouse – among other problems, tick control.

Ticks exist in three stages, each of which must obtain a feed of blood to survive and lay eggs. The tick spends only a small amount of time on the host and most in the layer of dead vegetation known as the mat. The main host for all tick stages is the hill sheep and only the immature stages exist on grouse. The tick transmits the disease louping ill which kills most grouse affected by it and many sheep. Sheep and grouse are the only two important hill animals which can amplify the disease; a vaccine is available for control in sheep. To discover if an area has ticks, several methods can be employed; such as the inspection of sheep, blanket drags and discussions with local farmers. The most effective form of control is the removal of poor quality vegetation with its thick mat layer. If this is not feasible, sheep (which harbour more than 95% of ticks) should be dipped correctly.

In Nidderdale, the tick population thrives in some of the bracken areas and we have been testing the idea that removal of this bracken, along with a suitable follow-up treatment, can result in a loss of mat, reduction in the tick population and the spread of vegetation beneficial to grouse and sheep production.

Chapter 25
The Management of Heather

Since grouse use heather for cover as well as for food, management must provide both long and short heather in a patchwork over the entire moor. The correct management of heather has not received the same attention as that devoted to grassland. Indeed, heather is frequently regarded as an almost inexhaustible resource which will always renew itself no matter how it is burned or grazed. This is a complete fallacy.

There is little doubt that a substantial increase in grouse numbers could be achieved on many sporting estates and upland farms if the existing heather was properly managed. Correct burning is the most important single requirement.

Burning

Equipment

When the moor is dry, fires can be easily started with a burning faggot of heather. However, a paraffin burner of the traditional type, or a pressurised flame gun gives better results.

Usually, the flames are controlled and extinguished by a beater or besom. Traditionally, this is an 8–9 ft. (2·5 m.) pole, with a triangular or circular piece of wire netting or a bunch of birch twigs bound on to one end. Alternatively, a beater may be made of aluminium alloy, with a frame about 12 × 18 in. (30 cm. × 46 cm.) welded on to a 7–10 ft. (2–3 m.) long handle at an angle of about 160°. Two or more layers of wire netting are bound on to the frame. A metal beater is almost indestructible and is easier to use than a wooden one, since the flames can be smothered rather than beaten out.

Heather fires often generate tremendous heat, making it impossible to approach the head of a fire to control or extinguish it, and a 'runaway' can result. To prevent this, 5-gallon (23 l.) knapsack sprayers containing a solution of a fire-retardant chemical (e.g. mono-ammonium phosphate or sodium alginate), as used by the Forestry Commission, should be on hand. A 200-gallon (909 l.) tank mounted on a lorry or tractor trailer is even more suitable if access is possible. Face masks and gloves allow one to work more effectively near the fire.

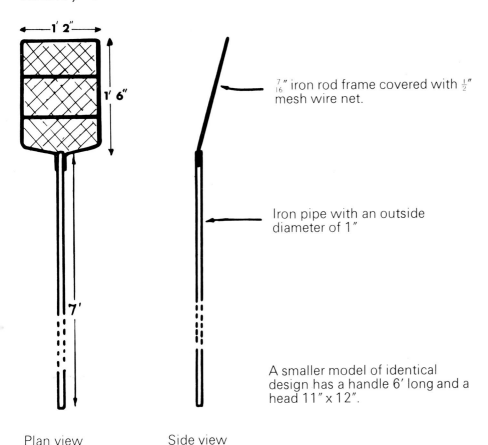

7/16" iron rod frame covered with 1/2" mesh wire net.

Iron pipe with an outside diameter of 1"

A smaller model of identical design has a handle 6' long and a head 11" x 12".

Plan view   Side view

139 Aluminium fire broom

Technique

Three men should attend a fire, two to control and eventually extinguish the head, and one to put out any subsidiary fires which may flare up at the edges. If the heather is very dry and long, and the wind strong, more than three men may be required to ensure adequate control.

Control can be greatly improved by the use of firebreaks. Permanent firebreaks, such as roads, streams or boggy areas may be used, and burning into an existing strip or patch of young heather will also slow down a fire, enabling it to be extinguished easily. It is most important to burn new strips at right angles to existing breaks. Commonly, a strip of old heather is burned parallel, and adjacent to, a road or a previous fire. This has the advantage that only one side needs to be guarded, but using the entire length of a previous strip as a firebreak nullifies the advantages of burning in strips. Two parallel and adjacent strips burned within a year or two of each other are of no more value to grouse than one wide strip and take twice as long to burn. On accessible ground with few stones, firebreaks can be created by rotavating strips of heather. At least four widths of the machine are necessary to be certain of stopping the head of a fire, but a break to guard the side of a fire can be produced with one pass of the machine.

It is important that a fire should attain the optimum temperature for successful regeneration; this has been found to be 600–800° F. (315–425° C.) at ground level. Lower temperatures result in incomplete combustion of old woody stems, and any layer of mosses and litter on the ground remains almost untouched. As explained previously, this is detrimental to regeneration, either from seed or from stools. On the other hand, a very hot fire will not only kill the heather plants outright (so preventing regeneration from stools), but may burn off the peat or raw humus at the soil surface, destroying all the heather seeds lying there. Subsequent regeneration is therefore long-delayed and, indeed, may never occur.

Some control over fire temperature can be obtained by considering both the weather and the growth phase of the heather. Burning should never be attempted when heather is damp with rain, snow, dew or hoar frost; the fire will not burn well and many long charred stems and a great deal of litter and moss will be left behind. Finely branched, dense heather 12–15 in. (30–38 cm.) high (building heather) is by far the easiest to burn successfully. However, even this type of heather should not be burned in a strong wind (more than about 10 m.p.h. [16 km.p.h.]), particularly if the vegetation is dry, because the fire will be too hot and troublesome to control.

It is difficult, if not impossible, to burn successfully in old heather which is rank and 'leggy', i.e. with long, bare stems and bushy crowns (mature or degenerate heather). Almost invariably, many unburnt stems and much moss will remain. Burning this type of heather in a strong wind should be particularly avoided, since the flames run quickly through the crowns of the plants without touching stems or ground. The only way to be certain of getting a clean burn in degenerate heather is to burn against the wind. With back-burning, the fire travels slowly, consuming everything. Consequently, regeneration is from seed, and therefore slow. Back-burning takes a great deal of time, which can ill be spared. The best way to avoid the need for it is to burn before the heather becomes degenerate.

Season

In Scotland, with certain exceptions, heather burning is restricted by the Hill Farming Act of 1946 to the period 1st October–15th April. In a wet spring, a landowner can obtain an extension to 30th April. On ground situated above 1,500 ft. (457 m.) the burning season can be extended to 15th May if application is made to the Secretary of State for Scotland.

Although the burning season lasts for some seven months, the actual number of days when heather can be burned is small. The weather is often damp which, combined with the cold and lack of sunshine, means that the heather is seldom dry. In eastern Scotland, in an average year, there are only about 20 days suitable for burning between October and April. In the wetter west, where autumn burning is seldom possible, the number is often less than 10.

The few days in the year which are suitable for burning are seldom fully utilised. Keepers are sometimes diverted to other, less essential, activities. Autumn burning is not always attempted because it is considered that spring firing gives better results. But experience at Kerloch moor in Kincardineshire has been that regeneration is better after autumn than spring burning. The belief to the contrary may have arisen because old heather on high wet ground is often burned at this time, and no matter when it is burned will always regenerate poorly. But this should not be a reason for neglecting opportunities for autumn burning. Every such opportunity must be taken throughout the legal season if heather is to be properly managed.

Rotation

Ideally, heather should be burned at an age when:

(a) It is no longer at its best as a source of food for grouse, not only in terms of its chemical composition, but also of its accessibility to the birds (grouse stand some 10–12 in. [25–30 cm.] high and most of the green shoots on heather taller than this are out of reach).
(b) It is at its densest, having covered nearly all of the ground and suppressed most other plants.
(c) There has not yet been an excessive build-up of litter and moss on the surface of the ground.
(d) The fire can be controlled easily.
(e) There will be a good, clean burn with few woody stems left behind.
(f) Regeneration after the fire will come quickly from stools, and not slowly from seed. (The criterion for judging the success of a fire is the speed with which the heather regenerates.)

These considerations all point to heather being burned when it is in the building phase, though patches of tall heather must be left scattered over the moor to provide shelter and nesting cover.

Burning at the pioneer stage is wasteful because heather is then highly nutritious and accessible to grouse. Moreover, ground cover is not complete in this phase and there may be other plants present which are of little or no value to grouse. Therefore burning gives these other plants (particularly bracken and the various grasses and sedges, which grow faster than heather) an opportunity to spread. In fact, overburning has been partly responsible for a decline in the abundance of heather on sheep grazings in Wales, northern England and south and west Scotland.

In the mature or degenerate phase, heather is long past its best as a food for grouse. The senility of the heather, the difficulty of controlling a fire, the abundance of mosses and the rapid accumulation of litter (at a rate of up to 5 cwt. per acre [627 kg. per h.] each year) all reduce the chances of getting a good clean burn followed by quick regeneration. Thus under-burning has the same end result as overburning; the dominance of the heather is weakened and moorland weeds such as bell-heather, bracken, mat-grass and deer-sedge become more abundant.

It is impossible to specify an exact optimum rotation between burns because heather growth and development vary according to climate, soil and the amount of grazing. In general, heather should be burned when it is in the late-building phase, i.e. 12–15 years old; or, in practical terms, when it reaches 12–15 in. (30–38 cm.) in height. However, heather growing in a sheltered glen with no grazing animals will reach the late-building stage in less than 12 years and must therefore be burned on a shorter rotation. Conversely, heather which is heavily grazed, or swept by strong winds on an exposed ridge, will take more than 15 years to reach the late-building phase and should be burned on a longer rotation. Indeed, exposed or heavily grazed heather may never need to be burned at all.

Pattern

In the early nineteenth century, when grouse shooting was a relatively unknown sport, heather burning was done by hill shepherds and moors were managed in much the same way as some deer forests today. Large areas were burned with each fire and consequently one tenth of the moor each year was burned. This benefited the sheep, which had an abundant and continuing supply of nutritious young heather.

Grouse requirements differ from those of sheep. Grouse are strictly territorial and more or less confined to small patches of ground. Sheep are not so territorial and like to wander over a larger area. The average size of grouse territories on a well-stocked moor may be less than 5 acres (2 h.). Hence it is necessary to have a large number of small patches of heather in different phases of growth scattered throughout the moor. One of the reasons why grouse are scarce on deer forests is because fires are usually large and the habitat is therefore unsuitable for the birds, even though the heather may be abundant.

There is no real conflict of interest between sheep-farming and grouse management. A moor well managed for grouse will be ideal for sheep. However, the converse is not necessarily true unless the fires are numerous, small and scattered in order to benefit grouse. The big problem is to find sufficient time, labour and money to burn in this way. It is easier to organise a few large fires each year than to burn the same total area in small patches. This is why it is so important to burn on every suitable day within the legal season. The shoot manager should regard heather burning as a matter of supreme urgency. A good day missed should give him as much concern as a farmer whose combine breaks down in the middle of harvest!

A minimum territory size of 5 acres (2 h.) suggests that an ideal size for a burnt patch might be something like 1 acre (0·4 h.). On most estates it is quite impracticable to burn such small patches as well as maintain a 12–15-year burning rotation, because of shortage of labour and time. Nevertheless, keepers must restrict the size of their fires to less than 5 acres (2 h.) if the burnt patch is to be square or circular. In practice, it is usually more beneficial, and certainly more efficient, to burn long narrow strips. These should not exceed about 30 yds. (27 m.) in width but may be as long as practicable. Hen grouse with broods are reluctant to stray farther than about 15 yds. (14 m.) from heather long enough to provide cover in an emergency. Thus a square burned patch of 1 acre (0·4 h.) has a large, unused central area, amounting to $\frac{3}{4}$ of an acre (0·3 h.), whereas a 1-acre (0·4 h.) strip, 140 yds. × 35 yds. (128 m. × 32 m.) is all utilised. Strips should always be burned, so that heather at least 6 in. (15 cm.) long is left on either side of them. The more the age classes of heather can be broken up, the better that ground will be for grouse, and the easier it will be to manage the heather in future.

Difficult ground

Some parts of a moor need to be burned with particular care. Screes or steep stony hillsides are especially susceptible to erosion of the soil. Regeneration of old heather in these places is usually slow, and in extreme cases may not occur at all because the soil is too dry. Without vegetation to bind the soil, rapid erosion can take place, and a once heathery slope be transformed into barren scree. Only heather in the building phase should be burned on a steep face, and the fire should never be in the direction of the slope, but always along the contour. In the case of late-mature or degenerate heather, the best policy is to refrain from burning.

Similarly, heather should not be burned on hill-tops or on exposed ridges where it is maintained as a short turf by the wind. Burning is not necessary in these places and can have disastrous results: growth is so slow that erosion may start. Care must also be taken on south-facing hillsides. The soil here is often very dry and a fierce fire may burn off all the humus from the surface. Consequently, regeneration of the heather will be seriously delayed, leading either to invasion by other plants, or erosion.

On wet, boggy areas with standing water, it is best to wait for a prolonged spell of dry weather and to burn out a large stretch at a time. The damp ground protects the heather stools from the heat of the fire and so regeneration is usually quick, provided the heather is young. The north-facing slopes of high hills are often difficult to burn because of late-lying snow. Burning in these places is best done in autumn.

Effects on soil

Critics of heather burning claim that it can lead to soil erosion and to losses in soil fertility. As indicated above, there is no reason why judicious burning, properly controlled, should lead to soil erosion. Its effect on soil fertility is a more complex question.

The ash deposited on the ground after a fire contains mineral nutrients such as calcium, phosphorus and potassium. These are eventually dissolved in rainwater, and it was thought at one time were lost to the regenerating heather through leaching and run-off. Moreover, almost all the nitrogen contained in heather is lost in the smoke from a fire. Nitrogen is one of the most important plant and animal nutrients. Some people argued that this loss, coupled with those from leaching and run-off, resulted in a serious depletion of fertility when burning was repeated over the years. But the nutrients deposited by rainfall and atmospheric dust in a 12–15 year period between fires may be sufficient to compensate for such losses and recent research has shown that the nutrients from heather are, in fact, almost wholly absorbed by the layer of humus at the soil surface and therefore are not lost. Soils without a layer of humus do not retain nutrients nearly as well, and some leaching occurs. Hence, on most moors, losses by leaching after a fire are probably insignificant. It is clear that the capability of a moorland soil to retain nutrients in this way will be destroyed if the surface humus or peat is burned off. This emphasises the importance of avoiding hot, slow fires.

Organisation

Burning must be properly organised and carried out according to a plan to achieve the best results. One of the most important considerations is to ensure that the keeper has enough help to fulfil this plan.

For example, on a moor in east Scotland with 9,000 acres (3,642 h.) of heather, it is necessary to burn about 600 acres (243 h.) each year to maintain a 15-year rotation. Since there are only about 15–20 days in the season when the weather is suitable for burning, 10–12 patches of about 3 acres (1·2 h.) must be burned each day. It is necessary to have at least three, and preferably four, teams of three men at work to do this. If labour is scarce, the heather will have to be burned in long, narrow strips of 10 acres (4 h.) or more to achieve the target of 600 acres (243 h.). It is important that extra areas should be burned in a good year, even though the target for that year has been achieved. This will make up for time lost in a wet year, or when snow lies late.

The only way to ensure that fires are not distributed haphazardly is to plan each season's burning beforehand. As an aid to planning all old fires should be plotted on a 6-in. (15 cm.) (1:10,560) map of the moor. The approximate size and location of each fire should be recorded, together with a note of the date of burning if known. It is then possible to contrive the best distribution of new fires before each burning season begins, and to assess the labour, equipment and transport needed. The person responsible for the burning plan should spend a day on the hill briefing those who will do the burning. The areas which have to be burned can be pointed out and problems discussed. This will go a long way towards ensuring the success of the plan.

Finally, neighbouring owners of woodland should always be informed if there is any intention of burning near their plantations. This fosters good relations, and they may offer extra labour in their own interests.

Other management methods

Cutting

The ideal of burning heather in small patches or long narrow strips on a 12–15-year rotation is rarely achieved because of shortage of labour. Cutting with a machine can be done in almost any weather. One machine commonly used is a Wolseley 'Junglebuster', or 'Swipe', cutting the heather with chains rotating at a height of about 6 in. (15 cm.).

After cutting, heather regeneration can be very good if all the cut material and surface litter is raked off, since the debris may otherwise inhibit regeneration from both stools and seed. The new growth largely comes from buds at the bases of cut stems, and regeneration is much faster than after burning. Cutting in spring gives better results than in autumn.

However, many places are inaccessible to a tractor, because of steep ground or stones, and must therefore be burned. It also takes much longer to cut than to burn. Even on the most suitable ground, it takes about two hours to cut 1 acre (0·4 h.). In practice, the cut heather and litter on the ground cannot always be cleared and consequently regeneration is disappointing. If the ground is suitable, a forage harvester makes the best job of debris disposal. All this is expensive.

Obviously, cutting is a supplement, and not an alternative, to burning. It is possibly most useful on degenerate heather where regeneration after burning is poor, and near woodlands where burning is hazardous.

Grazing control

If only a few small patches of young heather are available, grazing animals concentrate on them and the plants are nibbled right down to the ground or completely uprooted. Heavy grazing depresses heather growth and can cause a reduction in grouse numbers due to a shortage of long heather for cover. In areas where climate and soil are unfavourable to heather, severe grazing by sheep can completely eliminate the plant.

Some measure of grazing control can be exercised by judicious burning, to create a large number of scattered patches in old heather, so that the animals are dispersed and the damage to new growth is minimised. On land where grazing has suppressed but not eradicated heather, removal of sheep for 2–5 years may allow the plant to regain its dominance. Portable, high-tensile steel fencing can be used to exclude sheep from local areas.

Light grazing on pioneer heather can be beneficial by removing shoot tips and encouraging outward growth, so that cover of the ground is accelerated. Once young heather is established, grazing at the right intensity can maintain building heather in vigorous growth. Progress towards the mature and degenerate phases can be slowed down, or even stopped. Normally, most shoots produced by a heather plant are not grazed. They eventually die and fall to the ground as litter, or become woody and unpalatable. It is because of this under-exploitation by grazers that heather has to be burned every so often to remove the accumulated litter and woody shoots. If the heather is fully exploited by grazing animals, it does not have to be burned so frequently, but such grazing must be subject to proper control in the interest of good grouse moor management.

Grouse numbers can be high on cattle grazings. But allegations that these can be harmful to grouse interests have some foundation. Hill winterings for cattle pose special problems. The animals tend to congregate in the area where they are foddered. Consequently this is subject to intensive treading and dunging, which may eliminate the heather altogether. Also even small numbers of cattle will soon tread in and block open drains, thereby causing the establishment of wet patches.

Drainage

As mentioned before, heather never grows densely on wet, poorly drained land. Hence a well-planned network of open drains may improve the growth of heather on a wet moor and encourage the formation of a vigorous sward. Many moors were extensively open-drained during the late nineteenth and the early part of this century. However, shallow – 18-in. (46 cm.) – open drains affect a limited area on either side, and where rainfall is high it is a long, slow business to increase heather cover by draining.

Large-scale drainage is expensive and the benefits likely to accrue from it are difficult to assess. It may help to lessen the risk of attack by heather beetle, which seems to do most damage on boggy lands. It will make conditions less favourable to the fungal parasites of heather.

In north-eastern Scotland there are extensive areas of poorly drained ground, often on quite steep slopes. The peat layer may be only 18 in. (46 cm.) deep and the underlying soil is a coarse gravel with large boulders. Rainwater, which is acidified after percolating through heather litter, has caused leaching and produced a podsolised soil with an impervious pan at a depth of 2–3 ft.

(0·6–0·9 m.), causing waterlogging. Mole-draining with the aid of a crawler tractor and suitable tackle can provide an effective answer to this problem.

Fertilising

Both growth and feeding value of heather can be increased by applying nitrogenous fertiliser in spring. This also improves the breeding success of grouse and increases the stock when there are no other grazing animals present.

As a result, many people have supposed that fertilisers could be used in routine management. However, fertilising is expensive and the beneficial effects on grouse only last two or three years. If many sheep, cattle or deer are on the ground, fertilising will usually provide no more grouse, due to these animals grazing the fertilised heather very heavily.

Finally, fertilisers may have unknown side-effects, particularly on the soil. For example, repeated application of a nitrogenous fertiliser might induce deficiencies of mineral nutrients such as phosphorus or calcium. Hence at this stage until more is known about it, moor owners are advised not to apply fertiliser to heather.

Like cutting, fertilising can never be a substitute for burning, which is by far the first priority in managing heather.

Conclusion

Good heather management is fundamental to high stocks of grouse. Judicious and well-planned burning is the key factor in such management which can largely neutralise the ill effects of others. Haphazard and ill-considered burning will never allow a moor to realise its full potential.

Chapter 26
How to Distinguish Age and Sex

Young or old?

It is obviously essential for a wildlife scientist to be able to tell the age and sex of the specimens he examines. Game breeders will also require to separate young from old, and cocks from hens. In addition, shooting men like to record the proportion of young birds in the bag – certainly partridges – as it gives them an indication of the success of the previous breeding season. In poor reproduction years it warns them when they are in danger of shooting next year's breeding stock. And in the kitchen it will be as well to know whether a bird can be roasted or whether it must be destined for the casserole.

Two general tests: While young gamebirds may be distinguished from old ones by many different methods in the early part of the shooting season, there are only two tests which apply to most species throughout the whole of the shooting season.

All young gamebirds have a small blind-ended passage opening on the upper side of the vent. This passage, commonly known as the *bursa*, is believed to play some part in disease control. In all species it becomes much reduced or may close completely when the bird reaches sexual maturity, and the presence of a normal bursa is a certain test for a young bird. In ordinary hands the bursa test should not be attempted on live birds.

The second method (which unfortunately cannot be applied to the pheasant) is to examine the two outer primaries or flight feathers. In the partridge the pointed, lance-shaped tips of these feathers distinguish the young bird from the old, which has blunt-ended outer primaries. It should be mentioned that when feathers are wet, even blunt-ended ones can look pointed.

Young pheasants cannot be distinguished by this means, since, in contrast to other gamebirds, *all* the juvenile flight feathers are moulted. Partridge and grouse moult only eight of the ten sharply pointed juvenile feathers, and retain the outermost pair for approximately a year.

404

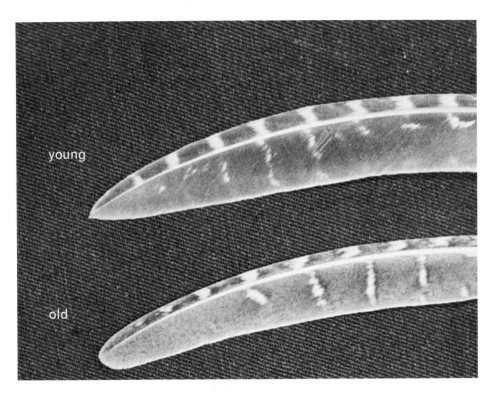

young

old

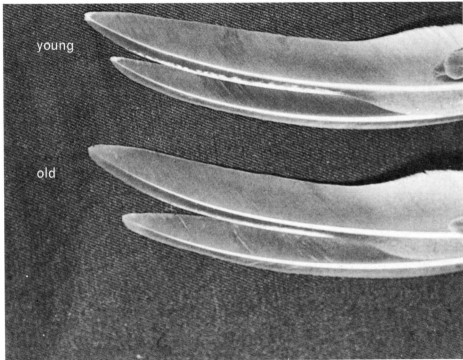

young

old

140 Above: Flight feathers of a young and an old grey partridge

Below: Flight feathers of a young and an old red-legged partridge

405

Grey partridge: In September and early October the familiar dark beak, yellowish legs and relatively soft bones of the young birds will readily differentiate them from the grey-beaked, grey-legged and hard-boned adults, but later in the season the simple flight feather test is to be recommended – the pointed primaries indicating a young bird. In September a few partridges in their second year may *not* have moulted these pointed primaries of the juvenile plumage, but these feathers will be faded and abraded to such an extent that the bird will be easily recognised as old.

The bursa test may be applied with a matchstick, burned at one end so that it is narrow but not too sharp, or the quill of a flight feather. With very gentle pressure the probe should penetrate about ½ in. (13 mm.) in a young bird, while in old birds the bursa will either be completely closed or, in some cases, open for only ¼ in. (6 mm.). It is unlikely that the busy keeper or shoot-owner will have the time to use the bursa test on a couple of hundred birds at the end of a day's shooting, but it is useful for small numbers and for otherwise doubtful specimens.

Red-legged partridge: The bursa is approximately the same depth in young birds as in the grey partridge (½ in. [13 mm.]). Another method of ageing redlegs is to inspect the two outer primaries – not for shape but for colour markings. The young bird has these two flight feathers tipped with cream*; sometimes other primaries not yet moulted will also show this cream tip.

Pheasant: The bursa test is relatively easily applied to both cock and hen pheasants. The bird should be laid on its back on the palm of the left hand while the thumb is used to bend back the tail and expose the vent. The opening of the bursa of a young bird will be seen to lie inside the opening of the vent on the side nearest the tail (see Figures 141 and 142). In young birds the depth of the bursa will be approximately 1 in. (25 mm.). In old birds the bursa may close completely (when the site of the opening is often marked by a slight bump) or remain open for about ¼ in. (6 mm.); very rarely up to nearly ½ in. (13 mm.). This is the only method for distinguishing young *hen* pheasants from old ones: early in the season young cocks may be separated from old ones by their blunt and relatively short spurs. Later in the season, surprisingly enough, the spurs of early hatched young birds can be as long and as sharply pointed as some old ones! The only certain means of distinguishing young from old, therefore, is again the bursa test.

Grouse: This species has been discussed in Chapter 24.

---

* In Spanish redlegs this cream-coloured tip is usually absent or very small indeed.

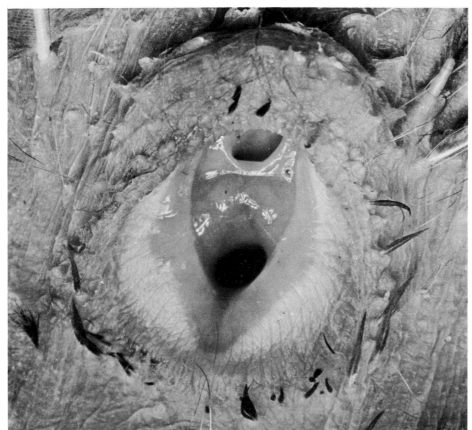

141 The bursa in a pheasant

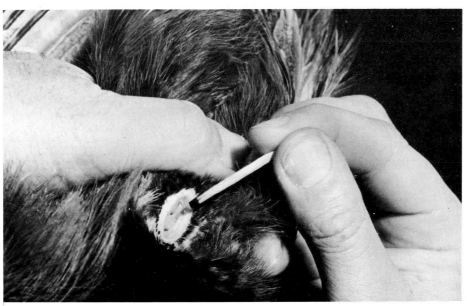

142 Method of applying bursa test

407

143 The wing of a
cock partridge

Mallard: Young and old mallard may be most certainly distinguished by the bursa test. Early in the season the appearance of the tips of the retrices (tail feathers) may serve as a guide, since those of young birds end with a notch – indicating where the extreme downy tip has broken off – while adult tail feathers are pointed.

Woodcock: The bursa test is applicable; made easy by slitting the cloaca. Oddly enough young woodcock will have the tips of the primaries ragged and worn: old birds will have undamaged tips!

Cock or hen?

Grey partridge: Provided they are well grown, young cock partridges may first be separated from young hens when they are ten weeks old. With hand-reared birds it may be safer to leave them until they are 11 or 12 weeks. The presence of median wing coverts ('shoulder feathers') which have only a light longitudinal stripe distinguishes the cock from the hen: the female has additional light transverse barring (see Figure 145). The dark brown 'horseshoe' on the breast is not in all cases a reliable method of sex distinction. In mature partridges the hen shows more greyish-white on the top of the head – an area which is usually grey-brown in the cock.

145 Wing covert feathers of the hen (left) and cock partridge (right)

Red-legged partridge: No plumage difference has been noted between cock and hen, although the adult cock is usually 3–4 oz. (85–113 g.) heavier than the hen. In old redlegs sex may be most readily distinguished by the knobbly spur on the

410

cock's legs. These may be occasionally present on the legs of hens, but they are usually very much smaller, and consist of a single protrusion. In young birds it is sometimes possible to feel the incipient spur of the cock even before it can be seen, but when sexing hand-reared stock it is wise to wait until they are about 14 weeks old – even then it can be tricky! The typical posture and behaviour of the males, when in a mixed pen, will sometimes help to distinguish them from the females.

Pheasant: The differences between cocks and hens are so well known that it would be superfluous to describe them. Occasionally birds occur which show the characteristic plumage of both sexes, and this is sometimes found in old hens which are assuming typical cock pheasant plumage, but cases may occur in young birds due to hormonal disturbances.

Grouse: The plumage differences between cock and hen grouse have been discussed in Chapter 24.

Mallard: While no difficulty will be experienced in separating adult ducks from drakes, sex is not readily distinguished in immature birds. However, when the young ducks are 7–8 weeks of age a combination of the following points should allow one to distinguish between the two sexes.

DRAKE	DUCK
Feathers show some grey vermiculation on flank in front of thigh	No grey vermiculation on flank
Wing coverts uniform in colour	Wing covert feathers have pale edges
Some glossy green feathers on top of head	Head feathers rarely glossy green
Beak usually dull greenish yellow	Beak usually brown

Index

Kale – *cont.*

as a release point, 259; sowing, 258, 261; types, 261

Knotgrass, 286

Larch, 172, 208

Laurel, *see* Common laurel; Portugal laurel

Laying pens: communal pens, 91; fixed, 90–1; for mallard, 325; management, 93–5; movable, 92–3; sectional pens, 91; siting, 93; types, 88–93

Leg-ringing, 161–3

Legg, P.B. trap, 67

Leopoldo, Aldo, 13

Lepco, 46

Leys, *see* Grass crops

Lice, 125, 384

Lime, 176

Linseed, 255, 262, 282

Little owl, 55, 56

Lloyd traps, 58

Long-eared owl, 55, 56

Lonicera nitida: described, 215; as flushing cover, 181; as hides, 318; in large woodlands, 204; around flight ponds, 307; on sloping sites, 207, 208; for small areas, 198–9, 200; in spinneys, 195, 196, 197; as windbreak, 172, 199, 307

Louping ill, 384

Lovat, Lord, 368

Lucerne, 42, 262, 282

Lupins, 263, 282

Magpies, 38, 50–1, 82; identifying traces of, 68

Maize: as game crop, 263–6, 282; for pheasant catchers, 88; and pheasants' food choice, 297

Malathion, 268

Mallard: ageing, 410; artificial incubation, 117; artificial nests, 330–3; bringing in wild duck, 314; buckwheat for, 249; decoys, 323; disease, 329; feeding, 312, 327–8, 338–40, 357–9; management after release, 327–8; and nest losses, 48; nesting rafts, 333–6; pinioning, 328; rearing, 322–9; release pens, 338; research, 357–9; sexing, 411; taking of eggs, 336n.; *see also* Wild duck

Mangolds, 266, 282

Maple, 176

Marsh plants, 356–7

Maywick Calor gas heater, 132, 134

Mebenvet, 148, 240, 244

Melanistic Mutant pheasant, 93–4, 99, 121

Metasystox 55, 274

Migration: grouse, 374–80; snipe, 360–1; woodcock, 364

Millet, 266

Ministry of Agriculture, 22, 65

Mink, feral, 57, 60, 65–6, 120, 344

Moles, 64–5, 119; identifying traces of, 70; and soil fertility, 379

Mongolian pheasants, 93

Moniliasis, 79, 125, 242

Moorhens, 56, 324, 333

Moors, 367; management, *see* Heather

Mountain ash, 176, 196, 197, 199

Movable pens: feather picking, 126–7; fields for, 125–6; rearing in, 122–9; releasing from, 126; siting, 125–6

Mustard, 32, 36, 194, 195, 203, 267, 269, 282

Nest boxes: for broodies, 103–4; for duck, 330–3

Nesting baskets, 330–3

Nesting rafts, 333–6

Nesting sites: artificial, 22–4; barrier smell protection, 72–3; cocksfoot grass, 33–4; field peas, 34; in grass crops, 22, 25–7; habitat requirements, 164–7; hedgerows, 22, 40, 71–3; identifying predators of, 67–70; management of duck, 336; predators and, 40; searching for, 71–2; spinneys, 191; use of brashings for, 214

'Netlon', 140, 231, 233, 236

Newcastle Disease, 130, 243–4; in ducks, 329

North of England Grouse Research Project, 9–10

Norway spruce (Christmas trees), 172, 182, 190, 204

Nursery pens, 141–2

Nusan, 117

Oak, 195, 196, 197, 199–200, 208

Oats, 252, 281, 297, 369

Oil drums; cleaning, 292; hopper construction, 290

Oil poppy, 267–8, 282

Oilseed rape, 268–70, 282

Old English Blackneck pheasant, 93, 99

Overcrowding, diseases and, 243

Owls, 55–6, 157, 158

Owner-farmers, 15

Oyster-shell, 96

Paddock-grazing, 27–30

Pairing, 80

Paraffin heaters, 131, 132, 135–7

Parsnip, 270, 282

Parsons Feeder, 292–4

Partridges: artificial incubation, 117; brooders for, 227–9; broodies for, 221, 222; clutch size, 73, 76; decline of wild, 38–43; egg laying dates, 71; feeding, 224–6; gapes, 39; hedgerows and, 16; hysteria, 79, 227; laying period, 76–7; nest losses, 38; nest sites, 16; pairing, 232–3; rearing, 220–38; rearing field sites, 221–2; releasing, 229–31; as a subject for management, 14; winter feeding, 286–8; winter losses, 38; wintering, 231–2; *see also* Grey partridge; Redleg partridge

418